Ministry of Agriculture, Fisheries and Food

C000083732

Reference Book 385

The nitrogen requirement of cereals

Proceedings of a Conference
organised by the Agricultural Development
and Advisory Service

September 1982

London: Her Majesty's Stationery Office

ISBN 0 11 242556 9

Foreword

Cereals are by far the most important arable crop in the UK. The area grown is now about four million hectares, with an annual production of about 20 million tons of grain.

In recent years, there have been marked changes in intensive cereal growing systems, especially for winter wheat. Increasing use of nitrogen fertiliser has played a large part in the development of these systems, and in the achievement of high yields. The present cost of nitrogen fertiliser used on cereals is about £180 million a year.

Response of cereals to nitrogen fertiliser is characterised by great variability between sites and seasons. Much research and experimental effort has been devoted to measuring and trying to establish the causes for this variation. Recommendations for nitrogen use on cereals have been developed on the basis of this large body of experimental work, but it is not yet possible to predict nitrogen requirements for individual crops with sufficient precision or reliability.

The problems of accurately predicting nitrogen requirements are increased by the complexities of transformation of nitrogen in the soil, and the many climatic and agronomic factors which interact to influence response to applied nitrogen.

This Conference arose out of the need to review comprehensively the large amount of relevant work done in recent years, and to try to establish a new strategy for the development of better methods of predicting nitrogen requirements.

The Conference was organised by the Soil Scientists of the Agricultural Development and Advisory Service (ADAS) and was held at Loughborough University in September 1982. The Conference brought together ADAS Soil Scientists and Agronomists, research workers from ARC Institutes and Universities, and representatives of commercial organisations and research workers from overseas.

The formal papers reviewed various aspects of work on the nitrogen response of cereals, while poster presentations covered some specific areas of recent work. At the end of the Conference, the participants divided into seven syndicate groups, each of which discussed and reported on a specific topic. It is hoped that the syndicate reports will provide a framework for the future planning and co-ordination of development work in this important field.

W Dermott
Head of Agricultural Science Service
ADAS

Contents

page

iii   Foreword

ix   Conference delegates

1   Introduction

5   Plant breeding – potential for improvement of yield and grain quality
    T J Riggs
19   Discussion

21   Cereal plant development – assessment and use
    E J M Kirby and Margaret Appleyard
39   Discussion

41   Dry matter production and crop yield – genetic constraints
    R B Austin
51   Discussion

53   Environmental effects on dry matter production
    P V Biscoe and V B A Willington
66   Discussion

69   Winter wheat yield variability
    L V Vaidyanathan

79   The supply of nitrogen from the soil
    D S Jenkinson
93   Discussion

95   Estimation of annual variations in leaching of residual nitrate under deep-
    rooted crops during winter
    I G Burns

103   Field measurements of the leaching of fertiliser nitrate
    J A Nicholsby and A Wild

107   Soil and fertiliser nitrogen use by winter wheat
    L V Vaidyanathan
118   Discussion

119   Recovery of ^{15}N-labelled fertiliser by winter wheat
      D S Powlson, G Pruden and D S Jenkinson

121   Uptake of fertiliser nitrogen by arable crops
      R J Dowdell, R Crees and D Christian

125   The effect of sowing date and of leaching on soil nitrogen supply for winter
      wheat, at Rothamsted and Woburn, 1981
      F V Widdowson, A Penny, R J Darby and E Bird

129   Uptake of nitrogen by barley in Scottish climatic conditions
      K A Smith, A Elmes and R S Howard

131   Effects of nitrogen on the growth and development of winter wheat
      V B A Willington and P V Biscoe

133   Design and interpretation of nitrogen response experiments
      B J George
149   Discussion

151   The response of winter wheat to nitrogen
      R Sylvester-Bradley, P M R Dampney and A W A Murray
175   Discussion

177   Nitrogen uptake of winter wheat
      H J Lidgate

183   Determining the nitrogen requirements for winter wheat using an
      experiment of Simplex design
      B J George and R J Skinner

191   Response of winter barley to nitrogen
      J P Grylls and J R Archer
208   Discussion

209   The response of spring barley to nitrogen
      P A Johnson
222   Discussion

223   Nitrogen for spring barley
      J D Whitear and M R J Holmes

227   Plant growth and composition as predictors of nitrogen requirements
      T Batey

233   An assessment of nitrate reductase activity as a predictor of nitrogen
      requirement of winter cereals
      R Sylvester-Bradley, P A J Barnard and P F W Hart

239   Nitrate reductase activity and the assessment of nitrogen status
L M J Verstraeten and K Vlassak

245   The basis of current nitrogen recommendations for cereals
P Needham
255   Discussion

257   Nitrogenous fertilisation of winter wheat in France: How is the balance to
be improved?
Ph. Viaux
264   Discussion

265   Modelling of the nitrogen requirement of cereals
P B Tinker and T M Addiscott
282   Discussion

283   Reports of syndicate discussions
285   Syndicate A   Relative merits of extensive and intensive experiments
287   Syndicate B   The role of ^{15}N in future experimentation
289   Syndicate C   Can the residual nitrogen from previous crops be better
quantified?
291   Syndicate D   Prospects for improving nitrogen prediction by soil and
plant analysis
293   Syndicate E   The relevance of growth and developmental stages for
nitrogen applications
295   Syndicate F   Prospects for improving the prediction of nitrogen
fertiliser requirements of cereal crops by modelling methods
297   Syndicate G   Opportunities for improved co-ordination of cereal
nitrogen experiments

Conference delegates

Ministry of Agriculture, Fisheries and Food

Archer F C   (Starcross)
Archer J R   (Cambridge)
Attwood P J   (Headquarters)
Bailey G A   (Reading)
Baldwin J H   (Cambridge)
Chalmers A G   (Wye)
Clare R W   (Rosemaund)
Cowton J M   (Terrington)
Dampney P M R   (Wolverhampton)
Davies Dr D B   (Cambridge)
Davies G R   (Bangor)
Davies Mrs S J   (Drayton)
Dermott W   (Headquarters)
Dight R J W   (Trawsgoed)
Farrar K   (Leeds)
Goodlass Dr G   (Shardlow)
Grylls J P   (Cambridge)
Hadden S W   (Leeds)
Harrod M F   (Cambridge)
Hewgill D   (Leeds)
Hodgson I H   (Starcross)
Hubbard K R   (Cambridge)
Hughes Dr A D   (Reading)
Jenkins J E E   (Leeds)
Johnson P A   (Shardlow)
Jones E   (Trawsgoed)
Jones J L O   (Cambridge)
King Mrs C M   (Reading)
LeGrice S   (FDEU, Cambridge)
Little Dr R C   (Headquarters)
Lord Miss E I   (Cambridge)

Marks M J   (Wye)
McDonald H G   (Gleadthorpe)
Needham P   (Headquarters)
Neild J R A   (Leeds)
Perks D A   (High Mowthorpe)
Rahn C R   (Cambridge)
Richardson S J   (Wolverhampton)
Royle Miss S M (Shardlow)
Rudd C   (Cambridge)
Scott Mrs J L   (Reading)
Sekhar N N C   (Shardlow)
Shaw Dr K   (Newcastle)
Skinner R J   (Cardiff)
Smith K A   (FWU, Reading)
Stevens D B   (Norfolk Agricultural Station)
Swain R W   (Shardlow)
Sylvester-Bradley Dr R (Wolverhampton)
Unwin R J   (Headquarters)
Vaidyanathan Dr L V   (Cambridge)
Vaughan Miss J   (Leeds)
Wadsworth G A   (Reading)
Ward J T   (Shardlow)
Webb J D   (Wolverhampton)
Whorton A P   (Bristol)
Wilkinson B   (Leeds)
Williams J H   (Wolverhampton)
Withers P J A   (Bristol)
Yarham D J   (Cambridge)

Invited delegates (non-MAFF)

Addiscott Dr T M A (Rothamsted)
Appleyard Miss M (Plant Breeding Institute)

Austin R B (Plant Breeding Institute)
Bache Dr B W (Macaulay Institute for Soil Research)

Batey Dr T (University of Aberdeen)
Biscoe Dr P V (Broom's Barn
  Experimental Station)
Bloom M T (Cambridge)
Cannell Dr R Q (Letcombe
  Laboratory
Cooke Dr G W (Rothamsted)
Dowdell Dr R J (Letcombe
  Laboratory)
Easson Dr D L (DANI)
Elmes Miss A (East of Scotland
  College of Agriculture)
Frost C A (East of Scotland
  College of Agriculture)
Gasser Dr J K R (ARC, HQ)
George B J (Rothamsted)
Greenwood Dr D J (National
  Vegetable Research Station)
Hollies J D (ICI, Billingham)
Holmes Dr J C (East of Scotland
  College of Agriculture)
Holmes M R J (Levington)

Jenkinson Dr D S (Rothamsted)
Jenkyn Dr J F (Rothamsted)
Kirby Dr E J M (Plant Breeding
  Institute)
Lidgate H J (Jealotts Hill)
Murray A W A (Rothamsted)
Nicholsby J A (University of
  Reading)
Penny A (Rothamsted)
Powlson Dr D S (Rothamsted)
Pruden G (Rothamsted)
Rayner Dr J H (Rothamsted)
Riggs Dr T J (Plant Breeding
  Institute)
Smith Dr K A (East of Scotland
  College of Agriculture)
Tinker Dr P B (Rothamsted)
Whitear J D (Levington)
Whitmore Dr A P (Rothamsted)
Widdowson F V (Rothamsted)
Willington Dr V B A (Broom's Barn
  Experimental Station)

Overseas delegates

Basstanie L U C (Centre for
  Agrobiological Research,
  Netherlands)
Belmans Dr C (Catholic University
  of Louvain, Belgium)

Dilz Dr K (Institute for Soil
  Fertility, Netherlands)
Verstraeten Dr L M J (Catholic
  University of Louvain, Belgium)
Viaux Ph (ITCF, France)

Introduction

The Conference opened with an introductory address by its Chairman, Dr G W Cooke.

In the first place I must say how much I appreciate the honour of having been invited by the Organisers to be the Chairman of this Conference. The subject – the use of nitrogen fertilisers on our cereal crops – is very important indeed, and I have had an interest in it for many years. I have observed the recent rapid changes in the amounts of nitrogen used and, in my view, this makes the present a very opportune time for the discussions that we are to have. So I will review briefly the past and present use of nitrogen fertiliser which forms the background for this Conference.

The total cost of fertilisers and lime to UK farmers in 1981 was £687 million, which was 13 per cent of their spending on 'inputs'. Cereals occupy about 4 million hectares in UK, about four-fifths of the area of arable crops. Before 1982 the record production was achieved in 1980 when 19.5 million tonnes of grain was produced; we are now hearing that the 1982 harvest will exceed 20 million tonnes, and that average yields for the whole country may be the highest on record.

Surveys of Fertiliser Practice suggest that cereals receive about 450 000 tonnes of nitrogen annually, which is about a third of the total amount of nitrogen fertiliser (about $1\frac{1}{3}$ million tonnes of N) used in UK. At present prices the cost of this nitrogen used on cereals is about £180 million; we must strive to ensure that this large expenditure is used by farmers to maximum advantage by being able to advise on the correct amounts to use and the best methods and times for applying the nitrogen. This fertiliser must also be used efficiently; in years past we have been aware of the low efficiency of the nitrogen used on cereals, perhaps no more than a third being recovered in grain and straw. But we will hear how high-yielding varieties grown by up-to-date practices, and protected from weeds, pests and diseases, can now yield so well that it is possible to account for 80 per cent or more of the nitrogen applied.

It is interesting to review the recommendations for the use of fertiliser nitrogen on cereals made in publications during the last 50 years, and to compare these recommendations with the amounts of nitrogen actually used by farmers. To simplify matters the recommendations I quote are for cereals grown on mineral soils with N Index 0. Table 1 summarises these changes in the amounts recommended and used (figures for use are the averages for all surveyed fields on each crop and therefore range over all N Indices from 0 to 2).

The first recommendations were made by Sir John Russell (1931) who prepared the official Bulletin for the Ministry. We do not have any estimate of the amounts of nitrogen used by farmers on their crops in the 1930s. Since the early 1940s the Surveys of Fertiliser Practice have provided reliable data that I believe is unique in the world. I have used results from the Surveys in the table. Accounts have been written of the early history of the Surveys (Yates and Boyd, 1965) and Reports are now published annually (Church, 1982) which show how much fertiliser is used on the main crops by farmers in England and Wales.

Table 1 The history of the amounts of nitrogen fertiliser recommended for, and used on, cereals from 1931 to 1981 (kilogrammes per hectare of N)

Year	Publication by	Winter wheat		Spring barley	
		Recommended	Used(a)	Recommended	Used(a)
1931	Russell	30	?	25	?
1941	Crowther and Yates	75	20(b)	75	20(b)
1957	Garner	80 (Stiff-strawed varieties)		80 (Stiff-strawed varieties)	
			50		35
		60 (Other varieties)		60 (Other varieties)	
1959	Cooke	100	50	100	35
1973	MAFF	100	90	100	73
1978	MAFF	125	125	100	83
1981	MAFF	150	162	100	98

(a) Amounts recorded as 'used' are averages of all fields surveyed.
(b) Survey of Fertiliser Practice data for 1943.

The foundation of present methods of advising on the amounts of fertilisers to be used on crops was laid in their classic paper by Crowther and Yates (1941). They summarised the results of all relevant experiments and showed how the exponential response curve could be used to derive the optimum dressing that returned most profit. They concluded that a generally-applicable optimum dressing was 75 kg/ha of N for cereals, but, because of the risk of lodging, they recommended that no more than 50 kg/ha of N should be used in practice. The first Surveys in the early 1940s showed that farmers applied only about 20 kg/ha of N for both wheat and barley. The next official Bulletin, written by H V Garner (1957), recommended up to 80 kg/ha of N for stiff-strawed wheats and barleys, but 60 kg/ha of N for other varieties. From a fresh review of the evidence in 1959 I concluded (Cooke, 1959) that 100 kg/ha of N should be recommended for winter wheat and spring barley; at that time farmers used half as much as this on wheat, and only a third as much on barley. This quantity, of 100 kg/ha of N, was also recommended in the next Ministry Bulletin (MAFF, 1973); by then farmers were using, on average, nearly as much nitrogen as was recommended for winter wheat, and three-quarters as much for spring barley. In the revised version of this Bulletin issued in 1979 (MAFF 1979), 125 kg/ha of N was recommended, and the Surveys showed that the average dressing used by farmers was as much as this figure. Finally, the last recommendation published from the Ministry that I have (MAFF, 1981) is for 150 kg/ha of N to be used on winter wheat; in 1981, when this Booklet appeared, the Surveys show that the average amount used by farmers was 162 kg/ha of N – that is more than the recommended amount.

The results of the latest Survey of Fertiliser Practice for 1981 showed that half of our wheat crops get between 150 and 200 kg/ha of N, and that 18 per cent of the fields surveyed had more than 200 kg/ha of N. Looking back over the series of Surveys published by Church (1982) we find that in the 13 seasons from 1966 to 1978 the rate of nitrogen used on winter wheat increased by only 39 per cent and the rate used on spring barley by only 6 per cent. In contrast, in the four seasons 1978 to 1981 the nitrogen used increased by 30 per cent for winter wheat, by 35 per cent for winter barley, and by 18 per cent for spring barley. These rapid increases are a response by farmers to several factors: current crop prices encourage farmers to secure the large yields that are now the targets of so many; the short-strawed varieties available have the capacity for giving large yields without lodging when fully-fertilised; the crops can be reliably protected from pests and diseases; and winter barley has become a very important crop.

Efficiency in the use of these large dressings of nitrogen fertiliser is a very important objective. At the average levels of yields now harvested our cereals recover in grain and straw about 400 000 tonnes of nitrogen. The total amount supplied by fertilisers, and in the organic manures given to cereals, is about 550 000 tonnes. As a scientist I can have no objective other than to be able to account for 100 per cent of the nitrogen applied to crops and, of course, to recover as much as possible in the harvest. The potentials of the new varieties that we have, and the range of agrochemicals that can protect them from pests and diseases, together with the improved agronomic practices of our good farmers, make my objective of high recovery of nitrogen a realistic target.

When farmers used much less fertiliser than was recommended it was not so important that the recommendations should be very precise. The present situation is quite different and we are at a crucial stage in the history of our use of nitrogen on cereals. There is a heavy responsibility on us to ensure that cereals receive sufficient nitrogen to achieve the full potential of the new varieties, and at the same time to ensure that this nitrogen is used with maximum efficiency, as little as possible being wasted by moving into the aerial or water environment to cause pollution.

The plans made for this Conference go far to achieve these objectives. In the first session we will consider the physiological aspects of the growth of cereals as they are affected by nitrogen. This joint activity of physiologists, plant breeders, and those concerned with crop nutrition, is a very important development of recent years. In our second session we will review the considerable body of recent evidence that we have from experiments that have tested the effect of nitrogen fertilisers on cereals. The third session will then consider how best to predict by modern techniques the amounts of nitrogen that should be recommended. Finally the outstanding questions that require detailed consideration will receive this in the important Syndicate discussions, and the conclusions of the Syndicates will be reported at the end of the Conference.

Finally, I must say how grateful those invited to the Conference are to the Organisers for giving us this opportunity to hear the latest information on the subject, and to discuss this as a basis for our common desire to work for a more rational and more efficient use of nitrogen to increase our cereal crops.

References

CHURCH, B.M. 1982. Use of Fertilisers in England and Wales. *Report of Rothamsted Experimental Station for 1981, part 2,* 123–128;
(See also earlier Reports by B. M. Church in this series)

COOKE, G.W. 1959. *Fertilisers and Profitable Farming.* London: Crosby Lockwood.

CROWTHER, E.M. and YATES, F. 1941. Fertiliser Policy in Wartime. *Empire Journal of Experimental Agriculture* **9**, 77–97.

GARNER, H.V. 1957. *Manures and Fertilisers.* Ministry of Agriculture, Fisheries and Food. Bulletin No. 36. London HMSO.

MAFF. 1973. *Fertiliser Recommendations.* Ministry of Agriculture, Fisheries and Food, Bulletin No. 209. London HMSO.

MAFF. 1979. *Fertiliser Recommendations.* Ministry of Agriculture, Fisheries and Food, GF1. London HMSO.

MAFF. 1981. *Lime and Fertiliser Recommendations No. 1 Arable Crops and Grassland.* Ministry of Agriculture, Fisheries and Food, Booklet 2191. Alnwick, Northumberland: MAFF (Publications).

RUSSELL, E.J. 1931. *Artificial Fertilisers in Modern Agriculture,* Ministry of Agriculture and Fisheries, Bulletin No. 28. London HMSO.

YATES, F. and BOYD, D. A. 1965. Two Decades of Surveys of Fertiliser Practice. *Outlook on Agriculture* **4**, 203–210.

Plant breeding–potential for improvement of yield and grain quality

T J Riggs
Plant Breeding Institute, Cambridge

Summary

National yields of wheat and barley have approximately doubled in the last 35 years. This increase has been due partly to improvements in crop husbandry and partly to the introduction of new varieties with greater genetic potential for yield and able to take advantage of high input management.

In the most successful breeding programmes several hundred crosses are made each year between carefully chosen parents. First selections are made amongst populations of a million or more single plants but the numbers are much reduced by selection in each generation. As the selections advance more resources are required for their evaluation. The time scale for producing a new winter wheat or barley variety is about 12 years but for spring cereals this may be reduced by selection in the southern hemisphere. More rapid production of true-breeding lines from the progeny of a cross can be achieved by inducing haploids and doubling their chromosome number or by using single seed descent.

Progress in breeding for yield has been measured by comparing the performances of a chronological series of varieties grown under conditions in which disease attack and lodging were prevented. Substantial genetic improvement for yield has been made in winter wheat and spring barley, particularly since the mid-1950s. These improvements have involved shortening the straw and increasing the 'harvest index' or ratio of grain weight to that of the total above-ground biomass. Harvest index is approaching its theoretical maximum, and the positive genetic relationship between straw length and yield suggests that further shortening of the straw would be undesirable. Breeders will, therefore, have to select for higher biomass either directly or indirectly. Physiologically, this will involve an increase in the rate of photosynthesis or a prolongation of photosynthetic capacity during grain filling.

The British market for wheat of biscuit making quality is about 0.6 million tonnes annually and is met by the home-grown crop but much of the high protein wheat required for bread making is imported. Progress has been made in breeding wheats with suitable milling texture and good protein quality but high yielding wheats tend to be low in protein quantity, particularly in the UK climate where grain filling is not normally restricted by high temperatures and drought stress. In addition, in wet harvests, sprouting may seriously reduce the quality of the grain. However, the possibilities for producing wheat of acceptable bread-making quality in the UK are much greater than generally supposed.

Between a fifth and a quarter of the barley crop grown in the UK is purchased by maltsters. Malting quality is a varietal characteristic but much affected by the conditions of crop growth. Apart from variety, the main criterion of acceptability is low grain nitrogen content. The negative relationship between yield and grain protein is, therefore, no impediment to the breeding of high yielding malting varieties. Rapid modification, i.e. enzymic hydrolysis of endosperm cell walls and protein during germination of the grain, is necessary so that a high proportion of the starch in the endosperm cells can be released for breakdown into fermentable sugars. The composition of the endosperm cell walls and the nature of the protein matrix surrounding the starch grains are important factors in determining the rate of modification. Genetic improvements have been made in the rate and ease of modification, and under modern malting regimes, the newest varieties yield considerably higher hot water extracts than the older ones.

Breeding methodology in cereals has changed little in principal since the 1950s but considerable logistical improvements have been made. Small-scale field and laboratory equipment and the development of computer systems for recording and analysing data have allowed the breeder to handle very much larger breeding populations with consequent improvements in the chances of success.

The future contribution of new techniques such as pollen irradiation and DNA transfer between widely differing species or genera are unpredictable but the need for intensive evaluation and selection will remain.

Introduction

National average yields of wheat and barley have risen from about 2.5 t ha^{-1} in the late 1940s to the current level of about 5.8 t ha^{-1} for wheat and 4.4 t ha^{-1} for barley. These increases are due partly to improvements in the management of cereal crops, involving the use of better machinery and of fertilisers, herbicides, fungicides and growth regulators, and partly to the success of plant breeders in improving the genetic potential for yield in these crops and making available new varieties that are able to take advantage of high input farming practices. In winter wheat yields of 10 t ha^{-1} are no longer uncommon and yields of over 13 t ha^{-1} have been recorded; in winter barley yields of 10 t ha^{-1} have been obtained.

Breeding methods

Modern wheat and barley varieties are bred and maintained as pure lines and there is therefore no exploitable variation within them. Genetic improvement is made by crossing chosen varieties and selecting amongst the progeny. Breeding programmes vary enormously in the number of crosses made each year but in general, the larger the programme the greater the chances of success. In the winter wheat programme at Cambridge the breeders normally make about 600 crosses each year and grow up to 2000 F_2 plants from each cross, giving an F_2 population of over one million plants, from which some 45000 are selected. These are grown as ear rows in F_3 and as families of ear rows and parallel yield

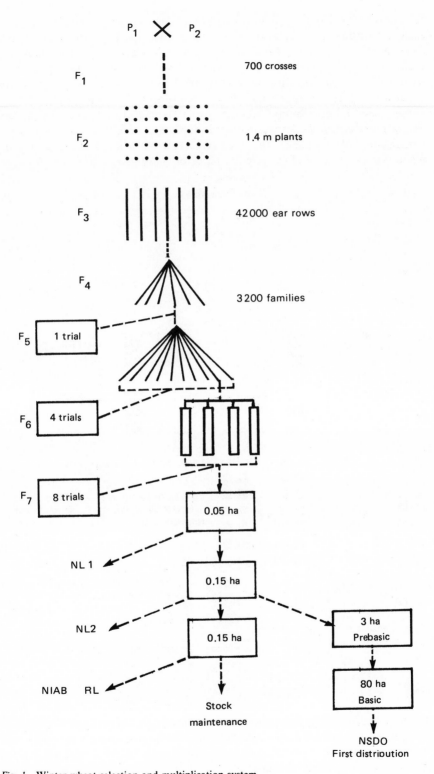

Fig. 1 Winter wheat selection and multiplication system.

7

assessment plots in subsequent generations (Figure 1). As the number of lines in each generation are reduced by selection the resources devoted to their assessment are increased. After six generations of selection five or six candidate varieties may be entered for National List Trials. Of these, perhaps two will receive provisional recommendation by the National Institute of Agricultural Botany after three years in trial. The normal time-scale from making a cross to first commercial distribution of a new variety is 10 to 12 years for winter wheat and winter barley. In spring wheat and barley, which do not have a cold vernalisation requirement, the time-scale can be reduced using a selection nursery in New Zealand (Figure 2). Three or more generations a year may be

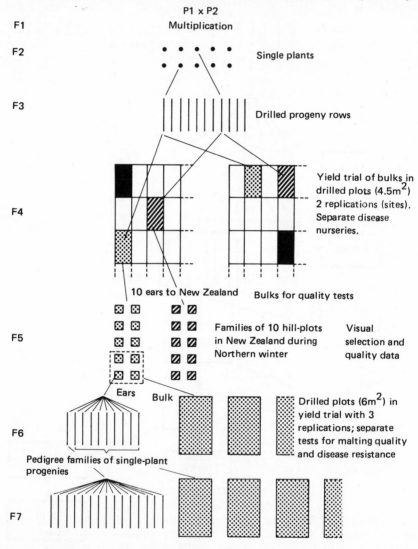

Fig. 2 A selection procedure for spring barley.

grown by using single seed descent (Riggs and Hayter, 1975; Riggs and Snape, 1979) though selection has to be deferred until homozygosity is achieved. In barley, and to a limited extent in wheat, it is possible to induce haploids, having only a single set of chromosomes. Subsequent chromosome doubling, by treating the plants with colchicine, results in doubled haploid lines which are completely homozygous. Thus, early generation hybrid lines can be made to produce pure breeding lines in a single generation, but this technique requires considerable expertise and labour.

Breeding for yield potential

Progress in breeding for higher yield may be assessed by growing trials in which varieties representing a chronological series are compared. Because wheat and barley are self-pollinating crops, varieties maintain their integrity over the years

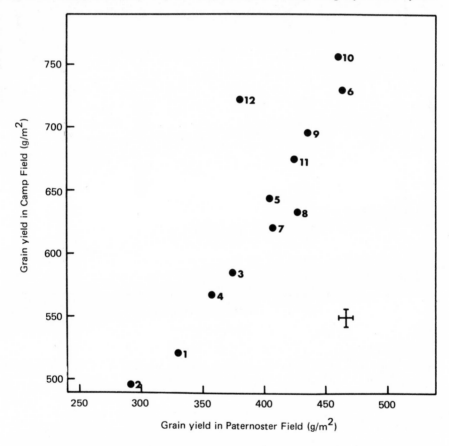

1 – Little Joss (1908), 2 – Holdfast (1935), 3 – Cappelle Desprez (1935), 4 – Maris Widgeon (1964), 5 – Maris Huntsman (1972), 6 – Hobbit (1977), 7 – Mardler (1978), 8, 9 – advanced breeding lines, 10 – Norman (1981), 11 – Armada (1978), 12 – Benoist 10483 (from Austen *et al.*, 1980a).

Fig. 3 Yields of winter wheat varieties grown at high fertility (Camp Field) and low fertility (Paternoster Field) in 1977–78.

and should perform as they did when originally released. However, the management practices of, say the 1940s and 1950s, were not the same as those employed today, and varieties grown then are generally too weak-strawed and susceptible to disease to be grown under modern fertiliser regimes and without fungicide protection. Experiments recently carried out at the Plant Breeding Institute compared old and new varieties of winter wheat (Austin *et al.,* 1980a) and of spring barley (Riggs *et al.,* 1981). In both sets of trials all varieties were protected by fungicides and in some trials lodging was prevented by supporting nets or frames. The experiments demonstrated that significant progress has been made in the genetic improvement of yield potential, particularly since the mid-1950s (Figures 3 and 4) and there is no sign of this trend declining. These yield

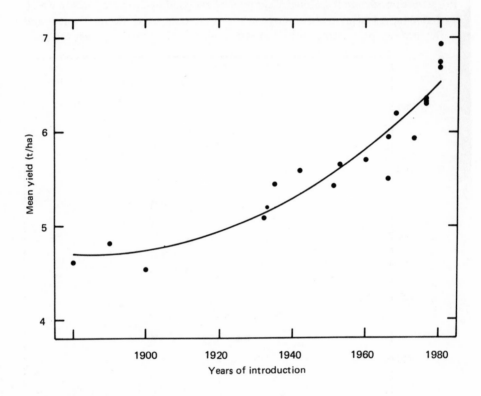

Fig. 4 Mean yields for 20 spring barley varieties plotted against year of introduction. Data from trials grown in 1978, 1979 and 1980 (from Riggs *et al.,* 1981).

increases have been accompanied by a change in the morphology of both crops as a result of a progressive reduction of straw length leading to greater resistance to lodging. The total above-ground biomass of modern varieties differs little from that of the older varieties but the proportion of that weight harvested as grain (harvest index) has increased remarkably from around 37 per cent to 50 per cent or more (Tables 1 and 2).

Table 1 Old and new varieties of winter wheat – yield, height and harvest index

		Yield t ha^{-1}	Height cm	Harvest index (%)
Little Joss	1908	5.9	142	36
Cappelle Desprez	1953	6.7	110	42
Maris Huntsman	1972	7.4	106	46
Hobbit*	1977	8.3	80	48
Mardler*	1978	7.1	77	49
Armada	1978	7.8	97	43
Norman*	1980	8.6	84	51

* Semi-dwarf varieties

Table 2 Old and new varieties of spring barley – yield, height and harvest index

		Yield t ha^{-1}	Height cm	Harvest index (%)
Plumage	1900	4.53	112	38
Spratt Archer	1933	5.19	92	41
Plumage Archer	1935	5.44	98	40
Rika	1951	5.42	85	45
Proctor	1953	5.65	84	42
Zephyr	1966	5.95	79	46
Julia	1968	6.20	77	45
Georgie	1976	6.30	72	50
Egmont	1980	6.93	83	48

In physiological terms, the partitioning of assimilates between straw and grain has been changed so that a greater proportion is stored in the grain. There is probably scope for further increase in harvest index up to about 60 per cent but there must clearly be a physiological limit if an adequate photosynthetic capacity is to be maintained.

Although in these two comparisons, over a range of varieties, there was a clear relationship between decreasing plant height and increasing yield, it is commonly found that within segregating generations from individual crosses, and in the absence of segregation for semi-dwarfing genes, there is a positive association between plant height and yield (Law *et al.,* 1978; Riggs and Hayter, 1975). Clearly, however, high yield can be combined with short straw and indeed many of the modern winter wheat varieties carry the semi-dwarfing gene *Rht2*. This gene, besides shortening the straw, increases grain number per ear and thus may actually improve yield. Nevertheless, amongst segregating material, all with the dwarfing gene, there is still some variation for height and the relationship between height and yield is still positive. This finding led Gale and Law (1977) to advocate a policy of selection for 'tall' dwarfs. In barley, the effect of dwarfing genes on yield is by no means always positive, and whereas for instance the *ert* or 'erectoides' dwarfing gene may increase the number of grains per ear, a compensatory decrease in the weight per grain usually occurs (Riggs and Hayter, 1975).

Further shortening of the straw in wheat and barley is probably undesirable, but limited increases in harvest index up to 55 to 60 per cent may be possible by extending the duration of the grain filling period and improving the leaf area index at anthesis. However, given that higher grain yields are to be achieved with harvest indices not very much higher than those currently recorded, it is obvious that the total above-ground biomass of the crop must be increased. This means that breeders will have to detect and exploit genetic differences in total dry matter production. At the present level of physiological efficiency of the wheat and barley crops, further increases in biomass may be limited by the availability of water and nutrients. Improvements in water economy, reductions in respiratory losses and an increase in the light-saturated rate of photosynthesis in individual leaves would seem to be desirable. Studies of hexaploid triticales in the UK have revealed a significantly greater capacity for biomass production than that of winter wheat (Gregory and Hampson, 1981). Whether this is due to an increased rate or duration of dry matter production is not yet known and may vary with season, but these results suggest that winter cereals in the UK have the genetical and physiological potential for very high biomass production.

Austin et al. (1981) measured photosynthesis of single leaves on field-grown plants of diploid and hexaploid wheats and found that the rate of photosynthesis was 36 per cent higher in the diploids than in the hexaploids. The varieties with higher photosynthetic rates had narrower and smaller leaves with greater mesophyll cell surface. Evans and Dunstone (1970) studied wild progenitors and cultivated wheats at the diploid, tetraploid and hexaploid levels. They concluded that the evolution of wheat had involved a parallel increase in grain and leaf size but coupled with a progressive reduction in the rate of photosynthesis per unit leaf area. However, the increased leaf area of cultivated wheats more than compensated for the reduced rate of photosynthesis and total photosynthesis per flag leaf blade was about four times as great in the cultivated tetraploids and hexaploids as in *Triticum boeoticum* which had the highest rate per unit leaf area.

The duration and rate of grain growth has tended to increase during evolution in wheat and the need to import carbohydrates from the leaves and stems has also increased (Evans and Dunstone, 1970). In barley the importance of stem reserves has been emphasised by Gallagher et al. (1975) and by Daniels et al. (1982). This might seem to be another reason why further shortening of the straw by breeding would be undesirable but the evidence for this is not clear (Austin et al., 1980b).

Riggs et al. (1981) found that even the oldest varieties of spring barley in their experiments yielded acceptably when prevented from lodging and protected from disease. Thus resistance to hazards is essential if the genetic potential for yield is to be realised. Breeders have made significant progress towards reducing losses due to such hazards as lodging, head loss, disease and drought. Stability of yield performance over a range of environments is an important property of modern cereal varieties.

Breeding for grain quality

The British climate is ideal for the production of exceptionally high yields of biscuit and feed wheats by world standards. The market for biscuit wheats is just over half a million tonnes annually and this is virtually all home-grown. The animal feed industry takes three to four million tonnes annually, mostly home-grown. Wheat suitable for bread-making, however, needs to be high in protein and much of it is imported from Canada, the USA, Eastern Europe and the Mediterranean area where high temperatures and moisture stress after heading restrict the period of grain filling, reducing yield and leading to high protein content. Greater uptake of home-grown wheat by the millers will depend on progress in breeding and on the adoption of agronomic practices which can help to offset deleterious climatic effects (Bingham *et al.,* 1981).

Hard milling texture is required in wheats suitable for bread-making; easy separation of the endosperm from the bran and a high proportion of endosperm to bran are required. Fortunately milling texture and clean separation of the bran are strongly varietal characters and independent of growing conditions. The flour must have high protein content of good quality and be relatively free of the enzyme α-amylase. This enzyme is a normal product of germination and may build up rapidly in the grain even before there is evidence of sprouting. Breeding for resistance to sprouting is relatively easy but even the most resistant varieties show deterioration if harvest is delayed. The hazard of sprouting is one of the most serious factors limiting the production of wheat for bread-making in the UK.

The quantity and quality of protein in the flour determines the mechanical properties of the dough, which should be strong and elastic enough to hold the CO_2 produced by fermentation, giving a loaf of large volume and springy texture. Protein quality is strongly heritable and prospects are good that breeders will be able to make improvements by increasing the proportion of the high molecular weight glutenins which are considered to be responsible for gluten strength (Payne *et al.,* 1980). A test based on the sedimentation rate of flour in a solution of sodium dodecyl sulphate (SDS) is proving useful for determining the protein quality of early generation selections. Protein *content,* however, is mainly dependent on environmental effects and although there are small differences between varieties these tend to be inversely related to yielding ability. Thus higher yielding varieties usually have lower protein contents (Pushman and Bingham, 1976; Blackman, 1980). Until fairly recently selection in wheat breeding programmes tended to be either for high yield or for good quality. Some progress has been made in the simultaneous improvement of both factors but the production of wheat of bread-making quality largely depends upon suitable husbandry and timely harvesting. Unless adequate premiums are offered for good quality wheat crops, farmers may not be persuaded to give these crops special treatment. The proportion of home-grown wheat used for bread-making has nevertheless increased in recent years and, with the introduction of new high quality spring wheats, likely to be available soon, this proportion could be further increased.

In contrast to wheat, the industrial consumers of that part of the barley crop not used for animal feed regard low protein content as one of the main criteria of acceptability. The production of malt for the brewing and distilling industries accounts for between a fifth and a quarter of the home-grown crop annually. Malting quality is a varietal characteristic and maltsters have strong preferences for particular varieties. However, the suitability for malting, even of good malting varieties, is very dependent upon growing conditions. When deciding whether to purchase a crop the maltster will consider first the variety and then the nitrogen content of the grain. A nitrogen content of around 1.5 to 1.6 per cent dry matter (DM) is preferred and grain of above 1.8 per cent DM will normally be rejected. Grain appearance and size are also criteria for suitability for malting. The grain should be plump, well-filled and thin-skinned; shrivelled, poorly filled grain is usually low in carbohydrate, high in protein and produces low malt extract. Local weather conditions, causing variation between districts in grain nitrogen content and grain size, are principally responsible for the fact that a large proportion of the production of barley from potentially malting varieties is not, in fact, suitable for malting (Sturgess and Knell, 1979). Drought stress, particularly during grain filling, was found by Morgan and Riggs (1981) to reduce grain size, increase grain nitrogen and reduce hot water extract (HWE).

The malting process involves germinating the grain under controlled conditions so that the starch in the endosperm is released from the cells and partially degraded to polysaccharides which can later be further degraded to fermentable sugars and extracted in hot water. High extract yield is dependent upon ease of modification and minimum loss through respiration and in production of roots and shoots. Varietal requirements of a good malting barley are that its grain should possess the minimum dormancy necessary to prevent sprouting in wet harvests, and that it should be capable of rapidly mobilising the enzymes necessary to break down the endosperm cell walls which should contain relatively low levels of ß-glucan. Within the cells the starch grains are embedded in a protein matrix which must be broken down during modification by proteolytic enzymes. Recent work has revealed that the composition of this protein varies between varieties (Shewry *et al.*, 1979) and may affect malting quality (Baxter and Wainwright, 1979).

Until the 1950s selection for malting quality in barley breeding programmes was not possible except on the basis of visual evaluation of the grain. The malting potential of a new variety was not known until large enough amounts of grain were available for a large-scale malt. This situation was improved when Whitmore and Sparrow (1957) developed a micro-malting test which could be applied to small samples (60 g) of grain. Using a modification of this technique (Gothard *et al.,* 1980), the Chemistry Department of the Plant Breeding Institute now processes 1500–2000 samples a year.

In the early stages of a breeding programme for malting quality the amount of available seed is too small and the number of samples too large for selection on the basis of tests involving malt production. Much progress has been made recently in the development of rapid predictive tests which may be used on large numbers of small samples. Some of these tests have been described and reviewed by Allison *et al.* (1979). All of them are conducted on ungerminated grain and measure a character or characters known to be closely correlated with HWE. Use of such tests enables the breeder to concentrate his attention early on those selections most likely to possess malting potential.

In a comparative study of the malting performances of old and new barley varieties grown in the glasshouse, Gothard *et al.* (1978) found little evidence of an improvement in malting ability between Plumage Archer (1920) and Ark Royal (1976). They concluded that there was little scope for further increases in potential HWE and that breeders should attempt to produce varieties which modify rapidly and hence achieve a higher proportion of their potential HWE in the shorter modification period now favoured by the industry.

Micro-malting tests conducted on field-grown barley from one of the experiments described by Riggs *et al.* (1981) do reveal increases in HWE from the older to the more modern malting varieties (Figure 5), reflecting the increases in grain yield (Figure 6). Indeed a possible explanation for the improvement in HWE is that the higher grain yields of the newer varieties are

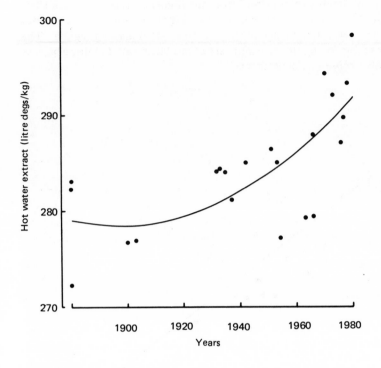

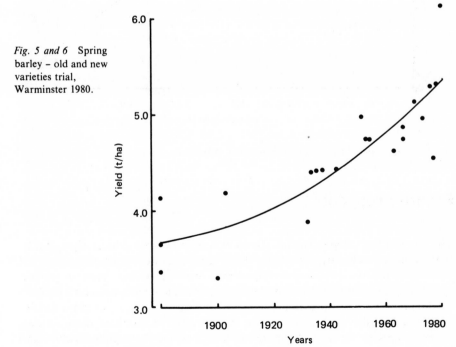

Fig. 5 and 6 Spring barley – old and new varieties trial, Warminster 1980.

associated with reduced grain nitrogen contents (Figure 7) and that this in turn is associated with higher HWE. However, the extract measurements were adjusted for grain nitrogen content and there was no correlation between the two characters. A more likely explanation is that the higher extracts obtained from the modern varieties resulted from their ability to modify rapidly in the shorter period (4 days) allowed in the tests and typical of modern malting regimes. The progress made in improving the ease and rate of modification of malting barleys is of considerable economic significance.

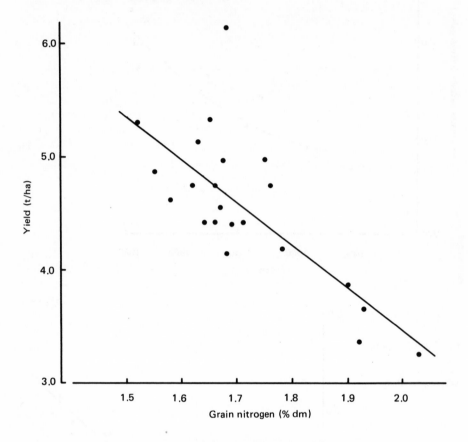

Fig. 7 Spring barley – old and new varieties trial, Warminster 1980.

Future prospects

The success of cereal breeding programmes in recent years has been largely due to improvements in logistics, enabling the breeder to handle much more material than was previously possible: small-plot machinery has been developed specifically for plant breeders so that sowing and harvesting need no longer be predominantly hand operations; tests for disease resistance and grain quality have been refined and adapted for screening large numbers of selections; developments in the field of electronics have enabled the rapid collection and processing of data so that decisions can be made with minimum delay and maximum objectivity. Further improvements of this sort will undoubtedly be made but it is probable that the main benefits have already been felt.

The trend in genetic improvement of yield as revealed by studies on old and new varieties does not yet appear to show signs of decline and there should be further scope for improvement using 'conventional' methods for another 10 years or so. A concept that might have immediate benefits for stability of yield and for the non-chemical control of major diseases is that of growing variety mixtures (Wolfe *et al.*, 1981). If this practice were to become widely accepted by farmers there might be implications for both breeders and physiologists in determining, for example, the best field types to be mixed for optimum exploitation of the environment.

Breeding for high biomass is likely to become important as further progress in improving harvest index slows; from the breeder's point of view this might be best achieved indirectly by continuing to select for high grain yield whilst maintaining high harvest indices. Extension of the growing period or an increase in growth rate seem inescapable requirements of such a policy.

Positive breeding for specific physiological objectives such as high photosynthetic rate or increased efficiency of nitrogen uptake and utilisation is likely to be impractical unless easily measured indices can be defined.

Exploitation of useful genes from wild relatives is hampered by the necessity for extensive back-crossing coupled with selection for the required genes. Recent work on *Nicotiana* by Jinks *et al.* (1981) and on spring barley by Hayter and Powell (pers. comm.) suggests that pollen irradiation may be a means of transferring limited amounts of genetic information from the male parent. Molecular genetics is receiving much attention, and investigations are being pursued at the Plant Breeding Institute into the use of recombinant DNA techniques for the isolation, characterisation and possible transfer of plant genes between species or genera. Initial success is likely to be achieved in crops other than the cereals, but whatever the developments in this field, the need for intensive evaluation and selection between progeny will remain the essential basis of cereal breeding programmes.

References

ALLISON, M.J., ELLIS, R.P., HAYTER, A.M. and SWANSTON, J.S. 1979. Breeding for malting quality at the Scottish Plant Breeding Station. *Report of the Scottish Plant Breeding Station 1978–1979:* 92–139.

AUSTIN, R.B., BINGHAM, J., BLACKWELL, R.D., EVANS, L.T., FORD, M.A., MORGAN, C.L. and TAYLOR, M. 1980a. Genetic improvements in winter wheat yields since 1900 and associated physiological changes. *Journal of Agricultural Science, Cambridge* **94**, 675–689.

AUSTIN, R.B., MORGAN, C.L., FORD, M.A. and BLACKWELL, R.D. 1980b. Contributions to grain yield from pre-anthesis assimilation in tall and dwarf barley phenotypes in two contrasting seasons. *Annals of Botany* **45**, 309–319.

AUSTIN, R.B., FORD, M.A., MORGAN, C.L. and PARKER, M.L. 1981. Photosynthesis in wheat and allied species *Annual Report of the Plant Breeding Institute, Cambridge 1980,* pp. 100–102.

BAXTER, E.D. and WAINWRIGHT, T. 1979. Hordein and malting quality. *Journal of the American Society of Brewing Chemistry* **37**, 8–12.

BINGHAM, J., BLACKMAN, J.A., ANGUS, W.J. and LONGBOTTOM, W. 1981. Breeding and management of wheat varieties. In: *The Yield of Cereals*, Royal Agricultural Society of England, Cereals Demonstration and Information Unit. 16–30.

BLACKMAN, J. A. 1980. Wheat physiology in relation to breeding. In: *The Yield of Cereals,* Royal Agricultural Society of England, Cereals Demonstration and Information Unit. 1–15.

DANIELS, R.W., ALCOCK, M.B. and SCARISBRICK, D.H. 1982. A reappraisal of stem reserve contribution to grain yield in spring barley (*Hordeum vulgare* L.). *Journal of Agricultural Science, Cambridge* **98**, 347–355.

EVANS, L.T. and DUNSTONE, R.L. 1970. Some physiological aspects of evolution in wheat. *Australian Journal of Biological Sciences* **23**, 725–741.

GALE, M.D. and LAW, C.N. 1977. The identification and exploitation of Norin 10 semi-dwarfing genes. *Annual Report of the Plant Breeding Institute, Cambridge, 1976*, pp. 21–35.

GALLAGHER, J.N., BISCOE, P.V. and SCOTT, R.K. 1975. Barley and its environment. V. Stability of grain weight. *Journal of Applied Ecology* **12**, 319–336.

GOTHARD, P.G., JENKINS, G. and MORGAN, A.G. 1978. Comparative malting performance of old and new barley varieties. *Journal of the Institute of Brewing* **84**, 332–336.

GOTHARD, P.G., MORGAN, A.G. and SMITH, D.B. 1980. Evaluation of a micro-malting procedure used to aid a plant breeding programme. *Journal of the Institute of Brewing* **86**, 69–73.

GREGORY, R.S. and HAMPSON, P.R. 1981. Hexaploid triticale: crop development. *Annual Report of the Plant Breeding Institute, Cambridge 1980*, p. 29.

JINKS, J.L., CALIGARI, P.D.S. and INGRAM, N.R. 1981. Gene transfer in *Nicotiana rustica* using irradiated pollen. *Nature* **291**, 586–588.

LAW, C.N., SNAPE, J.W. and WORLAND, A.J. 1978. The genetical relationship between height and yield in wheat. *Heredity* **40**, 133–151.

MORGAN, A.G. and RIGGS, T.J. 1981. Effects of drought on yield and on grain and malt characters in spring barley. *Journal of the Science of Food and Agriculture* **32**, 339–346.

PAYNE, P.I., HARRIS, P.A., LAW, C.N., HOLT, L.M. and BLACKMAN, J.A. 1980. The high-molecular-weight sub-units of glutenin: structure, genetics and relationship to bread-making quality. *Annales de Technologie Agricole* **29**, 309–320.

PUSHMAN, F.M. and BINGHAM, J. 1976. The effects of granular nitrogen fertilizer and a foliar spray of urea on the yield and bread-making quality of ten winter wheats. *Journal of Agricultural Science, Cambridge* **87**, 281–292.

RIGGS, T.J. and HAYTER, A.M. 1975. A study of the inheritance and inter-relationships of some agronomically important characters in spring barley. *Theoretical and Applied Genetics* **46**, 257–264.

RIGGS, T.J. and SNAPE, J.W. 1977. Effects of linkage and interaction in a comparison of theoretical populations derived by diploidized haploid and single seed descent methods. *Theoretical and Applied Genetics* **49**, 111–115.

RIGGS, T.J., HANSON, P.R., START, N.D., MILES, D.M., MORGAN, C.L. and FORD, M.A. 1981. Comparison of spring barley varieties grown in England and Wales between 1880 and 1980. *Journal of Agricultural Science, Cambridge* **97**, 599–610.

SHEWRY, P.R., FAULKS, A.J., PARMAR, S. and MIFLIN, B.J. 1979. The storage protein (hordein) polypeptide pattern of barley (*Hordeum vulgare* L.) in relation to varietal identification and disease resistance. *Journal of the National Institute of Agricultural Botany* **15**, 34–50.

WHITMORE, E.T. and SPARROW, D.H.B. 1957. Laboratory micro-malting technique. *Journal of the Institute of Brewing* **62**, 397–398.

WOLFE, M.S., BARRETT, J.A. and JENKINS, J.E.E. 1981. The use of cultivar mixtures for disease control. In: Jenkyn, J.F. and Plumb, R.T. (eds.) *Strategies for the Control of Cereal Disease.* Blackwell Scientific Publications, Oxford. 73–80.

Discussion

Dr Little asked Dr Riggs to comment on the potential for genetic manipulation. Dr Riggs explained that the techniques involved removing small sections of DNA from one organism and transferring them to another organism which already had most of the desirable characteristics, e.g. a stiff straw gene from wheat into barley. The foreign DNA was fused with the DNA of the host, and the whole plant had to be regenerated from this cell. Such regeneration was possible with some species, e.g. potatoes but with cereals it was unlikely to be possible for several years.

Mr Wadsworth asked if biomass production would increase in future, perhaps with even larger dressings of nitrogen. Dr Riggs said that the genetic variation in biomass production had not so far responded to selection for yield.

M Viaux questioned whether there could be climatic restrictions on harvest index. In France, harvest indexes of about 60 per cent had been recorded, and work published in W Germany quoted similar figures. Dr Riggs remarked that harvest indexes as high as 60 per cent were rare in the UK – the usual maximum was 50–55 per cent, and was fairly stable. Several participants agreed, and finally *Mr Needham* suggested there might be differences in the definition of harvest index – the UK figure was usually based on grain as a percentage of above-ground dry matter.

Cereal plant development – assessment and use

E J M Kirby and Margaret Appleyard
Plant Breeding Institute, Cambridge

Summary

Appearance of leaves, tillers and ear emergence, which characterise plant development are the result of the activity of the shoot apex. At first the apex produces leaf primordia and later spikelet initials which differentiate to form the floral organs. These changes give the apex characteristic, recognisable forms. Leaves appear at a constant rate in relation to degree days. The total number of leaves per shoot varies with genotype, date of sowing and other factors. Tiller initiation and growth is closely related to leaf growth. Stem elongation starts when the apex is at about anther primordium stage. The growth of each internode is correlated with growth of the subtending leaf. Because of differences in number of leaves and tillers, apex stages are not well correlated with growth stages and there is variation in the date at which comparative apex stages are reached in different crops. Therefore, it may be important to assess apex development stage when applying certain treatments or estimating the affect of stress.

Plant development

The concept of development is concerned with increase in complexity of form and/or increase in number of parts. Thus the increase in number of leaves on the main shoot or on the plant is a measure of advancing development. Shooting, boot formation and ear emergence likewise indicate the differention and maturation of the ear and further development of the plant. All the organs of the shoot arise as primordia which are initiated by changes in patterns of cell division and growth at the shoot apex. The physiological and morphological changes at the apex presage changes in external form of the plant.

Thus there are different levels at which development of the plant may be described, ranging from gross external form (e.g. 'fully-tillered') to physiological criteria at the cellular level (e.g. 'floral initiation'). While there is general agreement about the necessity to describe and record crop development, the level at which such descriptions should be made and the criteria which should be used are often not adequately defined. A prime consideration must be where and how a particular treatment or environmental stress affects plant growth or final yield. In some cases the plant response to a treatment is related to the activity of cells in the shoot apex or in other meristems. When a treatment is

21

applied at certain stages of development such a response may produce changes which lead to a reduction in yield. Therefore, it may be important to know the critical stage and to be able to assess it.

In this paper, changes which occur at the shoot apex are outlined and development of leaves, tillers and internodes is described. The relationships between shoot apex, leaf and tiller development and growth stage are discussed. Variation in the timing of development is described. Most emphasis is put on the early part of the life cycle and changes after ear emergence are not considered.

Shoot apex development

The shoot apex forms in the seed during embryo development on the parent plant. When the seed is mature the embryo has already initiated three or four leaf primordia. After germination more leaves are initiated on the dome-shaped apex. After a full complement of leaves for that shoot has been initiated a phase of spikelet initiation follows and an embryo ear is formed. The transition from vegetative to floral phase is marked by elongation of the apex, which becomes cylindrical in form. Spikelet primordia are first recognised at the double ridge stage. After the double ridge stage, spikelet development proceeds and the primordia of florets and of floral organs are laid down in sequence. At about the time when spikelet initiation is complete, stem elongation and rapid ear growth begins. During this sequence there is a continuum of development of the apex, but it is possible to recognise and define a number of different stages, usually by reference to the appearance of the most recently initiated organ. Details of apex development are contained in a number of research papers and a general review and description of cereal plant development has been published recently (Kirby and Appleyard, 1981).

Leaf development and emergence

Growth and emergence of leaves is of central importance to crop growth and yield, but the number of emerged leaves is also a parameter of development.

Leaf initiation occurs early in shoot development and all the leaves that will later grow and expand are present when only from three to six of those leaves have emerged. Except in very cold weather, the time from initiation of one leaf to the next is three to four days, while the time from the emergence of one leaf to the emergence of the next is six to 10 days.

In the field, leaf emergence on a shoot may vary from very low rates (0 to 0.05 leaves per day) in winter to rates of about 0.15 leaves per day in April and May. However, when the rate of leaf emergence is expressed in terms of accumulated degree days (heat units, thermal time) it appears to be constant over the complete period of leaf emergence (Figure 1). The rate of leaf emergence on the main shoot varies from about 0.006 to 0.02 leaves ($°C$ day)$^{-1}$ depending on variety, date of sowing and other factors, possibly rate of change of daylength (Baker, Gallagher and Monteith, 1980). There is also evidence that base temperature (the temperature at which leaf emergence ceases) varies (Kirby, Appleyard and Fellowes, 1982). Thus the number of emerged leaves on the main shoot measures the progress of plant development up to ear emergence. Each leaf is an increment in the life cycle, and appears only after a predictable number of day degrees.

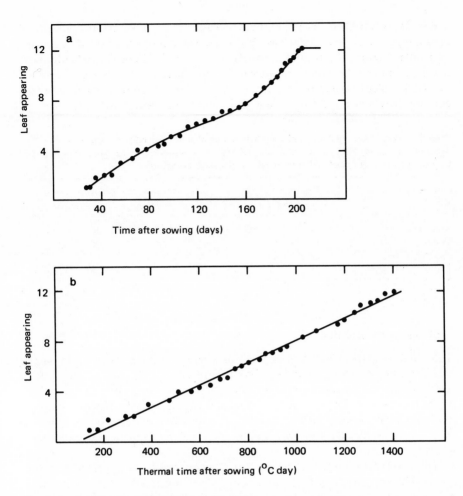

Fig. 1 Leaf appearance in Huntsman winter wheat
a) plotted against days after sowing and
b) plotted against thermal time (accumulated temperature or degree days) (From Gallagher, 1976).

The total number of leaves on the main shoot varies by about twofold. Some spring barley varieties sown at high latitudes (e.g. Scotland) may form as few as seven or eight leaves, while winter varieties sown in East Anglia early in September produce 14 or 15 leaves on the main shoot. Variation in total number of leaves is chiefly due to variation in genotype, temperature, daylength, plant population and soil fertility. For example, the effect of date of sowing is shown in Table 1.

Table 1 Number of leaves on the main stem in relation to sowing date Cambridge 1980/81

Sowing	Norman	Highbury	Igri	Ark Royal
September	14	11	15	12
October	11	11	13	11
November	10	10	12	11
February	11	9	10	10

23

Because of variation in total number of leaves, the number of emerged leaves does not have a constant relationship with apex development. As will be shown in a later section, the beginning of stem elongation is correlated with apex development and the number of internodes (and therefore the number of leaves) involved in stem elongation is more or less constant. Therefore, the number of emerged leaves at a particular stage of development varies (Table 2).

Table 2 Effect of sowing date on relation between number of emerged leaves and apex stage for winter wheat, variety Norman, at Cambridge 1980/81. Final number of leaves, number of emerged leaves at double ridge stage and at terminal spikelet stage are shown.

Sowing date	Final number of leaves	Number of emerged leaves:	
		at double ridges	at terminal spikelet
September	14	8	10
October	11	7	8
November	10	6	7
February	11	7	8

Leaf emergence and tillering

Tiller buds arise from meristems in the axils of leaves. A ridge of tissue is initiated and a swelling develops around its flank to form a prophyll primordium. Later, as leaf primordia are initiated the meristem becomes a shoot apex similar to that of the main shoot. The apex follows a similar course of development to that of the main shoot, first initiating a number of leaves, then spikelets on the embryo ear. The prophyll and leaves grow and the tiller emerges from the subtending leaf sheath.

Tiller buds are initiated in the axil of the coleoptile and the lower leaves of the plant. They do not form in the axil of the leaves which will subtend elongated internodes on the stem, with the exception of the leaf subtending the lowermost internode and sometimes the leaf distal to it. For example, on the main shoot of a spring barley plant with 10 leaves, five primary tiller buds (TC to T4) are initiated. The growth and emergence of leaves and the initiation, growth and emergence of tillers are closely in phase with each other. The initiation of a tiller can be seen when the subtending leaf is fully expanded (Kirby and Faris, 1970) and emerges when two further leaves have expanded (Kirby and Riggs, 1980; Masle-Meynard and Sebillotte, 1981). Thus it is possible to predict the potential production of tillers from leaf emergence data (Table 3).

Initiation of tiller buds appears to be little affected by environmental factors, but the growth of the tiller buds is affected by a number of factors (which may be inter-related), e.g. nutrient availability and plant population. Thus the number of tillers produced may only be equal to potential for a short period of development.

Tillers have fewer total leaves than the main shoot and the number of leaves appears to be related to tiller position. A typical sequence, illustrated by spring barley in which 10 leaves were formed on the main shoot was TC, eight leaves; T1, seven leaves; T2, seven leaves and T3, six leaves. Because fewer leaves are formed and the period of leaf initiation is shorter the interval between bud

24

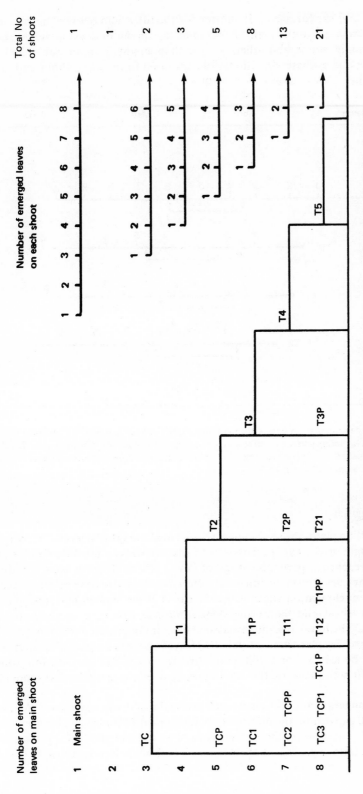

Table 3 Diagram to show the relationship between leaf emergence and tillering. The scheme illustrates potential tillering under ideal conditions.

initiation and ear formation is shorter for the tiller than between germination and ear formation in the main shoot. Thus the spread of developmental stages between main shoot and tillers is less than might be anticipated and ear emergence and anthesis are almost synchronised in the main shoot and tillers (Figure 2).

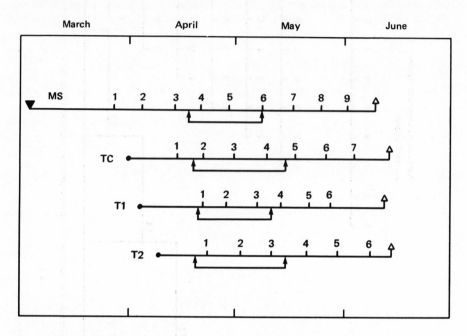

Fig. 2 The development pattern of the main shoot (MS), coleoptile tiller (TC), and tillers 1 and 2 (T1 and T2), for spring wheat Kolibri sown on 2 March. The symbols are ▼ sowing time, ⬥──⬥ ear initiation phase, ↑ ear emergence. The numbers above the lines represent the number of expanded leaves (from Stern and Kirby, 1979).

Stem elongation

In the seedling plant, the shoot apex is found at about ground level. The increase in stem length, which carries the ear upwards, occurs only when the floral shoot apex has reached a particular stage of development. There is some variation between varieties, and environmental differences may also have an effect, but in general stem elongation starts when the ear is at the stamen initiation phase.

In both wheat and barley the stem comprises from five to six elongated internodes. The lower internodes, associated with tillers, do not elongate. Thus in a spring barley plant with a total of 10 leaves on the main stem, the internodes subtended by leaves 4 or 5 will be the first to elongate (Figure 3). In a winter barley plant with 14 leaves, the first internode to elongate will be that subtended by leaf 9.

Stem elongation and leaf emergence proceed in a definite sequence. As a leaf reaches full expansion, the internode begins elongation and grows for a length of time equal to the time for the emergence of two leaves (Figure 4). Each successive internode starts to grow as the previous one is about half its final length (Figure 5).

26

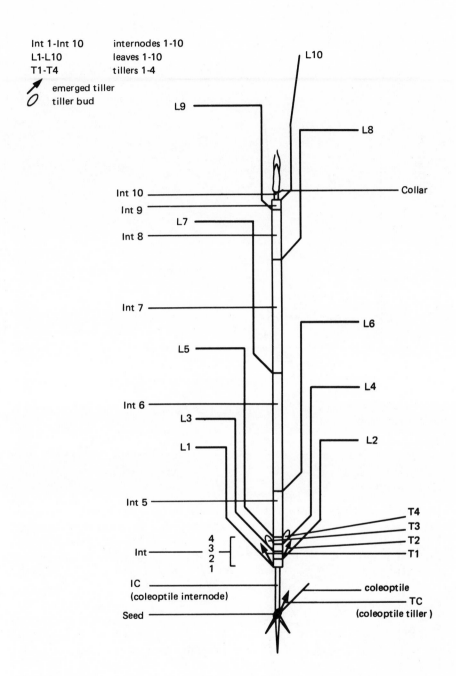

Fig. 3 A diagram of a spring barley plant to show the position of tillers and elongated internodes. This plant has 10 leaves on the main shoot and is shown at the time of flag leaf emergence.

27

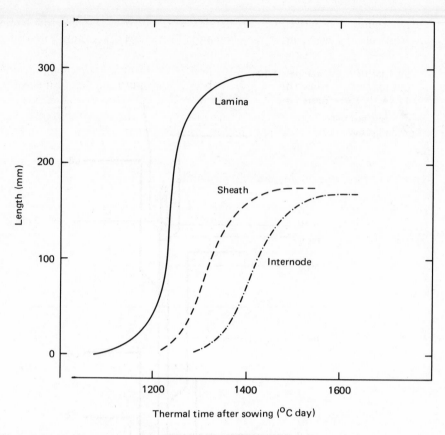

Fig. 4 Length of the lamina, sheath and internode of leaf 7 in Huntsman winter wheat in relation to thermal time (from Gallagher, 1976).

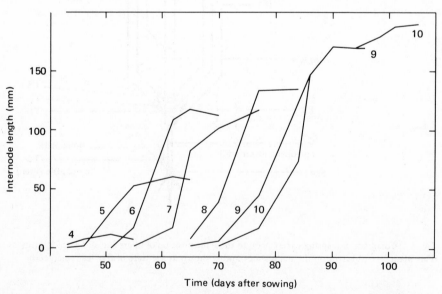

Fig. 5 Length of internodes 4 to 10 plotted against days after sowing in Proctor spring barley.

28

The beginning of stem elongation heralds the period of maximum growth rate of the shoot (and therefore of the plant and of the crop). For example in winter wheat during the pre-stem elongation phase the rate of growth of the shoot was, at most, 40 mg day^{-1} (Figure 6). In the period following the beginning of stem elongation, stem growth proceeded at about 75 mg day^{-1} and rapid ear growth, which started after stem elongation, contributed about 35 mg day^{-1}. During most of the period of rapid growth leaves are not growing and only the stem and ear contribute to shoot growth. Further evidence that rates of dry matter accumulation are high in stems and ears may be adduced from considering the distribution of dry matter in the mature plant. Of the total dry matter at ear emergence the stems and ears together comprise about 60 per cent.

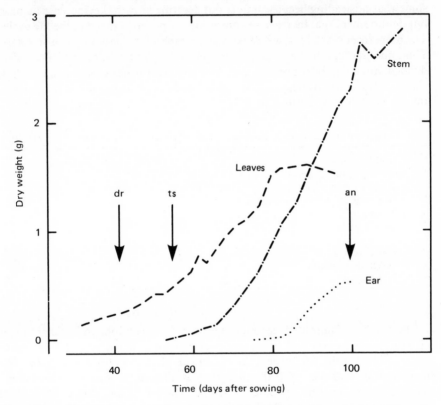

Fig. 6 Dry weight of leaves, stem and ear and stage of development of the main shoot of Cappelle winter wheat. dr, double ridges; ts, terminal spikelet; an, anthesis (from Brooking and Kirby, 1981).

Variation in plant development

Generally, progress of a crop through its life cycle is measured by calendar date (e.g. encapsulated in phrases such as 'the dry mass of the crop on such a date was') or by the superficial appearance of the crop or plant (e.g. 'severe frost was experienced as tiller emergence began'). Where crop response depends on plant development, particularly on the physiological condition of the shoot apex and

29

differentiating organs, it is necessary to consider how well either calendar date or external criteria predict apex development.

Growth stage scales

There are internationally accepted standards of definition and description of plant form available for many crops. The best known and most widely used standards for cereals used in Britain are the 'Feekes' scale (Large, 1954) and the 'Zadoks' code (Zadoks, *et al.*, 1974; Tottman and Makepeace, 1979). These scales are based on 'growth stages' of the plant, although the term growth stage is somewhat misleading because it does not describe growth (i.e. increase in mass) but development (i.e. increase in complexity or progress through the life cycle). The more recent system, the Zadoks code, is expected to be adopted as standard. This code changes the basis of description as the plant develops and the code is divided into a number of sections, each of which is further subdivided (Table 4). These sections may overlap, e.g. sections 1 and 2, or may be sequential phases in the life cycle, e.g. sections 5 to 9.

Table 4   Principal growth stages of the 'Zadoks' decimal code (Zadoks, Chang and Konzak, 1974)

0	Germination
1	Seedling growth (number of unfolded leaves on main shoot)
2	Tillering (number of tillers)
3	Stem elongation (number of detectable nodes)
4	Booting
5	Ear emergence
6	Anthesis
7	Milk development
8	Dough development
9	Ripening

The number of unfolded leaves on the main shoot (Zadoks code, Section 1) is an objective criterion and because leaves emerge at equal intervals of degree days, it divides the life cycle into a number of meaningful increments. The temperature response of leaf emergence is known or can be ascertained, particularly in relation to date of sowing (Baker *et al.*, 1980). Thus plant development can be precisely described in terms of number of emerged leaves and, knowing about temperature trends, the number of leaves at some future date may be estimated.

Questions arise as to how far a Zadoks Section 1 score (a count of the number of unfolded leaves on the main shoot) describes the state of the shoot apex or other developmental parameters, e.g. stem elongation. Is a plant with a specified number of leaves comparable with another plant with the same number of leaves but sown at some other date or treated in some other manner? Are plants of different varieties with the same number of emerged leaves sown under comparable conditions at the same stage of development? The answer to these questions is no. Studies show that the number of emerged leaves does not give a good indication of apex stage or other associated characters. Winter barley or

Number of emerged leaves on main stem

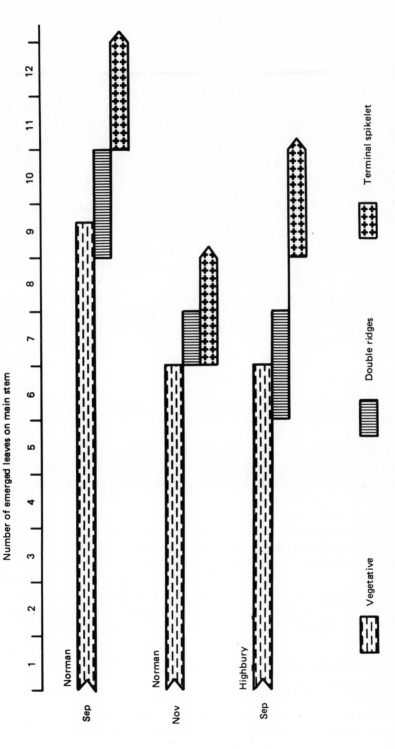

Fig. 7 Number of emerged leaves on the main shoot versus stage of development for Norman winter wheat and Highbury spring wheat at Cambridge. Norman was sown in mid–September and mid–November. Highbury was sown in September at the same time as Norman. In some cases more than one developmental stage occurs at the same number of emerged leaves. This was particularly noticeable in the November sown Norman where all stages from double ridges to terminal spikelet were observed on plants with seven emerged leaves.

winter wheat sown on different dates differ in apex stage at a particular leaf number and contrasting varieties sown at the same time, achieve different stages of development at the same leaf number (Figure 7). This figure shows the contrast between a winter and a spring variety, but differences have also been found between, for example, spring barley varieties differing in ear type (6-row v. 2-row). The basis for this variation is probably due to variation in total number of leaves formed on the shoot and a good correlation exists between final number of leaves and number of unfolded leaves at a particular stage (Table 2).

It is well established that there is no relation between Zadoks Section 2 scores (number of tillers) and development (Tottman, 1977). This may easily be seen by inspection of data where a treatment affecting plant growth, such as nitrogen or plant population, has a large affect on tiller number, but has little or no affect on plant development. Therefore the formulation of recommendations in terms of number of tillers for timing of treatments should be avoided.

The systematic scoring of Zadoks Section 1 and Section 2 in parallel does have considerable value and conveys information about tillering in relation to potential tillering. For example, if the comparative scores for two different crops were 1.5, 2.1 and 1.5, 2.4 then, by reference to the relation between number of leaves and number of tillers (Table 3), it is clear that in the second plant tillering is proceeding at potential, whereas in the first plant tillering is severely restricted.

Section 3 of the Zadoks code is mostly based upon stem elongation, measured by 'number of nodes detectable'. As already shown, the elongation of an internode is closely related to the emergence of its subtending leaf. Like leaf emergence, therefore, a period between the commencement of elongation (or other comparable stage) of two successive internodes is a definable period in terms of accumulated degree days and similarly is a predictable process. As already shown stem elongation starts at a known stage and the same number of elongated internodes is always involved. This reinforces the usefulness of this criterion as a description of plant development.

The problems in the use of Section 3 reside in the definition of stages described. Sub division 3.0 is a special case, for pseudo stem erection is an almost undefinable character which is so subjective as to be of little value. It is more objectively defined by French agronomists who use the description 'ear at 1 cm' (tip of the ear 1 cm above the plane of tillering) (Couvreur et al., 1980). In stage 3.1 and succeeding stages the definition of detectable nodes is open to debate. To the botanists, a node means a region on the stem where a leaf is attached, whereas the farmer thinks of the enlarged sheath base of the leaves which arise on the elongated stem (knot or pulvinus to the botanist). The definition of node detectable will be more rigorously defined in a new edition of the BCPC booklet, but the most satisfactory definition of a node is probably by reference to an elongated internode associated with it; for this purpose an internode has elongated when it exceeds 10 mm. On this criterion internode elongation and Zadoks Section 3 become more or less synonymous and precisely describe plant development over the period.

During the period before ear emergence (Zadoks stage 4 and succeeding stages are not considered in the paper) growth stage scores may not give much information about apex development. If the response to treatment or environment is mediated through apex development then direct observation may give information which cannot be obtained otherwise.

Variation in plant development in the field

Another consideration important in relation to the timing of treatment or assessment of crop response to environment is the degree to which development varies between crops. Cereal husbandry techniques vary in many respects, for example in the variety used and date of sowing, and these factors may affect the time at which developmental events occur.

An important husbandry variant is time of sowing. A winter cereal may be sown from early in September until November and a few crops may even be sown in January or February. It has already been shown that time of sowing has significant effects on plant morphology (e.g. number of leaves). In winter barley, early-sown crops may have reached the double ridge stage at the beginning of November, while in later sown crops this stage may not be achieved until two or three months later (Figure 8). The time at which maximum number of primordia is reached and the time of the beginning of stem elongation show similar, though less extreme variation.

There are also appreciable differences between varieties. For example Huntsman and Talent sown on the same day may vary by almost a month in the time at which double ridges become detectable (Figure 9). The differences in ear type and spikelet number between wheat and barley are the basis for the different patterns of ear development seen in these crops (Figure 9). Finally, year-to-year differences in weather may result in significant differences in the time at which comparable stages of development are attained (Figure 10).

Relation between stage of development and husbandry

The stage of apex development may be crucial for timing some agronomic treatments. This has been firmly established for some practices and a good example of this is the timing of application of herbicides containing 2,4–D and MCPA. In other cases the relationship has not been clearly shown and this may be because relevant plant development data have not been recorded in parallel with the regime of treatments. Furthermore, a knowledge of the course of development in the cereal plant may suggest hypotheses as to the likely response to treatment. Such hypotheses could be tested and may lead to the improvement of practices. An example of this is the apparent relation between stem growth and rate of plant growth. An objective of current fertiliser practice is to ensure that nitrogen does not limit growth during the time when it is most rapid (Lidgate, 1981). The most rapid growth occurs following terminal spikelet formation and this appears to be a critical stage for the main application of nitrogen top dressing. However, the timing of application is complicated by low temperatures, the need for nitrogen to be dissolved in the soil solution and the possibility of leaching due to heavy rain.

Systematic recording of apex development may enable predictions to be made about effects of environmental stress. For example, frost damage or winter kill is more severe on floral apices than on vegetative apices. An early sown variety with

33

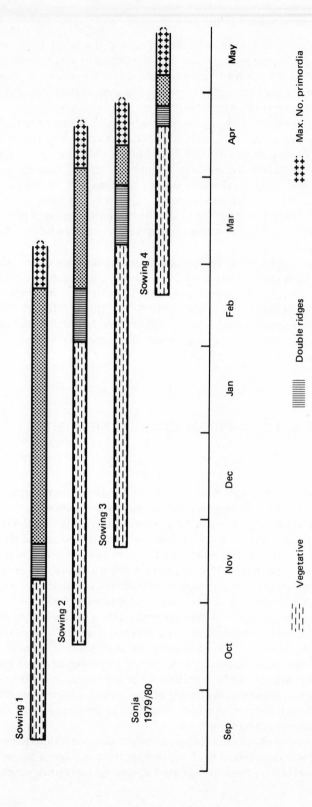

Fig. 8 Timing of stages of development of main shoot of Sonja winter barley sown in mid–September (1), mid–October (2), mid–November (3) and mid–February (4).

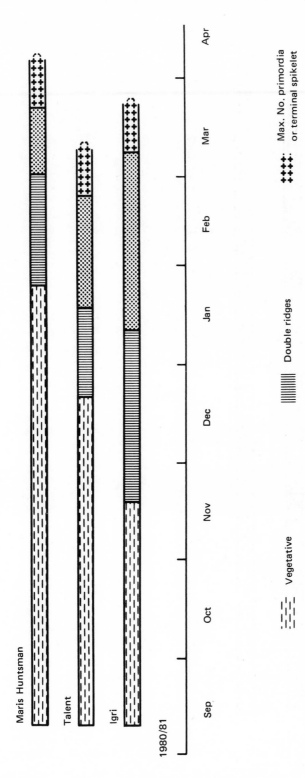

Fig. 9 Timing of stages of development of main shoot of winter wheat and winter barley sown in mid–September.

35

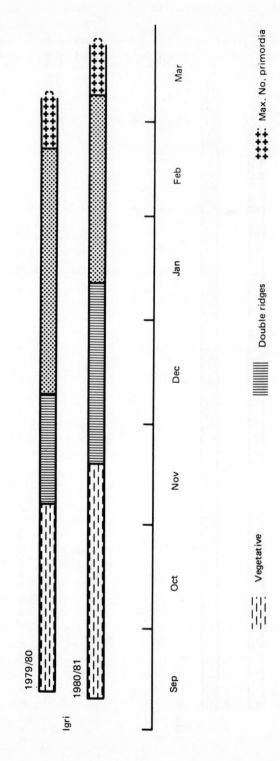

Fig. 10 Timing of stages of development of Igri winter barley sown in 1979 and 1980.

low vernalisation response which may reach the floral stage before Christmas, is likely to sustain more damage than one at the vegetative stage. Meiosis is another example of critical stage of development. Drought, (Saini and Aspinall, 1982a) high temperature (Saini and Aspinall, 1982b) and possibly low temperatures (frost) at about the time of meiosis have been shown to induce sterility and reduce grain number per ear.

Assessment of development

In this paper it has been shown that there is considerable variation in plant development patterns. Modern husbandry techniques involve use of growth regulators and herbicides. It is likely that the efficacy of these substances would be improved if they were applied at defined stages of plant development and it is relevant to consider how to assess development most easily. Essentially for a technique to be useful it should have certain basic features. Ideally the criteria used for research and development should also be applicable for use by the farmer. It must assess directly the development of the organ which may be affected by treatment at certain critical stages. Alternatively the assessment may be made on other characters which are closely correlated in all environments.

A technique which may become available and may form a valuable adjunct to other methods of assessment is computer simulation of development. Major factors which affect development have been identified and responses of the plant to them have been quantified. Integration of the various response functions in a computer program could produce a plant development model which when supplied with the appropriate parameters of, for example, genotype, time of sowing and weather data would estimate plant development. A number of such models is under construction including that co-ordinated by the Yield Variation Group of the ARC.

The assessment of growth stages, while conveying valuable information about some aspects of plant development, often is not a good guide to apex development. Some improvement in growth stage techniques may be effected by identifying external features which have a better correlation with fundamental differences in development. An example is the use of the length of the longest sheath (>5 cm) which has replaced 'pseudo stem erection' (Tottman, 1977). Such criteria should be objective and based on measured characters rather than on subjective assessments of growth rate or position (e.g. pseudo stem erection).

Some information can best be obtained by direct observation. This is a relatively simple technique. A stereoscopic microscope is essential but otherwise the equipment needed is very simple. With a little experience an apex can be prepared and its stage of development assessed in a few minutes. Observation of apex development relates directly to research results and may allow estimation of future development and convey numerical or quantitative information about the plant.

References

BAKER, C.K., GALLAGHER, J.N. and MONTEITH, J.L. 1980. Daylength change and leaf appearance in winter wheat. *Plant, Cell and Environment* 3, 285–287.

BROOKING, I.R. and KIRBY, E.J.M. 1981. Interrelationships between stem and ear development in winter wheat: the effects of a Norin 10 dwarfing gene, Gai/Rht$_2$. *Journal of Agricultural Science* 97, 373–381.

COUVREUR, F., INGOAT, G. and MASSÉ, J. 1980. Les stades du blé. Institute Technique des Céréales et des Fourages, Paris.

GALLAGHER, J.N. 1976. The growth of cereals in relation to weather. PhD thesis, University of Nottingham.

KIRBY, E.J.M. and APPLEYARD Margaret. 1981. *Cereal Development Guide.* NAC Cereal Unit, Stoneleigh.

KIRBY, E.J.M., APPLEYARD Margaret and FELLOWES Gwynneth. 1982. Effect of sowing date on the temperature response of leaf emergence and leaf size in barley. *Plant, Cell and Environment* 5, 447–484.

KIRBY, E.J.M. and FARIS, D.G. 1972. The effect of plant density on tiller growth and morphology in barley. *Journal of Agricultural Science* 72, 281–288.

KIRBY, E.J.M. and RIGGS, T.J. 1978. Developmental consequences of two-row and six-row ear types in spring barley. *Journal of Agricultural Science* 91, 207–216.

LARGE, E.C. 1954. Growth stages in cereals. Illustrations of the 'Feekes' scale. *Plant Pathology* 3, 128–129.

LIDGATE, H.J. 1981. Matching nitrogen with cereal crop needs. In: Yield of cereals, Course papers 1981, NAC Cereal Unit, Stoneleigh.

MASLE-MEYNARD, J. and SEBILLOTTE, M. 1981. Etude de l'hétérogénéité d'un peuplement de blé d'hiver. II. Origine des différentes catégories d'individu de peuplement; éléments de description de sa structure. *Agronomie* 1, 217–224.

SAINI, H.S. and ASPINALL, D. 1982a. Effect of water deficit on sporogenesis in wheat (*Triticum aestivum* L.) *Annals of Botany* 48, 623–633.

SAINI, H.S. and ASPINALL, D. 1982b. Abnormal sporogenesis in wheat (*Triticum aestivum* L.) induced by short periods of high temperature. *Annals of Botany* 49, 835–846.

STERN, W. and KIRBY, E.J.M. 1979. Primordium initiation at the shoot apex in four contrasting varieties of spring wheat in response to sowing date. *Journal of Agricultural Science* 93, 203–215.

TOTTMAN, D.R. 1977. The identification of growth stages in winter wheat with reference to the application of growth-regulator herbicides. *Annals of Applied Biology* 87, 213–224.

TOTTMAN, D.R. and MAKEPEACE, R.J. 1979. An explanation of the decimal code for the growth stages of cereals, with illustrations. *Annals of Applied Biology* 93, 221–234.

ZADOKS, J.C., CHANG, T.T. and KONZAK, C.F. 1974. A decimal code for the growth stages of cereals. *Weed Research* 14, 415–421.

Discussion

Mr Skinner asked whether day length affected floral development in the apex. Dr Kirby replied that the rate at which spikelet primordia formed in the ear was a function of day length, especially in spring barley. When spring barley crops grown in Scotland and Cambridge were compared, similar rates of spikelet formation were seen despite the 3 degree C lower average temperatures in Scotland, because of the longer days in Scotland. The components of growth discussed in his paper were mainly affected by temperature, he said. However, the rate of emergence of leaves was 0.01 leaves per degree day for September sowings and 0.02 leaves per degree day for February sowings, and this might be related to the rate of change of day length when the first leaf emerged.

Dr Sylvester-Bradley commented that the nitrogen application affected leaf emergence and increased leaf size. Nitrogen also affected tiller production. He wondered how this fitted in with the close correlation between leaf and tiller development described. Dr Kirby pointed out that he had been describing the potential emergence of tillers as related to the number of leaves. This potential took many weeks to be realised. The prediction worked well for the first four to six leaves and then broke down, presumably due to some stress factor. Therefore, the relationship could be used to assess how far a crop was falling behind its potential. He referred to Dr Biscoe's work (this volume pages 53–65), which showed that nitrogen had no effect on rate of leaf emergence but did affect leaf size.

Dry matter production and crop yield – genetic constraints

R B Austin
Plant Breeding Institute, Cambridge

Summary

Success in breeding for higher yield in wheat and barley has been associated with a progressive reduction in plant height and straw weight, biomass yields having remained constant. It is suggested that there is only limited scope for continuing this trend. Further increases in yield will depend on breeding for increased biomass, whilst maintaining the highest possible harvest index (grain : biomass ratio). It is argued that increases in biomass will be achieved through increases in the rate, rather than in the duration of growth. During grain filling, increased dry matter production could be achieved by selection for greater leaf area, maintenance of photosynthetic activity, and possibly by combining the high photosynthetic rates of some wild diploid wheats with the large leaf area of the hexploids. Some ways of increasing dry matter production would increase the water requirement of the crop, and so would be ineffective, or less effective, on soils prone to drought. However, high photosynthetic rate per unit leaf area, would increase dry matter production but not the water requirement of the crop.

If breeders are successful in producing higher yielding varieties in the future these will require more fertiliser nitrogen to achieve their potential. Uptake during the grain filling period may be critical.

To maximise cereal production, it is suggested that it will be necessary to breed varieties for particular soils and climatic regions.

Introduction

Since phenotype is the resultant of genotype and environment, genetic constraints have to be viewed in the context of a particular environment. In UK cereal growing areas the weather varies from year to year and from site to site and there are also changes in those elements of the environment that are under the control of the farmer, mainly fertiliser use, rotation, soil condition, weeds, pests and diseases. While there have been only relatively small trends in the climate during this century, chemical and mechanical aids to husbandry have totally transformed the elements of the environment which are under the control of the farmer. This new, more favourable, environment has required altered plant types to exploit it maximally. Breeders have been concerned to make these alterations, and as Riggs (1984) has shown they have been very successful. To recap, the genetic gains have been the consequence of breeders' objectives to reduce plant height so that crops can benefit from more nitrogen fertiliser, without lodging. The reduction in height has led to a reduction in stem weight and a matching increase in grain weight, total above ground dry matter yields at maturity (biomass) having remained essentially invariant. Harvest index (grain dry matter as a per cent of biomass) of the varieties grown at the beginning of this century was about 30 per cent but in modern varieties is about 50 per cent.

A limit to harvest index

In considering genetic constraints to obtaining higher yield the obvious first consideration is whether, and if so by how much, it will be possible to increase harvest index beyond about 50 per cent, while not increasing biomass. The arguments presented elsewhere for wheat (Austin *et al.*, 1980), are repeated here. They are based on data for four semi-dwarf varieties giving a grain yield (dry matter basis) of 7.07 t/ha. The dry weights of the other components at harvest were, in t/ha : stem and sheath 4.53, chaff 1.39 and leaf lamina biomass 1.43. This dry weight distribution gave a harvest index of 49 per cent.

Consider the consequences if it were possible to reduce stem and sheath weights to half these values (as ratios are being considered, the absolute values are not important). Assuming no change in biomass and that half the stem and sheath weight was transferred to the ears, mostly to the grain but enough to the chaff to retain the existing grain : chaff ratio, the new distribution of dry weight would be grain 8.95, chaff 1.78, leaf laminae 1.43 and stem and sheath 2.26. These values give a harvest index of 62 per cent and an increase in grain yield of 26 per cent over that observed for the varieties. It seems unlikely that varieties having such a small stem weight would be useful in agriculture. If stem number and height were to remain the same, more grain would have to be supported on thinner and presumably weaker straw. This would make for unacceptable susceptibility to lodging. Alternatively if the stems were shorter, it might be difficult to achieve adequate light distribution over the leaves, thus limiting photosynthesis and biomass. Also, susceptibility to splash borne diseases would be greater and the crops would be more at risk from weed competition.

Breeding for higher biomass

These arguments suggest that breeding may be approaching the limit to harvest index in wheat. The situation is similar in spring barley, the best varieties of which also have a harvest index of about 50 per cent (Riggs *et al.*, 1982). The only alternative for achieving further genetic gain in yield of wheat and barley is to increase the biomass whilst maintaining harvest index. Assuming a common starting weight, this could result either from lengthening the period of growth or from increasing growth rates, or a combination of the two. In winter wheat, there seems little scope for increasing the duration of the crop life cycle. The same is probably true for winter and spring barley. In wheat, modern varieties flower about a week earlier than the old ones, though differences in maturity time do not appear to have been quantified. There is much genetic variation in flowering time and maturity, reflecting the expression of genes for photoperiodic sensitivity, vernalisation requirement and possibly earliness *per se*. It is fairly straightforward to produce experimental genotypes differing in flowering date and maturity, and to assess the consequences for yield and yield stability. Work on winter wheat with this aim is in progress at the Plant Breeding Institute.

The other approach, though of course not mutually exclusive, is to breed for faster growth rate. Nitrogen fertiliser gives faster growth and, within limits, increases yield by increasing biomass (nitrogen also reduces harvest index, though usually not by a similar proportion to the increase in biomass). Elevated atmospheric carbon dioxide concentration has the same effect, though does not appear to reduce harvest index (Sionit *et al.*, 1981). Thus, barring other limitations such as water, more biomass can be produced at the radiation and temperature levels which prevail in the UK and is associated with higher grain yield. The question is, is there *genetic* variation which will achieve the same result? Growth rates can be increased in winter cereals by selecting for reduced vernalisation requirement, but experience suggests it would be difficult to retain a safe level of winter hardiness in such types, at least with wheat and barley. It is by no means assured that the extra growth in winter would contribute to increased yield. If, as is sometimes observed, reduced vernalisation requirement is associated with increased apical dominance and reduced tillering, few, though larger tillers would be produced which would show accelerated development, early flowering and low yield. On the other hand, if more tillers were produced, drought or nitrogen stress could cause the death of a greater proportion, so that the number of fertile tillers would be relatively unchanged, as compared with 'normal' varieties. In practice, it is likely to be possible, given sufficient effort, to select for increased tillering whilst maintaining winter hardiness and, except when there is severe drought in April and May, no increase in tiller mortality (Innes *et al.*, 1982).

There are likely to be disadvantages associated with too rapid growth rate in April and May, the period of rapid leaf and stem growth in winter wheat. Increased vegetative growth during this period may, through competitive effects, adversely affect ear development, resulting in reduced harvest index. Thus to be useful, plant types will need to have appropriately *balanced* increases in the growth rates of all organs, so that harvest index is at least maintained.

All this reasoning is valid only if water and nitrogen are available *ad libitum*. If, as frequently happens, this is not so there will be penalties from too rapid use of the limited supplies. Some implications of this will be discussed later in this paper.

Modelling dry matter production during grain filling

The most obvious way to achieve further genetic gain in grain yield is to increase either the rate or duration of grain filling. Daily potential photosynthesis during the grain filling period can be calculated as a function of various plant attributes. As little of the carbon assimilated during grain filling is incorporated into organs other than the grain, photosynthesis, less respiration, can be equated to grain carbon. This scheme provides a means for exploring the effects of varying the plant attributes which can influence carbohydrate supply for grain filling. As presented here, it is assumed that the capacity of the grains to accept carbohydrate is not limiting, that water and nutrients are freely available and that pests and diseases are absent. There is evidence (Scott *et al.*, in press) that the potential size of grains, i.e. their capacity to accept carbohydrates and proteins during grain filling, may be limited by genotype and by the environment during ear development. Also, increasing the assimilate availability during ear development by carbon dioxide enrichment, increases yield by increasing the number of fertile florets per ear (Krenzer and Moss, 1975). Certainly the numbers of grains/m^2, the product of number of ears/m^2 and number of grains/ear is largely determined by anthesis (Day *et al.*, 1978; Fischer, 1970; Innes and Blackwell, 1981). There is likely to be a strong correlation between number of grains/m^2 and leaf area index at anthesis (ALAI). The latter is a parameter in the model described below and so to the extent that it will be shown that potential yield is a function of ALAI, pre-anthesis effects on grain number are taken into account, implicitly if not explicitly.

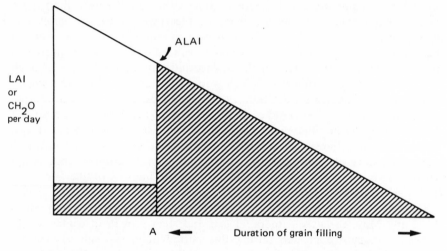

Fig. 1 Schematic representation of changes in leaf area index and daily photosynthesis with time during grain filling. Hatched areas represent grain dry matter. The pre-anthesis dry matter contribution is protein remobilised from vegetative organs to the grain.

Details of the model have been given by Austin (1982) and are based on the canopy photosynthesis model of Monteith (1965). Throughout the grain-filling period the leaf area index of a wheat canopy declines and there is an associated decline in daily photosynthesis. The total carbohydrate available for grain filling is calculated by summing the daily carbohydrate production, and is equivalent to the triangular shaded area in Figure 1. Daily photosynthesis was calculated from the model of Monteith (1965) modified by Patefield and Austin (1971). In this model the relationship between photosynthesis per unit leaf area and irradiance is described by a two parameter rectangular hyperbola and the distribution of irradiance over the leaves is described as a function of the proportion of the photosynthetically active radiation not intercepted by unit leaf area index (s) and the light transmission of individual leaves. Canopies with preponderantly upright leaves have a high value of s. Irradiance is assumed to vary sinusoidally with a maximum at midday. The equations describing these relationships are combined to enable daily potential photosynthesis of the crop to be calculated. Leaf area index is assumed to decline linearly over the grain filling period from an initial value (ALAI) at anthesis, to zero at maturity. The decrease in the photosynthetic capacity of green tissue resulting from its senescence is allowed for by assuming that the light saturated rate of photosynthesis remains constant for the first 15 days after anthesis but declines linearly with time thereafter, becoming zero at the end of grain filling. This simplification is consistent with some experimental data. In favourable seasons, with disease-free crops growing on fertile soils, the onset of senescence is considerably delayed.

Several studies (e.g. Austin *et al.*, 1977; Pearman *et al.*, 1981) have shown that about 40 per cent of the carbon assimilated during grain filling is lost by 'dark' respiration. This value is assumed for the standard case.

A daily total of photosynthetically active solar radiation of $8.4\,MJ\,m^{-2}\,day^{-1}$ is assumed. This is close to the long–term average for June and July in central and eastern England. Of this 33 per cent is taken as being intercepted by the ears, which are assumed to contribute 15 per cent to the photosynthesis of the canopy (Olugbemi *et al.*, 1976). At very high ear densities such as would occur in high yielding crops the ears may intercept more than 33 per cent and so contribute proportionally more to canopy photosynthesis.

To complete the calculation of yield, it is taken that grain protein originates from that in the vegetative organs and is already present at anthesis (Austin *et al.*, 1977). The protein content is taken as 12 per cent (dry weight basis). Any contribution to grain filling from carbohydrate stored in the vegetative organs before anthesis is likely to be small under good growing conditions and is neglected. Total grain dry matter is converted to yield in t/ha at 15 per cent moisture content (fresh weight basis).

Using the model based on these assumptions, the calculated potential yield is 12 t/ha. Making reasonable assumptions about the yield of vegetative dry matter, as detailed by Austin (1982), this yield is likely to be achieved with a harvest index of 52 per cent, i.e. little or no increase on present values.

Effects of particular attributes on dry matter production during grain filling

The model enables the effects on potential yield of varying some crop characteristics to be calculated (Figure 2). As expected, yield is strongly dependent on leaf area index at anthesis (ALAI) and on the duration of the grain filling period. At the potential yield of 12 t/ha, a 1 per cent increase in ALAI or duration of grain filling would increase yield by 0.75 per cent. A 1 per cent increase in light saturated photosynthetic rate (P_{max}) would have a smaller effect, 0.5 per cent, while a 1 per cent delay in the time of onset of leaf senescence would increase yield by only about 0.1 per cent. Such comparisons are only meaningful if coupled with information on the likely genetic improvement in these attributes. It must also be borne in mind that there are likely to be detrimental consequences of some of these changes so they have to be set against the benefits. A high ALAI may make the crop especially sensitive to water stress (Innes, private communication) and may be associated with an increased crop water use both prior to anthesis and during grain filling. The benefits from high ALAI may only be achieved in crops with erect leaves, but erect leaves may be detrimental if there is a pre-anthesis drought. Increase in the duration of the grain filling period may be achieved by advancing anthesis but this may give less opportunity for the development of the vegetative organs and ears, and so be detrimental. Alternatively it can be achieved by delaying ripening, which would be undesirable for rotational reasons. There would appear to be no penalty from delaying the onset of leaf senescence: indeed this has been an objective in both wheat breeding at the Plant Breeding Institute and of corn breeding in the U.S. corn belt and is believed to have contributed to genetic gain in yield, at least in corn (Duvick, private communication; Duvick, 1977).

The attribute which deserves close scrutiny is light saturated photosynthetic rate (P_{max}), one of the parameters describing the relationship between irradiance and photosynthesis. The equation used is only an approximation to the observed relationship. If both parameters are varied, photosynthesis is increased equally in percentage terms at all light intensities. This change would give a matching increase in daily photosynthesis and crop yield. P_{max} can vary markedly with genotype, considering the genus *Triticum* as a whole (Table 1). The other parameter, a measure of quantum efficiency of photosynthesis at low light intensity, appears to be relatively invariant. If only P_{max} varies the effects on daily photosynthesis and yield are less in percentage terms than the variation in P_{max}, particularly in dull weather.

Table 1 Photosynthetic and other characteristics of flag leaves of wild and cultivated *Triticum* species

	P_{max} mg CO_2 $dm^{-2} h^{-1}$	Leaf width mm	Leaf area cm^2	Mean plan area per mesophyll cell μm^2	Stomatal conductance to water vapour $cm\ s^{-1}$	Chlorophyll content mg dm^{-2}
Wild diploids						
T. thaoudar	42	7.2	8.9	1070	0.56	4.4
T. urartu	43	8.7	7.8	940	0.58	5.8
Wild tetraploids						
T. dicoccum	32	10.5	12.1	1820	0.46	4.5
T. dicoccoides	35	8.2	9.6	1710	0.57	5.6
Cultivated tetraploid						
T. durum	28	15.9	22.0	1560	0.62	5.2
Cultivated hexaploids						
T. aestivum*	28	15.0	18.4	1970	0.57	4.9

* Mean of five cultivars.

As shown in Table 1 wild diploid wheats have a P_{max} some 50 per cent greater than hexaploid bread wheats. This is not associated with a greater stomatal conductance so that cause of the difference must be at the anatomical and/or biochemical level. An obvious possibility is that the leaves with high P_{max} have more photosynthetic 'machinery', but of the same or similar efficiency. Judging from their chlorophyll content (only one measure of amount of photosynthetic machinery) this is not so. It is not yet known whether the same applies to other parts of the photosynthetic machinery, particularly the enzymes of the Calvin

46

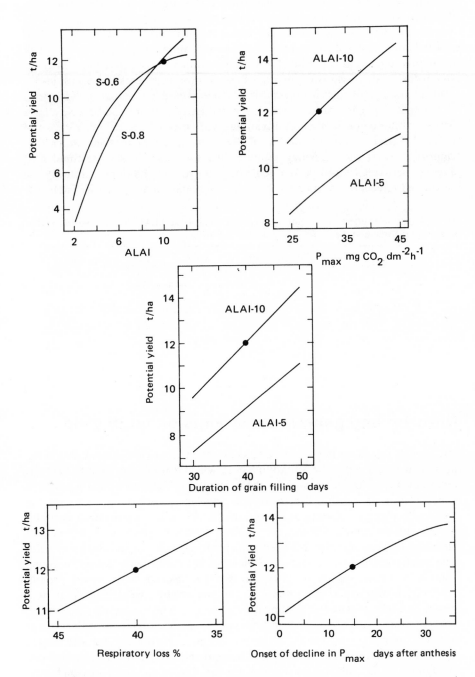

Fig. 2 Calculated effects on potential yield of varying leaf area index at anthesis (ALAI), sunflecked area fraction(s), Pmax, duration of grain filling, respiratory loss, and time of onset of decline in Pmax.

● represents the standard case for all model parameters.

cycle. In view of the very strong association with leaf and cell size, it is tempting to suppose that cell size is an important factor determining P_{max}, possibly through its effects on the length of diffusion pathways (both for the influx of CO_2 and the export of assimilates to the veins). Insufficient is known to assess the relative importance of these factors, and others, and these aspects are currently being investigated at the Plant Breeding Institute and elsewhere. Attempts are also being made to transfer the high P_{max} of diploid wheats to hexaploids.

Of course, yield improvements in practice would not need to depend on changing a single attribute. Indeed, provided that there were no adverse effects on ear development, it might be advantageous to breed for both higher P_{max} and reduced ALAI. Such varieties would be more efficient in their water use. Improved water use efficiency would reduce the losses in yield (estimated to average between 10 and 20 per cent) due to drought. Examples showing the calculated effects of varying attributes in combination are given in Table 2.

Table 2   Calculated effects on potential yield of wheat of varying ALAI, P_{max}, the time of onset of senescence (SENO) and the duration of grain filling (DUR).

		SENO 15 P_{max}		SENO 30 P_{max}	
		30 yield (t/ha)	40	30	40
ALAI	DUR				
7.5	40	10.9	12.6	12.1	13.9
	50	13.2	15.2	14.6	16.7
10	40	12.0	13.8	13.5	15.4
	50	14.4	16.7	16.1	18.5

Nitrogen and genetic constraints on grain yield

Nitrogen is important both for its effects on growth and yield, and as part of the protein in the grain. The suitability of a wheat variety for breadmaking is determined by many factors under the control of different genes. High protein concentration is needed for making an elastic, stable dough, though the composition of the protein is important too. Protein concentration is under genetic and environmental control. As Riggs (1984) has reminded us, there is a strong negative correlation between grain protein concentration and grain yield. The relationship is such that high yielding varieties, while generally giving somewhat greater yields of grain protein per hectare, have lower protein contents. Is the negative correlation, and the implied yield penalty at high protein content, inevitable? Among a wide range of wheat varieties Austin et al. (1977) found a strong correlation between the nitrogen content of the crop at anthesis, and total dry weight at anthesis. This occurred because dry weight varied much more than did nitrogen content. Heavy plants at anthesis may, though not necessarily, have low harvest index. This could be one reason for the negative correlation. The other reason is concerned with leaf senescence. If senescence is early, i.e. the duration of grain filling is short, leaves will die and their nitrogen be relocated to the grains when less carbohydrate has been formed than if senescence is later. The effects of these relationships would be reduced if it were possible to breed for greater nitrogen uptake during grain filling. Unfortunately nitrogen uptake requires active, probably growing, roots, but the roots are the losers in a competitive battle for assimilates during grain filling (Morgan and Austin, 1983). This effect would only be alleviated by an increase in the supply of assimilate, i.e. a higher rate of crop photosynthesis.

If higher yielding varieties are produced and these are required to have similar, if not increased, grain protein concentration to those presently grown, their nitrogen offtake will be greater, implying with present practice, a greater nitrogen requirement. Thus it will be important to examine limitations, both soil and genetic, to nitrogen uptake during grain filling, and try to overcome them.

Varieties for particular soils and climatic regions

It is widely accepted that genetic adaptability over a range of environments is achieved only at the expense of fitness in particular environments. Thus if it were possible to recognise regions in the UK which regularly were drier or warmer than others, varieties most suited to these conditions could be produced and would be different from those most suited to moist and cool areas. Similarly, light soils with low available water holding capacity (AWC) will require, for achieving maximum yields, varieties with different characteristics than heavy soils with high AWC. Whether it is economically justified to produce varieties of a crop (e.g. winter wheat) for particular climates and soils depends on the likely benefits in terms of yield, compared with the increased costs of breeding, trailling, producing and distributing the seed. Although there is insufficient information to make a good estimate of the likely benefit, a minimum would probably be that production would be increased by 5 per cent, equivalent to about 0.3 t/ha on a yield of 6.0 t/ha. At £120/tonne this would be worth £36/ha. Assuming seed costs £200/tonne and that it is sown at 0.15 t/ha the cost of seed is £30/ha. The element in farmers' seed costs attributable to breeders' costs and margins is probably about £2/ha. If twice as many varieties were produced, these costs would approximately double. Allowing for seed producers' and merchants' extra cost margins the additional cost to the farmer would be between £4 and, at maximum, £10. Thus the benefits from better fitness – £36/ha in this example – would exceed the costs by between 3.6 and 9 fold. This example suggests that breeding for specific environments and soils could be cost effective. A considerable R and D effort would be needed to obtain a reasonable quantification of the likely benefits, and a careful economic study would be needed to assess the increased costs. Experience at PBI from character analysis with wheat strongly suggests that further progress in breeding for higher yield will depend on producing varieties with high biomass. Attributes making for high biomass yield vary with environment, so general purpose varieties will inevitably be compromises and will not enable the production potential of the UK cereal growing area to be fully exploited. There would be implications for agronomy and fertiliser practice. For each soil/climatic zone, with its 'own' varieties, optimum cultural practices would need to be worked out. Fertiliser practice already takes account of soil variation, but recommendations could be made with more confidence if variety performance were more predictable, as a result of using purpose-bred varieties.

References

AUSTIN, R.B. 1982. Crop characteristics and the potential yield of wheat. *Journal of Agricultural Science, Cambridge* **98**, 447–453.

AUSTIN, R.B., BINGHAM, J., BLACKWELL, R.D., EVANS, L.T., FORD, M.A., MORGAN, C.L. and TAYLOR, M. 1980. Genetic improvements in winter wheat yields since 1900 and associated physiological changes. *Journal of Agricultural Science, Cambridge* **94**, 675–689.

AUSTIN, R.B., EDRICH, J.A., FORD, M.A. and BLACKWELL, R.D. 1977. The fate of the dry matter, carbohydrates and ^{14}C lost from the leaves and stems of wheat during grain filling. *Annals of Botany* **41**, 1309–1321.

AUSTIN, R.B., FORD, M.A., EDRICH, J.A. and BLACKWELL, R.D. 1977. The nitrogen economy of winter wheat. *Journal of Agricultural Science, Cambridge* **88**, 159–167.

AUSTIN, R.B., MORGAN, C.L., FORD, M.A. and BHAGWAT, S.G. 1982. Flag leaf photosynthesis of *Triticum aestivum* and related diploid and tetraploid species. *Annals of Botany* **49**, 177–189.

DAY, W., LEGG, B.J., FRENCH, B.K., JOHNSTON, A.E., LAWLOR, D.W. and JEFFERS, W. de C. 1978. A drought experiment using mobile plot shelters: the effect of drought on barley yield, water use and nutrient uptake. *Journal of Agricultural Science, Cambridge* **91**, 599–623.

DUVICK, D.N. 1977. Genetic rates of gain in hybrid maize yields during the past 40 years. *Maydica* **12**, 187–196.

FISCHER, R.A. 1970. The effect of water stress at various stages of development of yield processes in wheat. In: *Plant Response to Climatic Factors* (ed. R.O. Slatyer). Proceedings of the Uppsala Symposium, Paris: UNESCO, 1973.

INNES, P. BLACKWELL, R.D., AUSTIN, R.B. and FORD, M.A. 1981. The effects of selection for number of ears on the yield and water economy of winter wheat. *Journal of Agricultural Science, Cambridge* **97**, 523–532.

INNES, P. and BLACKWELL, R.D. 1981. The effect of drought on the water use and yield of two spring wheat genotypes. *Journal of Agricultural Science, Cambridge* **96**, 603—610.

KRENZNER, E.G. and MOSS, D.N. 1975. Carbon dioxide effects on yield and yield components in wheat. *Crop Science* **15**, 71–74.

MONTEITH, J.L. 1975. Light distribution and photosynthesis in field crops. *Annals of Botany* **29**, 17–37.

MORGAN, C.L. and AUSTIN, R.B. 1983. Respiratory loss of recently assimilated carbon in wheat. *Annals of Botany*, **51**, 85–95.

OLUGBEMI, L.B., AUSTIN, R.B. and BINGHAM, J. 1976. Effects of awns on the photosynthesis and yield of wheat, *Triticum aestivum*. *Annals of Applied Biology* **84**, 241–250.

PATEFIELD, W.M. and AUSTIN, R.B. 1971. A model for the simulation of the growth of *Beta vulgaris* L. *Annals of Botany* **35**, 1227–1250.

PEARMAN, I., THOMAS, S.M. and THORNE, S.N. 1981. Dark respiration of several varieties of winter wheat given different amounts of nitrogen fertiliser. *Annals of Botany* **47**, 535–546.

RIGGS, T.J., HANSON, P.R., START, N.D., MILES, D.M., MORGAN, C.L. and FORD, M.A. 1981. Comparison of spring barley varieties grown in England and Wales between 1880 and 1980. *Journal of Agricultural Science, Cambridge* **97**, 599–610.

RIGGS, T.J. 1984. Plant breeding — potential for improvement of yield and grain quality. Ministry of Agriculture, Fisheries and Food, Reference Book 385, *The Nitrogen Requirement of Cereals*, pp. 5–18. HMSO, London.

SCOTT, W.R., APPLEYARD, M., FELLOWES, G. and KIRBY, E.J.M. 1983. Effect of genotype and position in the ear on carpel and grain growth and mature grain weight of spring barley. *Journal of Agricultural Science, Cambridge* **100**, 383–391.

SIONIT, N., MORTENSEN, D.A., STRAIN, B.R. and HELLMERS, H. 1981. Growth response of wheat to CO_2 enrichment and different levels of mineral nutrition. *Agronomy Journal* **73**, 1023–1027.

Discussion

Mr Holmes commented on recent successes of grass breeders in producing varieties with increased dry matter production. Perhaps cereal breeders could learn from them. Mr Austin agreed, but pointed out that other attributes might be more important. Indeed farmers usually sowed mixtures of grasses, so reducing the impact of high dry matter varieties.

Dr Greenwood was interested in the suggestion that different varieties might be suited to different soils, and asked if this was based on variety trials. He felt there might be advantages in growing a wider range of varieties, e.g. in disease resistance. Mr Austin agreed, but commented that diversity within a small area might not be increased by having varieties for different soil types. The main evidence for his suggestion had not come from variety trials because, by the very method of selection, any varieties which failed to perform well in most situations were discarded early. However work on genotypes selected for particular characters had shown differences in environmental response. For example low-tillering wheats had more stable yields after early drought, but high-tillering wheats performed better in the absence of water stress. Low-tillering wheats might therefore be more suitable for light soils.

Environmental effects on dry matter production

P V Biscoe and V B A Willington
Broom's Barn Experimental Station, Higham, Bury St. Edmunds, Suffolk

Summary

The importance of dry matter production for high yields of modern cereal varieties is established. A framework for investigating the effect of environmental factors on dry matter production is described, based on the concept that growth is proportional to the amount of radiation intercepted. This approach is used to provide a clearer understanding of how specific environmental factors and nitrogen influence dry matter production either by the amount of radiation intercepted or by the efficiency with which radiation is converted to dry matter. A distinction is made between the effect of environmental factors on the rate of dry matter production and on the duration, which is primarily governed by the rate of crop development.

Introduction

The environment is a major variable affecting cereal production and a knowledge of how it influences crop performance during different seasons is important for several reasons. First, it assists research scientists trying to interpret the results of experiments where the same treatments have been applied in different years. This is because the seasonal effects are usually far larger than those attributable to the treatments (e.g. Krentos and Orphanos, 1979) and if general response patterns are to be identified then an understanding of how the environmental factors influence development, growth and yield is required. Second, when high yields are achieved in particular circumstances it enables reasons for the yield to be elucidated. Finally, it should enable farmers to respond to variations in the weather during a season so that different cultural operations can be timed, in relation to the crop and not the calendar, to achieve consistency of production.

While the need for a clear understanding of the influence of environmental factors on crop productivity can be convincingly made, its solution is less obvious. The most common approach has been to correlate the year-to-year fluctuations of yield with corresponding weather, usually expressed in terms of monthly averages of temperature, rainfall and sunshine. This began last century with Laws and Gilbert (1880) and has continued until the present (e.g. Robertson, 1974). In general, this statistical type of approach has failed to provide any clear relationships between the weather and crop yields and when Yates (1969) reviewed what was nearly a century of endeavour he was pessimistic about the progress that had been made. Considering how factors such as temperature and radiation are naturally correlated and how they interact in determining the rates of physiological processes it is not unexpected that such studies have made only limited progress.

In this paper we propose a framework for investigating the effect of environmental variables on the growth and yield of cereals. This will be used to identify the specific effects of individual weather variables on first, the physiological processes governing the rates of dry matter production and second, the duration of growth.

Dry matter production and yield

Before considering how different environmental variables influence the production of dry matter, its importance for grain yield, which is only part of the total dry matter produced, must be assessed. An analysis of the variations in harvest index, defined as the ratio of grain dry weight to total dry weight, for a range of cereal crops both winter and spring sown, has shown that while yields varied greatly, variations in harvest index tended to be small and usually less than 10 per cent of their mean value (Gallagher and Biscoe, 1978). This is well illustrated by Figure 1 which shows data from spring barley crops grown at

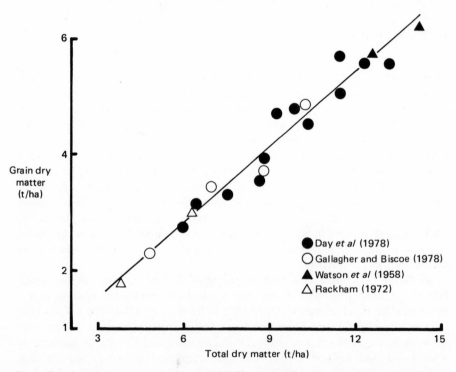

Fig. 1 Relationship between grain dry matter yield and total dry matter for spring barley crops.

different sites, in different seasons and exposed to a range of experimental treatments. In an extreme case Day *et al.* (1978) imposed a drought for different lengths of time during the development of a spring barley crop, including the whole of the life cycle and despite a two-fold range of total dry matter production between treatments the harvest index varied little. Similarly, measurements made on wheat during the hot, dry summer of 1976 showed that the harvest index of Huntsman fell from the usual 0.45 to 0.37, a small response considering how extreme the weather was (Gallagher *et al.*, 1976). Thus, with modern varieties, changes in harvest index tend to be small and so the weather predominantly influences grain yield by its effect on total dry matter production.

A framework for investigation

The strong correlation that has been demonstrated between the rate of dry matter production and the amount of radiation intercepted (Gallagher and Biscoe, 1978) provides the basis for an analytical framework to identify the effects of environmental variables on dry matter production. Figure 2 illustrates this relationship between intercepted radiation and crop growth rates for wheat and barley grown at different sites in England and in different seasons.

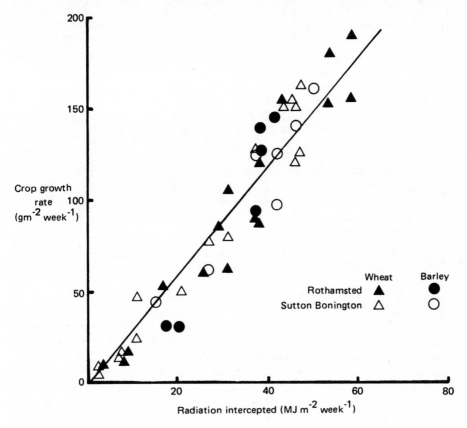

Fig. 2 Relationship between the rate of dry matter production and the amount of radiation intercepted.

Acceptance of this relationship enables dry matter production during a growing season to be considered as the product of (a) the total amount of radiation intercepted and (b) the efficiency of its conversion to dry matter, i.e. the slope of the line in Figure 2. Analysis of dry matter growth in terms of intercepted radiation draws attention to the basic difference between radiation falling on a field and on the foliage within that field, and provides a means of assessing the effect of seasonal variations in radiation receipts on dry matter growth. In contrast, differences in intercepted radiation are a consequence of variations in the seasonal pattern of leaf area production and persistence, which depend on environmental factors such as temperature and rainfall and on soil factors such as fertiliser. In the absence of constraints, e.g. pests and diseases, the conversion of intercepted radiation to dry matter by cereal crops proceeds with an almost constant maximum efficiency. The actual efficiency with which intercepted radiation is used can be compared with the maximum efficiency so providing a powerful means of investigating the effects of environmental variables, e.g. temperature, rainfall or agronomic treatments, e.g. nitrogen fertiliser. Figure 3 summarises the analytical approach that has been proposed and illustrates how it will be used throughout this paper to examine the effect of individual environmental factors on dry matter production.

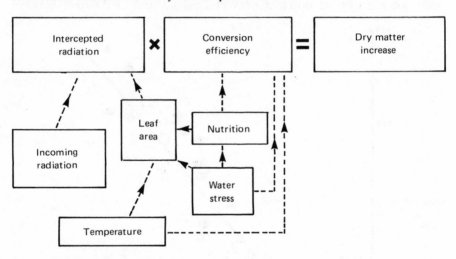

Fig. 3 Diagrammatic presentation of an approach to analyse the effects of environmental factors on the dry matter production by cereals.

Radiation receipts

Table 1 shows that during the period when cereal crops are growing quickly the standard deviation of the monthly mean values of radiation, at any one site, is about ±10 per cent. The standard deviation decreases to about ±6 per cent if the radiation receipts are averaged over several months. Exceptionally, the seasonal and monthly variations in radiation receipts can be large. For example, the maximum value recorded for June at Broom's Barn is 2.8 MJ m^{-2} d^{-1} above average (Table 1), which is equivalent to an additional 1.5 t/ha of dry matter assuming that 90 per cent is intercepted and is converted with an efficiency of 2 g/MJ. It has been suggested, therefore, that the normal variations in radiation

Table 1 Long-term average (1966–1982) of solar radiation receipts MJ m^{-2}d^{-1} at Broom's Barn, Suffolk for the months April to July inclusive

	April	May	June	July	April–July
Mean	11.2	15.4	17.0	15.0	14.7
SD	1.50	1.63	1.96	1.63	1.03
Max	13.5	19.0	19.8	17.6	16.3
Min	9.0	12.8	13.5	11.7	12.5

receipts can account for only a minor part of the seasonal differences in dry matter production and yield (Monteith, 1981).

Radiation interception

It has long been recognised that the major reason for differences in yield between sites and seasons is the amount of green leaf area produced and retained by crops (Watson, 1947). While the early studies extensively investigated correlations between crop growth and leaf area index, L, (defined as the area of green lamina, sheath and ear, per unit ground area) it was only later that the relationship between L and the interception of radiation was quantified (Monsi and Saeki, 1953). Subsequently, relationships between L and the proportion of radiation intercepted have been widely investigated and except for extreme variations in leaf angle an L of 4 will intercept more than 80 per cent of the incident radiation (Szeicz, 1974). It is evident, therefore, that dry matter production will be limited by environmental factors which restrict early leaf growth, i.e. until an L of 4 is achieved and which cause premature and rapid leaf senescence.

Leaf area production

Following emergence, when the number of leaves will depend on the established plant population, leaf area growth is governed by the rates of leaf appearance and leaf expansion and by the final leaf size. The appearance of successive leaves on a cereal plant strongly depends on temperature (Baker *et al.*, 1980) and is used as an index of the plant's development (Zadoks *et al.*, 1974). Figure 4 shows that in the absence of water stress leaf extension is linearly related to temperature and rates of extension during the day (open circles) and night (closed circles) fall on the same response line. Leaf extension ceases only when the temperature falls to about 0 °C. Friend (1966) has shown that final leaf size also increases with increasing temperature; the largest leaves being produced at 20 °C. In the absence of other constraints temperature is therefore the major environmental factor governing the early leaf growth of cereals.

This dependence of leaf growth on temperature may explain the apparent success of the recent trend for earlier sowing of winter cereals. On average, air temperature decreases by about 4 °C per month from September to November, consequently earlier drillings will generally emerge quicker and have faster rates of leaf appearance and expansion. During the winter earlier sown crops will have large L's but because radiation receipts are small, 2.5 MJ m^{-2}d^{-1} on average, even large differences in the proportion of radiation intercepted will cause relatively small differences in dry matter production. However, as radiation receipts

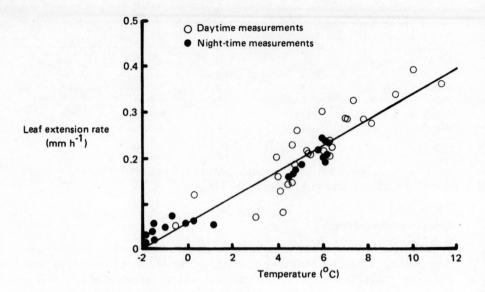

Fig. 4 Response of leaf extension rate to temperature.

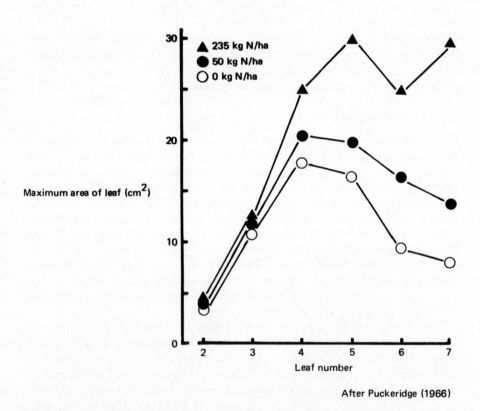

After Puckeridge (1966)

Fig. 5 Increase in the area of individual wheat leaves to nitrogen fertiliser.

increase rapidly in the spring, reaching 11 MJ m^{-2} d^{-1} in April, earlier sown crops will have faster rates of dry matter production because of the larger L.

At this time of the year on days with long periods of bright sunshine water stress can develop during the afternoons which will slow the rate of leaf expansion (Gallagher and Biscoe, 1979) and decrease the size of individual leaves (McCree and Davis, 1974). Thus the crop would have a smaller L, decreasing the proportion of radiation intercepted and so restricting the potential rate of dry matter production.

It is also during the spring that nitrogen fertiliser can exert a major influence on crop growth. Nitrogen does not affect either the number of leaves produced on an individual stem or the rate at which they appear but it considerably increases the size of individual leaves (Figure 5) (Puckeridge, 1966). Because the rate at which successive leaves appear is governed by temperature the effect of the nitrogen fertiliser will be to increase the rate of leaf area expansion (Gallagher, 1976) and provided that this is concommitant with an increase in the proportion of radiation intercepted then the rate of dry matter production will be faster.

Leaf area persistence

During early summer (May/June) cereal crops should be intercepting most of the incident radiation. Once the ears have emerged no new green tissue will be produced and subsequent dry matter production depends on the performance of the existing L. As most of the grain weight at harvest is provided by dry matter growth after anthesis, increasing the persistence of the green leaf area is an important criterion for good yields.

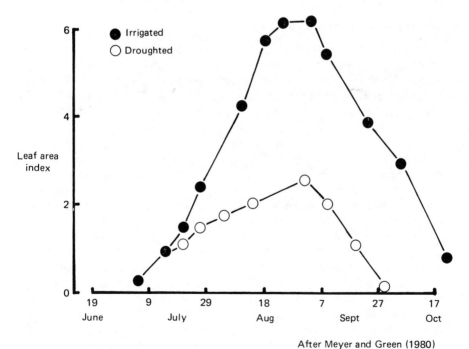

After Meyer and Green (1980)

Fig. 6   Effect of irrigation on the leaf area index of a wheat crop.

59

Drought and high temperatures, which are often associated in the summer, are the two environmental factors most likely to decrease leaf area persistence. Measurements of L in winter wheat crops during 1976, a year of severe drought and 1977, a cool, wet summer, showed that in 1976 L persisted for only 28 days after anthesis, compared to 42 days in 1977 (Gregory et al., 1981). Meyer and Green (1980) grew wheat crops under different irrigation treatments in a dryland area of southern Africa and found that the predominant effects of drought were on leaf area production and persistence (Figure 6). Recent experiments on spring barley at Rothamsted have used mobile shelters to withhold rain from the crops and so study the effects of drought, independently of those associated with temperature and radiation differences (Day et al., 1978). It has previously been shown (Figure 1) that the drought treatments caused large differences in total dry matter growth, which were strongly correlated with yield. The main reason for these differences in dry matter growth was the reduction in amount of radiation intercepted, caused by the adverse effect of drought on leaf area growth (Legg et al., 1979). Thus, with the occurrence of a drought cereal yields will be largely determined by the amount of radiation intercepted; effects of drought on the efficiency of conversion of intercepted radiation to dry matter are only of secondary importance (Legg et al., 1979).

In crops that are inadequately supplied with nitrogen leaf senescence tends to be rapid because the demand for nitrogen by young, rapidly growing plant organs, e.g. leaves and grains, cannot be met by absorption through the roots. The deficit appears to be made up by the translocation of nitrogen from mature, fully expanded leaves (Williams, 1955) which disrupts the leaf cells and causes premature senescence (Milthorpe and Moorby, 1974).

Conversion of intercepted radiation

While the results from the Rothamsted shelter experiment showed that the major effect of a prolonged drought was to decrease the interception of radiation, it has been shown that shorter periods of water stress, i.e. days with prolonged periods of bright sunshine, affect the efficiency of conversion of intercepted radiation to dry matter (Biscoe and Gallagher, 1977). It has also been found that during bright days following cold nights the rate of dry matter production is less than expected from a knowledge of the intercepted radiation (Takeda, 1976).

An analysis of the relationships between intercepted radiation and dry matter production for a limited number of crops suggests that the addition of nitrogen fertiliser may increase the efficiency of conversion by about 10 per cent at the most (Gallagher and Biscoe, 1978). This difference is very much smaller than that expected from laboratory-based experiments which have shown that the rate of leaf photosynthesis at a given irradiance is positively correlated with the nitrogen concentration of the leaf (Natr, 1972). A series of detailed measurements of the photosynthetic characteristics of leaves in winter wheat crops showed that there was no difference in the photosynthesis–light response curves between leaves from crops given either no nitrogen fertiliser or 146 kg/ha of N, although the nitrogen concentrations of the leaves were 3.6 per cent and 4.3 per cent respectively (Figure 7). In both crops the rate of leaf photosynthesis slowed as the leaves aged and the decrease was proportional to the amount of nitrogen translocated from the leaf and not the nitrogen concentration per se.

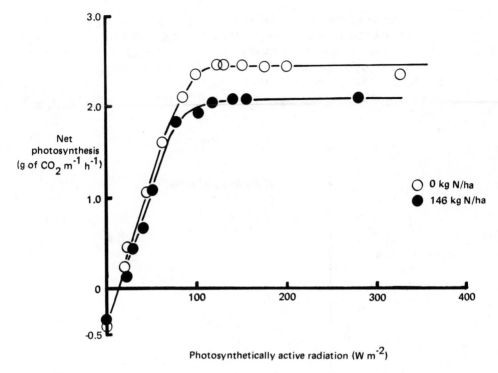

Fig. 7 Photosynthesis light-response curve of flag leaves from winter wheat crops given no nitrogen fertiliser or 146 kg/ha of N.

(Gregory *et al.*, 1981). These results have implications for the interpretation of the laboratory-based experiments and for the role of nitrogen fertiliser in cereal crops. In many of the previous experiments the different nitrogen concentrations were either created by suddenly withholding nitrogen from the rooting medium or achieved by measuring leaves at different times during their ontogeny. In both cases photosynthesis measurements were made on leaves from which nitrogen was being translocated because it was either the main source of nitrogen for the meristems or part of natural senescence. As nitrogen was lost from the leaves the rate of photosynthesis decreased and this decrease was wrongly related to the prevailing nitrogen concentration. In cereal crops although much of the nitrogen in the grain at harvest is already present in the crop at anthesis (Austin *et al.*, 1977), if nitrogen continues to be taken up after anthesis then less of the nitrogen for grain growth will be supplied by the leaves and the rate of photosynthesis should remain relatively unchanged.

Dry matter production and development

So far, this paper has concentrated on examining the ways that different environmental factors influence the rate of dry matter production. It was shown earlier that cereal yields are closely related to the total amount of dry matter produced, which depends in part on the rate of dry matter production but also on the duration of the growth period. In cereals this duration is a function of crop development, i.e. the progress of the crop from germination to maturity. Temperature is the main environmental factor governing crop development and development rate is positively correlated with temperature (cf. Kirby and Appleyard, this volume pages 21–38), consequently the time taken to complete a defined stage in the crop's development will be shorter as the temperature increases.

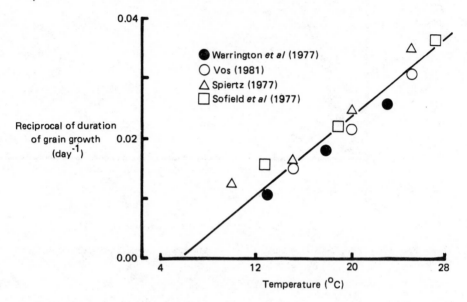

Fig. 8   Effect of temperature on the duration of the grain filling period in wheat.

This aspect of dry matter productivity is well illustrated by considering the period of grain growth. Figure 8 shows that the duration of grain growth gets shorter as the mean temperature increases. If the radiation receipts and the proportion that is intercepted are relatively constant then the amount of dry matter produced will be expected to decrease as temperature increases. Using growth chamber facilities to control both radiation and temperature Spiertz (1977) has shown that a temperature increase from 15 to 25 °C causes a reduction in the mean weight per grain from 44 to 32 mg. Brocklehurst et al. (1978) demonstrated the importance of dry matter production for grain growth by comparing the grain growth of wheat which had been shaded, to decrease incident radiation by 50 per cent, with an unshaded crop. The duration of grain filling was unaffected, because both crops experienced the same temperature, but shading caused a 18 per cent decrease in the mean weight per grain. Similarly, it has been shown that the application of nitrogen fertiliser does not influence the duration of grain growth (Spiertz, 1978) but crops given nitrogen at flag leaf emergence had heavier grain. The nitrogen increased leaf area persistence, enabling more radiation to be intercepted and increasing the total amount of dry matter produced.

Nix (1976) has attempted to quantify the relationship between growth, regarded as a function of radiation, and development, which is governed by temperature, using the concept of a photothermal quotient. This quotient expresses the light energy available per unit of development and provides a ratio between the potential supply of assimilates (radiation receipts) and the potential requirement for assimilates by the plant (mean temperature). Using the results from a series of experiments Rawson and Bagga (1979) have shown that the number of grains per plant, which is a major determinant of yield, is strongly correlated to the photothermal quotient for the development period emergence to anthesis.

The variations in mean temperature tend to be larger than those for irradiance, particularly when averaged over the main growing season for cereals. As temperature governs the rate of crop development, and hence the length of the growing season, and accepting that radiation receipts vary little, it would be expected that the better cereal yields should be obtained in the coolest summers. Monteith (1981) recently examined this view by relating wheat yields for the east midlands of England in the years 1963 to 1978 to mean air temperature during May, June and July. Figure 9 shows the results of this exercise and the negative

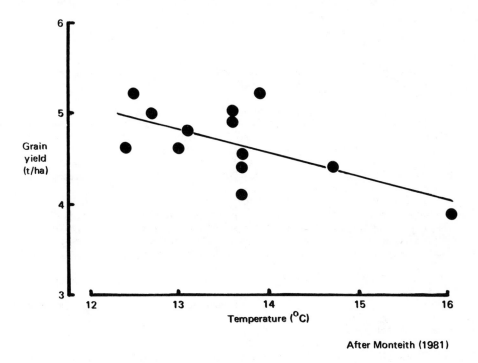

After Monteith (1981)

Fig. 9 Relationship between wheat yields in the east midlands of England between 1963 and 1978 and the mean air temperature for the months May, June and July.

correlation produced indicates that at 14 °C there is a 6 per cent yield decrease for a 1°C increase in temperature. This analysis provides an explanation for the reports of systematically better yields in Scotland and northern England compared with southern England (Biscoe, 1981); a difference that has recently been proved by a direct comparison (Kirby and Ellis, 1980).

This paper has attempted to provide an understanding of how seasonal variations in the environment can influence cereal growth. In doing so it has introduced the concept of intercepted radiation as a major discriminant of growth and shown how it can provide a valuable framework for the analysis of crop growth. Such a framework is essential because as more and more data are collected from field experiments our understanding of the relationship between the physical environment and biological response is increasingly confounded by complexity. This framework has been used to show how specific environmental variables influence the dry matter productivity of cereal crops so that when agronomic treatments are applied, e.g. nitrogen fertiliser (the main subject of this publication) then the crop's response can be identified despite the capriciousness of our weather.

Acknowledgements

V B A Willington is financed by a grant from ICI plc.

References

AUSTIN, R.B., FORD, M.A., EDRICH, J.A. and BLACKWELL, R.D. 1977. The nitrogen economy of winter wheat. *Journal of Agricultural Science, Cambridge* **88**, 159–167.

BAKER, C.K., GALLAGHER, J.N. and MONTEITH, J.L. 1980. Daylength change and leaf appearance in winter wheat. *Plant, Cell and Environment* 3, 285–287.

BISCOE, P.V. 1981. Climatic change and cereal production in Britain. In: *Climatic change and European Agriculture* (eds. Burrage, S.W. and Carr, M.K.V.), pp. 36–42. Wye College, London.

BISCOE, P.V. and GALLAGHER, J.N. 1977. Weather dry matter and yield. In: *Environmental Effects on Crop Physiology* (eds. Landsberg, J.J. and Cutting, C.V.), pp. 75–100. Academic Press, London.

BROCKLEHURST, P.A., MOSS, J.P. and WATKIN WILLIAMS. 1978. Effects of irradiance and water supply on grain development in wheat. *Annals of Applied Biology* 90, 265–276.

DAY, W., LEGG, B.J., FRENCH, B.K., JOHNSTON, A.E., LAWLOR, D.W. and JEFFERS, W de C. 1978. A drought experiment using mobile shelters. *Journal of Agricultural Science, Cambridge* 91, 599–623.

FRIEND, D.J.C. 1966. The effects of light and temperature on the growth of cereals. In: *The Growth of Cereals and Grasses* (eds. Milthorpe, F.L. and Ivins, J.O.), pp. 181–199. Butterworths, London.

GALLAGHER, J.N. 1976. The Growth of Cereals in Relation to weather. Ph.D. Thesis, University of Nottingham.

GALLAGHER, J.N., BISCOE, P.V. and HUNTER, B. 1976. Effects of drought on grain growth. *Nature* **264**, 541–542.

GALLAGHER, J.N. and BISCOE, P.V. 1978. Radiation absorption, growth and yield of cereals. *Journal of Agricultural Science, Cambridge* 91, 47–60.

GALLAGHER, J.N. and BISCOE, P.V. 1978. A physiological analysis of cereal yield. II Partitioning of dry matter. *Agricultural Progress* 53, 51–70.

GALLAGHER, J.N. and BISCOE, P.V. 1979. Field studies of cereal leaf growth. III Barley leaf extension in relation to temperature, irradiance and water potential. *Journal of Experimental Botany* 30, 645–655.

GREGORY, P.J., MARSHALL, B. and BISCOE, P.V. 1981. Nutrient relations of winter wheat. 3. Nitrogen uptake, photosynthesis of flag leaves and translocation of nitrogen to the grain. *Journal of Agricultural Science, Cambridge* 96, 539–547.

KIRBY, E.J.M. and ELLIS, R.P. 1980. A comparison of spring barley grown in England and Scotland. 2. Yield and its component. *Journal of Agricultural Science, Cambridge* 95, 111–116.

KRENTOS, V.D. and ORPHANOS, P.I. 1979. Nitrogen and phosphorus fertilisers for wheat and barley in a semi-arid region. *Journal of Agricultural Science, Cambridge* 93, 711–717.

LAWES, J.B. and GILBERT, J.H. 1880. Our climate and our wheat crops. *Journal of the Royal Society of Agriculture of England Series 2* 16, 173–210.

LEGG, B.J., DAY, W., LAWLOR, D.W. and PARKINSON, K.J. 1979. The effects of drought on barley growth: models and measurements showing the relative importance of leaf area and photosynthetic rate. *Journal of Agricultural Science, Cambridge* **92**, 703–716.

MCCREE, K.J. and DAVIS, S.D. 1974. Effect of water stress and temperature on leaf size and on size and number of epidermal cells in grain sorghum. *Crop Science* **14**, 751–755.

MILTHORPE, F.L. and MOORBY, J. 1974. *An Introduction to Crop Physiology.* Cambridge University Press, London.

MONTEITH, J.L. 1981. Climatic variation and the growth of crops. *Quarterly Journal of the Royal Meteorological Society* **107**, 749–774.

MONSI, M. and SAEKI, T. 1953. Uber den Richtfaktor in den Pflanzengesellschaften und seine Bedentuing fur die Stoffproduktion. *Japanese Journal of Botany* **14**, 22–52.

NATR, L. 1972. Influence of mineral nutrients on photosynthesis of higher plants. *Photosynthetica* **6**, 80–99.

NIX, H.A. 1976. Climate and crop productivity in Australia. In: *Climate and Rice* (ed. Yoshida, S.). IRRI Philippines.

PUCKRIDGE, D.W. 1963. The influence of competition for light on the dry matter production and ear formation of wheat plants. M. Agric. Sci. Thesis, University of Adelaide (cited in Bunting, A.H. and Drennan, D.S.H. Some aspects of the morphology and physiology of cereals in the vegetative stage. In: *The Growth of Cereals and Grasses* (eds. Milthorpe, F.L. and Ivins, J.D.), pp. 20–38. Butterworth, London.

RACKHAM, O. 1972. Responses of the barley crop to soil water stress. In: *Crop processes in controlled environments* (eds, Rees, A.R., Cockshull, K.E., Hand, D.W. and Hurd, R.D.), pp. 127–138. Academic Press, London.

RAWSON, H.M. and BAGGA, A.K. 1979. Influence of temperature between floral initiation and flag leaf emergence on grain number in wheat. *Australian Journal of Plant Physiology* **6**, 391–400.

ROBERTSON, G.W. 1974. Wheat yield for 50 years at Swift Current, Saskatchewan in relation to weather. *Canadian Journal of Plant Science* **54**, 625–650.

SOFIELD, I., EVANS, L.T., COOK, M.G. and WARDLAW, I.F. 1977. Factors influencing the rate and duration of grain filling in wheat. *Australian Journal of Plant Physiology* **4**, 785–797.

SPIERTZ, J.H.J. 1977. The influence of temperature and light intensity on grain growth in relation to the carbohydrate and nitrogen economy of the wheat plant. *Netherlands Journal of Agricultural Science* **25**, 182–197.

SPIERTZ, J.H.J. 1978. Weather and nitrogen effects on rate and duration of grain growth and on grain yield of wheat cultivars. *Proceedings of Eucarpia Workshop on Crop Physiology and Cereal Breeding.* Wageningen, 17–22.

SZEICZ, G. 1974. Solar radiation in crop canopies. *Journal of applied Ecology* **11**, 1117–1156.

TAKEDA, G. 1976. Ecological studies on the photosynthesis of winter cereals. I. Diurnal changes in the photosynthesis of two rowed barley under field conditions in winter. *Proceedings of the Crop Science Society of Japan* **45**, 17–24.

TSUNODA, S. 1972. Photosynthetic efficiency in rice and wheat. In: *Rice Breeding.* IRRI, Philippines, 471–482.

VOS, J. 1981. Effects of temperature and nitrogen supply on post-floral growth of wheat, measurements and simulations. *Agricultural Research Report* 911, PUDOC, Wageningen, 1–164.

WARRINGTON, I.J., DUNSTONE, R.L. and GREEN, L.M. 1977. Temperature effects at three developmental stages on the yield of the wheat ear. *Australian Journal of Agricultural Research* **28**, 11–27.

WATSON, D.J. 1947. Comparative physiological studies on the growth of field crops. I. Variations in net assimilation rate and leaf area between species and varieties and within and between seasons. *Annals of Botany* **11**, 41–76.

WATSON, D.J., THORNE, G.N. and FRENCH, S.A.W. 1958. Physiological causes of differences in grain yield between varieties of barley. *Annals of Botany* **22**, 321–352.

WILLIAMS, R.F. 1955. Redistribution of minor elements during development. *Annual Review of Plant Physiology* **6**, 625–645.

YATES, F. 1969. Investigation into the effects of weather on yields. *Report of Rothamsted Experimental Station for 1968, Part 2.* 46–49.

ZADOKS, J.C., CHANG, T.T. and KOWZAK, C.F. 1974. A decimal code for the growth stages of cereals. *Weed Research* **14**, 415–421.

Discussion

Dr Dilz quoted Dutch experience that a late nitrogen top-dressing on winter wheat could have a large effect on yield, and in some trials up to one–third of the total nitrogen uptake was after anthesis. A top-dressing just before ear emergence could give an additional 400 to 600 kg/ha grain. A discussion followed in which Mr Austin said that late nitrogen did indeed increase green leaf area duration, and therefore might in principle prolong grain filling and increase yield. However in ADAS experience, the effects on yield were small.

Dr Vaidyanathan questioned Mr Austin's hypothesis that if we could raise the harvest index of winter wheat from 49 per cent to 62 per cent, we would increase the non-grain component in the ear from 10 per cent to 12 per cent of the total; he had found that this component was very stable. Mr Austin said that the 10 per cent figure was based on measurements, but he did not know how constant it would be if harvest index changed.

Dr Vaidyanathan asked Dr Kirby whether, once tiller buds were produced, their emergence and growth could be inhibited, for example by cutting off incident light with a collar at the stem base. Dr Kirby agreed that many factors might prevent tiller buds from developing into tillers. However he thought that the experiment referred to involved a collar exerting pressure at the base of the stem, and that this pressure was much greater than would normally be experienced by the plant. This implied that it was not a light effect, and *Dr Vaidyanathan* wondered how, in that case, we could explain the increased tillering observed with shallower drilling. Dr Kirby suggested that with deep drilling, nutrients translocated from the seed were diverted to form the first internode rather than to form tillers.

Dr Tinker expressed concern at the dangers of ignoring growth below ground. Although extractable roots might make up less than 10 per cent of total dry matter, there were claims in the literature that 20 per cent or more of photosynthate might be directed below ground. He wondered how this affected Mr Austin's approach. Mr Austin replied that in experiments in controlled environments he had found that, after anthesis, very little leaf carbon assimilate went to roots if ears were present. However, sterile tillers or those with ears removed diverted much more assimilate to the roots. He had concluded that the roots competed poorly with ears for any assimilate. Dr Biscoe commented that in his work at Sutton Bonnington, the relationship between intercepted radiation and dry matter production had been adjusted to take account of dry matter diverted to roots.

Dr Jenkyn remarked that although most carbohydrate in grain was produced after anthesis, in some circumstances, e.g. high temperatures, the stem contribution could be important. Should we conclude that normally stem reserves were not being used? If so, he wondered whether we could manipulate plants to release them. Mr Austin explained that if the growth of the stem structure were stopped before anthesis by drought, soluble carbohydrates would build up before photosynthesis fell off, and could contribute up to 40 per cent of stem dry matter. At anthesis, these soluble carbohydrates would be mobilised to the grain and could contribute significantly to yield (1 to 2 t/ha). In more normal seasons this accumulation did not start until anthesis and reached a maximum 10 days later. The actual contribution to yield was about 1 t/ha, which was smaller as a percentage of a normal yield. Dr Biscoe commented that his own data from years with water stress agreed with Mr Austin's figures.

Mr Hubbard enquired how far sink capacity affected this. Would there be more transfer from the stem if a high sink capacity (e.g. high grain number) were present, and was this a factor in recent yield increases? Mr Austin stated that even in normal crops no unused soluble carbohydrate was left in stems and leaves at maturity. In other words they acted as a temporary buffer store. Dr Dilz confirmed Dr Biscoe's suggestion that work in Holland had shown that sink capacity could be satisfied while there was still green tissue. This had happened in 1962 and in 1978, and they presumed that the ear had been unable to accept any more assimilate.

Winter wheat yield variability

L V Vaidyanathan
ADAS, Cambridge

Average national and regional yield changes

National average winter wheat yields have increased during the post-war years from 2.31 t/ha in 1946 to 5.59 t/ha in 1981. There are considerable annual fluctuations occurring more or less similarly in all ADAS Regions and also reflected broadly in average yields of other cereals, suggesting some effect of countrywide macroclimatic features.

Three distinct periods are evident. The following pattern is seen, when averaged over all Regions (Table 1).

Table 1 Average winter wheat yields t/ha at 85 per cent DM – 1946 to 1981

In each period –
Yield in a given year = Yield at start of period + (Annual change in yield) × (No. of years from start of period)

$$Y_n = Y_1 + b \cdot (X_n - X_i)$$

Region	Early period 1946–1961		Middle period 1962–1972		Late period 1973–1981	
	Y_1	b	Y_1	b	Y_1	b
North	2.215	0.0901	4.073	0.0292	4.492	0.0964
Yorks. and Lancs.	2.315	0.0947	4.024	0.0260	4.288	0.1805
Wales	1.944	0.0759	3.614	0.0373	3.542	0.2963
West Midlands	2.183	0.0768	3.953	–0.0021	4.051	0.1770
East Midlands	2.492	0.0775	4.181	–0.0103	4.175	0.1762
South West	1.871	0.1075	3.878	0.0127	3.951	0.2212
South East	2.146	0.0795	3.839	0.0149	4.011	0.1791
East	2.495	0.0787	4.142	0.0058	4.127	0.2206
SE of b		0.0182		0.0319		0.0432

1) 16 years, 1946–1961 inclusive, with annual increase of 0.119 t/ha from 2.31 to 4.21 t/ha;
2) 11 years, 1962–1972 inclusive, with annual increase of 0.005 t/ha from 4.27 to 4.33 t/ha;
3) 9 years, 1973–1981 inclusive, with annual increase of 0.147 t/ha from 4.27 to 5.59 t/ha.

These are data obtained from the annual Agricultural Census (MAFF).

Increase in farm mechanisation, change in rotations with emphasis shifting to mixed arable or all arable, modest increase in fertiliser nitrogen usage and the availability of herbicides would account for the improvement seen in the period up to the early sixties.

The virtually stagnant middle phase up to the early seventies seems to correspond to the predominance of wheat varieties liable to severe damage from diseases and lodging if inputs like fertiliser nitrogen were increased. Depressed market value of the product was perhaps a disincentive for intensifying husbandry.

The later period from the early 1970s onwards is closely associated with:
1) Increase in the proportion of area sown with improved varieties, beginning

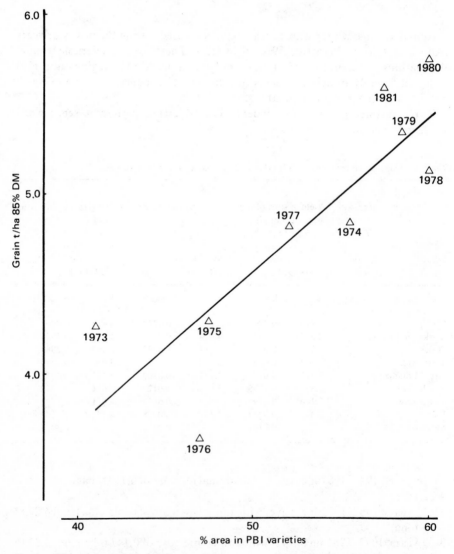

Fig. 1a Winter wheat yield change related to area sown with improved varieties.

with Maris Huntsman and soon overtaken by the short, strong-strawed cultivars with much improved harvest indices; data from NSDO.

Yield t ha^{-1} (85 per cent DM) = 0.246 + 0.0866 × per cent area in new varieties, (r^2 = 0.721, Figure 1a).

2) Increase in proportion of crops receiving plant protection treatments.
Yield t ha^{-1} = 4.26 + 0.0197 × per cent area sprayed, (r^2 = 0.584, Figure 1b).

3) Increase in spring nitrogen top dressing; data from the Survey of Fertiliser Practice.
Yield t ha^{-1} = 1.762 + 0.0253 × kg ha^{-1} nitrogen fertiliser, (r^2 = 0.712, Figure 1c).

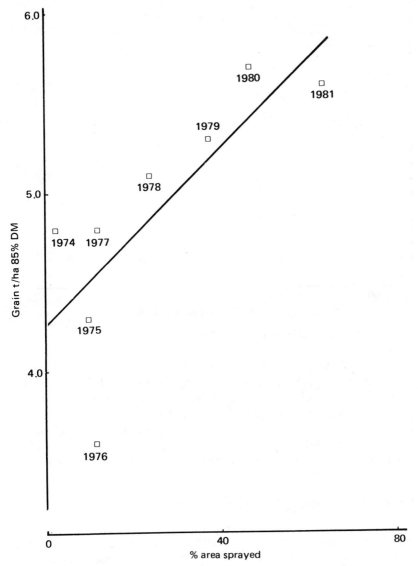

Fig. 1b   Winter wheat yield change related to area receiving plant protection treatment.

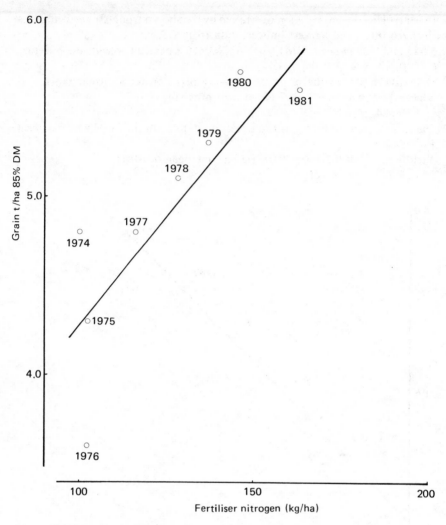

Fig. 1c Winter wheat yield change related to fertiliser nitrogen use.

The latter two factors would have been influenced by the increased market value of the crop. This period is also notable for the further shift in rotational strategy to continuous cereals or combinable crops under reduced autumn soil cultivations and substantial increase in the use of herbicides.

There are significant differences in rates of change in yield between Regions. Explanation of these and annual fluctuations may emerge from models seeking to link yields to seasonal and local weather and environmental factors.

Factors influencing yield variation

Observations on crops grown in the same field in successive seasons or on several crops during one season (ADAS Eastern Region Annual Reports) reveal some notable features.

Nutrient and water supply and root activity are the most likely to be affected by soil properties. Seasonal conditions and husbandry practices influence the effects of pests, diseases and weeds. Occasionally, yield variations are well accounted for by (1) mineral nitrogen content of soil at the beginning of spring growth and/or (2) the extent of root disease (take-all) or (3) weed competition (Figures 2, 3 and 4).

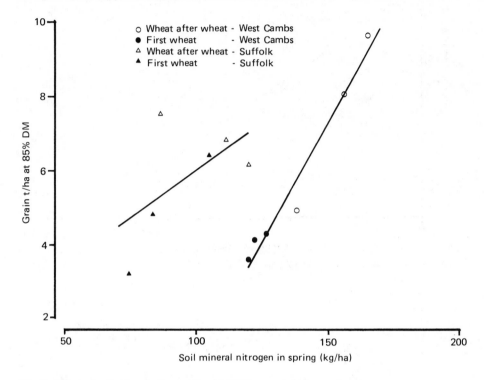

Fig. 2 Effect of soil mineral nitrogen on yield 1981 – several sites.

Response to spring fertiliser nitrogen was measured during 1974–1981 on several sites, with differing soil nitrogen supply, in different varieties. Yields were in the range 2.24 to 7.49 t ha^{-1} (85 per cent DM) without fertiliser nitrogen and 4.00 to 12.23 t ha^{-1} with optimum nitrogen. The optimum nitrogen level was in the range 0–280 kg ha^{-1} and varied over the seasons within a field and between fields in one season. However, yields at optimum nitrogen were closely related to yields achieved solely from soil nitrogen supply, accounting for over 85 per cent of variance.

Yield with optimum N t ha^{-1} (85 per cent DM) = 0.486 + yield with no fertiliser nitrogen × 1.636, r^2 = 0.854 (F = 141, 24 df, Figure 5).

This evidence adds little to our understanding of mechanisms and processes involved, but emphasises that site potential strongly influenced by the growing season determines the yield achieved.

Rainfall distribution, incident photosynthetically active radiation, its efficient interception and use and the temperature regime are all inter-related determinants of total growth achieved, Gallagher and Biscoe (1978).

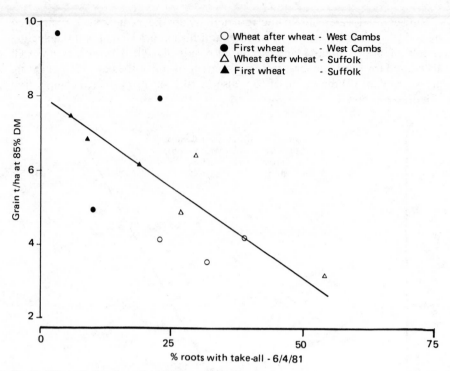

Fig. 3   Effect of take-all on yield 1981.

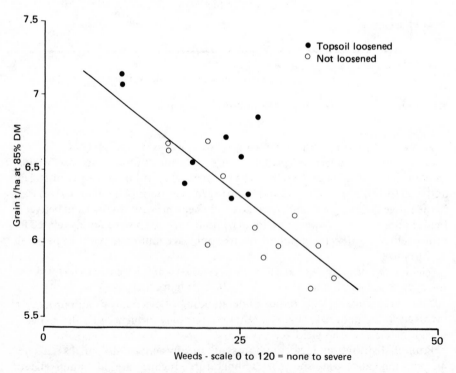

Fig. 4   Weed effect on yields of continuously direct drilled wheat 1981 – single site.

74

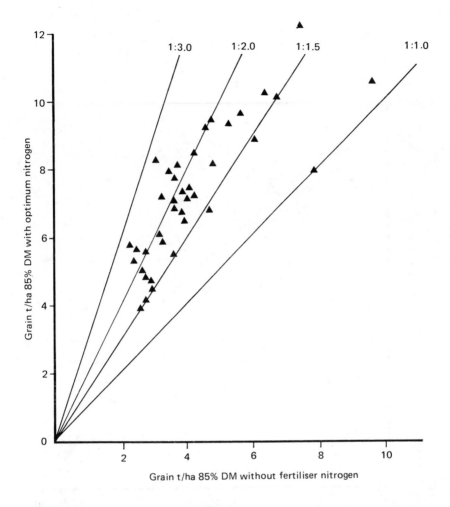

Fig. 5 Yields with optimum and no fertiliser nitrogen.

Partitioning of the accumulated dry matter and nutrients between grain and other parts is variety–dependent, Austin *et al.* (1980) and also subject to seasonal factors, Gallagher *et al.* (1976).

Temperature during the grain growth phase may also influence the growth rate and its duration and so the size of the yield, Proctor (1963), Thorne (1971), Masse (1981), besides drought as suggested by Gallagher *et al.* (1976). Tissue temperature may be a physiologically significant factor responding to the intensity and duration of sunshine directly incident on the tissues, through its spectral composition, especially the far-red and infra red components. Figure 6 shows a significant negative association between yields achieved in several sites in successive seasons (1973–81) and the sunshine – hours for July accounting for over 50 per cent of variance.

Yield t ha^{-1} (85 per cent DM) = 8.97 – Sunshine hours in July $\times$ 0.017, r^2 = 0.502 (F = 28, 28 df, Figure 6).

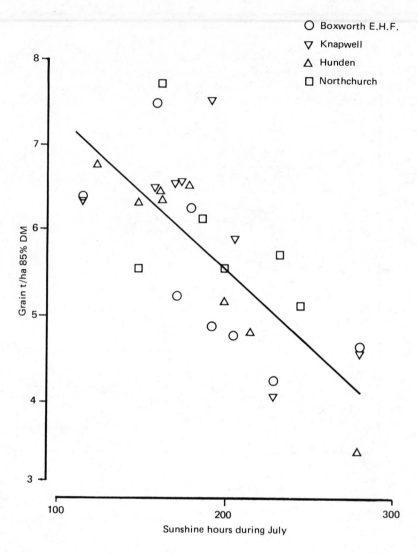

Fig. 6 July sunshine effect on winter wheat yield.

Cumulative potential evaporation or net potential evaporation (allowing for rainfall) during this or other extended periods were less satisfactory correlants.

Acknowledgement

Mr B J George, Department of Statistics, Rothamsted Experimental Station, Harpenden, helped with statistical analyses.

References

MAFF. Agricultural Statistics England and Wales, MAFF – data source for annual average yields.

AUSTIN, R.B., BINGHAM, J., BLACKWELL, R.D., EVANS, L.T., FORD, M.A., MORGAN, C.C., and TAYLOR, M. 1980. Genetic improvements in winter wheat yields since 1900 and associated physiological changes. *Journal of Agricultural Science, Cambridge* **94**, 675-695.

GALLAGHER, J.N., and BISCOE, P.V. 1978. Radiation absorption growth and yield of cereals. *Journal of Agricultural Science, Cambridge* **91**, 47-60.

GALLAGHER, J.N., BISCOE, P.V., and HUNTER, B. 1976. Effects of drought on grain growth. *Nature* **264**, 541-542.

NSDO, National Seed Development Organisation, Newton Hall, Newton, Cambridge – data source for area sown with improved varieties.

PROCTOR, J.M. 1963. An experiment to determine the effects of date of sowing on the yield and quality of harvesting peas 1953–56. *Journal of Agricultural Science, Cambridge* **61**, 281-289.

MAFF. Survey of Fertiliser Practice. Fertiliser use on farm crops in England and Wales, 1974–1981.

MASSE, J. 1981. La maturation du blé dépend surtout du climat, *Perspectives Agricoles* **51**, 13-19.

THORNE, G.N. 1971. Effects of temperature on grain growth in wheat. *Rothamsted Experimental Station Report, Part I*, p. 106.

The supply of nitrogen from the soil

D S Jenkinson
Rothamsted Experimental Station, Harpenden

Summary

The decomposition of plant material in soil can conveniently be regarded as taking place in two phases, a rapid decay during the first year, leading to a much slower process lasting many years. At the end of the first year about 13 kg of nitrogen is tied up in organic form per tonne of dry plant material added. If the plant material originally contained less nitrogen than this, the deficit is made up by immobilising inorganic nitrogen from the soil; if more, the excess nitrogen is mineralised. About a tenth of the immobilised nitrogen is released during the second year, and ever diminishing quantities in succeeding years.

Neither the various chemical tests nor the biological tests for predicting the nitrogen supplying capacity of a given soil are satisfactory for large scale advisory work under UK conditions and it is unlikely that better soil tests will alter this situation. It is much more likely that improved predictions will come from refinements to the N Index, a system for assessing nitrogen supplying capacity from cropping history. Computerized systems are now being introduced for keeping farm records on a field-by-field basis and these, updated by weather information and by computer-run models of transformations undergone by soil nitrogen, are likely to form the basis for improved predictions.

Introduction

With rare exceptions, more than 90 per cent of the nitrogen in agricultural topsoils is in organic combination. This stock of organic nitrogen is subject to slow mineralisation (defined as the conversion of nitrogen from organic to inorganic form) and the nitrogen thus mineralised is replaced by organic nitrogen produced during the death and decay of plants and animals. The process is set out in Figure 1, which shows an idealised nitrogen cycle in a topsoil carrying winter wheat. In this diagram, soil nitrogen is segregated into seven compartments, four inorganic (exchangeable NH_4^+, non-exchangeable NH_4^+, NO_2^- and NO_3^-) and three organic (nitrogen in roots, nitrogen in microbial biomass and organic nitrogen not in roots or biomass).

An authoritative book, edited by F J Stevenson, has just appeared (1982) on nitrogen in agricultural soils. With this book as background, my aim in the present paper is to consider how our present knowledge on the mineralisation and immobilisation of nitrogen in soil can be related to the prediction of the nitrogen supplying capacity of a given soil.

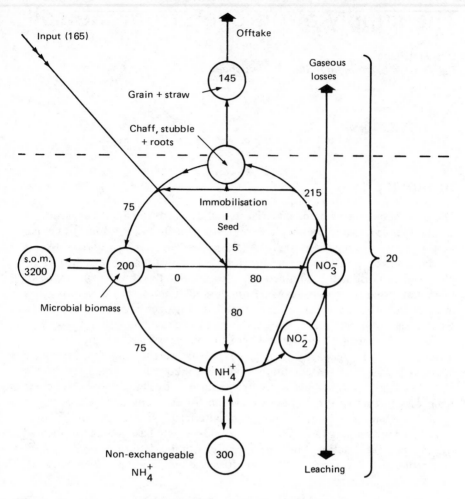

Input (165)

Offtake

145

Grain + straw

Chaff, stubble + roots

Gaseous losses

215

Immobilisation

Seed

75

5

s.o.m. 3200

200

0

80

NO_3^-

20

Microbial biomass

80

NO_2^-

75

NH_4^+

Non-exchangeable NH_4^+

300

Leaching

Fig. 1 Nitrogen cycle under continuous winter wheat receiving NPKMg fertiliser annually (Broadbalk plot 08, section 1). All figures are rounded (usually to the nearest 5 kg) to avoid any spurious appearance of precision, and relate to the topsoil (0–23 cm) only (Jenkinson, 1982).

Mineralisation and immobilisation of nitrogen in soil

Biological and non-biological immobilisation

An uptake of inorganic nitrogen during the decomposition of a substrate in soil, known as 'immobilisation', can take place at the same time as mineralisation. In consequence, a change in the mineral nitrogen content of a soil containing decomposing plant material gives only *net* mineralisation or immobilisation, i.e. the difference between gross immobilisation and gross mineralisation.

The immobilisation of nitrogen in soil was studied intensively between 1920 and 1950, recently there has been a revival of interest, mainly because of the introduction of isotopic techniques, which allow gross mineralisation and immobilisation measurements to be made. The topic has been repeatedly reviewed; by Jansson (1958), by Bartholomew (1965), by Allison (1973), by Campbell (1978) and by Jansson and Persson (1982). Mathematical modelling of immobilisation (and related nitrogen transformations in soil) has been reviewed by Tanji and Gupta (1978).

Immobilisation of inorganic nitrogen can occur by both biological and non-biological processes (for a review see Allison, 1973). Thus plant material and peat can react chemically with ammonia at pH levels above 8, particularly in the presence of oxygen, resulting in the formation of complexes in which the ammonia is bound in a non-exchangeable form (Mortland, 1958). Nelson and Bremner (1969) showed that NO_2^- decomposed chemically in acid soils, part of the nitrogen being released in gaseous forms and part immobilised in the soil organic matter. Again, certain soils containing illitic and vermiculitic clay minerals can fix NH_4^+ in the clay lattice, the ammonium thus fixed being rendered largely non-exchangeable (Nommik, 1981). However, these chemical processes are of minor importance in mature topsoils within the pH range 5–8 and the subsequent discussion will be confined to biological immobilisation.

Nitrogen transformations during the early stages of decomposition of plant material

Immobilisation is illustrated in Figure 2, which shows the uptake of nitrogen by straw supplied with sufficient mineral nitrogen to ensure that microbial activity was not restricted by nitrogen deficiency. In this particular example, immobilisation reached its peak (known as the 'turning point') after 3 weeks, long after the peak rate of evolution of carbon dioxide.

Whether immobilisation or mineralisation predominate when a given substrate is added to soil depends primarily on the nitrogen content of the added organic matter. In Jensen's (1929) classical work, lucerne, which is rich in nitrogen (3.5 per cent) mineralised nitrogen right from the start, whereas with wheat straw (0.5 per cent nitrogen) there was net immobilisation throughout the six-month period of the experiment. Materials with intermediate nitrogen contents occupy intermediate positions, a common pattern being a short period of immobilisation, followed by mineralisation. As a rough generalisation, material with a nitrogen content of less than 1.2–1.3 per cent (corresponding to a C/N ratio of about 30) will immobilise soil nitrogen (and fertiliser nitrogen, if present) throughout the early weeks (and often months) of incubation. With more than 1.8–2.0 per cent nitrogen (corresponding to a C/N ratio of about 20), mineralisation usually occurs within a week or so, if not immediately. However, per cent nitrogen is a fallible guide to whether or not a given material will immobilise nitrogen during the early stages of decomposition; a lignified material with a low nitrogen content may well immobilise less nitrogen than a more decomposable plant material containing more nitrogen (Rubins and Bear, 1942).

There will be competition for inorganic nitrogen when plants grow on a soil in which heterotrophs are actively decomposing organic matter of wide C/N ratio. In this situation the heterotrophs invariably succeed, at the expense of the plants (and of nitrifiers, when there is competition for ammonium, Jansson, 1958).

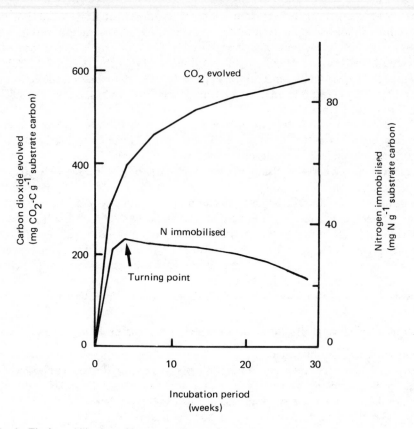

Fig. 2 The immobilisation of inorganic nitrogen by wheat straw decomposing in soil (Nommik, 1962).

The quantity of organic nitrogen remaining in plant material that has decomposed for one year

The decomposition of plant material in soil can be represented by a two stage process, a relatively rapid initial phase, during which about two-thirds of the plant carbon is lost, followed by a sharp transition to a much slower phase (Jenkinson, 1977). Setting aside the initial phase, different plants and different parts of plants decompose to a remarkably similar extent over a period of a year or so. Thus, although ryegrass roots initially decomposed more slowly than green ryegrass leaves, by the end of a year there were no significant differences between the percentages of root and leaf carbon retained in the soil (Jenkinson, 1977). About a third of the added carbon was retained in the soil when green ryegrass leaves (Jenkinson, 1977), green maize (Oberlander, 1973), mature wheat straw (Führ and Sauerbeck, 1968) or the forage legume medic (Ladd, Oades and Amato, 1981) were allowed to decompose for one year in the field. Allison, Sherman and Pinck (1949) found (in laboratory experiments), that 34 per cent of the carbon in green oats remained in the soil after one year; the corresponding figures for nitrogen-supplemented wheat straw was 38 per cent, for whole green soybean plants 28 per cent and for mature maize stalks 38 per cent. Siegel (1940)

82

found that 31 per cent of the carbon in a cereal straw of C/N ratio 167 remained in the soil after one year in the field; when supplemented with inorganic N to bring the C/N ratio to 20 the corresponding retention was again 31 per cent and with a C/N ratio of 10 it was 26 per cent.

These findings, that about a third of the carbon from plant materials remains in the soil after a year in the field, combined with the observation that the C/N

Fig. 3 Organic nitrogen released from plant material that has decomposed for one year, assuming that dry plant material contains 40 per cent C and that one-third of the added plant C remains in the soil after one year.

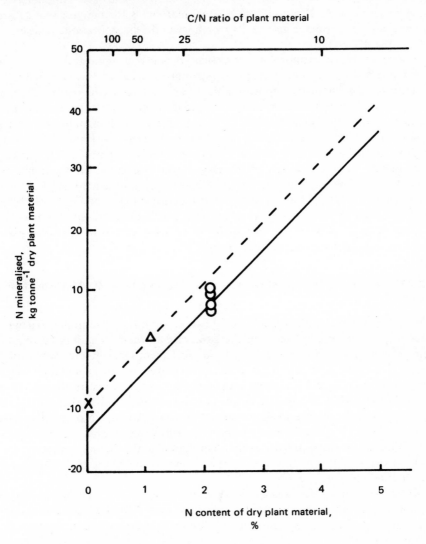

— C/N of the residual plant C assumed to be 10.
--- C/N of the residual plant C assumed to be 15.
× Sorensen (1981); cellulose decomposing in two different soils at 20 °C.
○ Ladd *et al.* (1981); medic decomposing in four different soils under field conditions.
△ Myers and Paul (1971); oat straw decomposing in the field.

ratio of well drained and near-neutral agricultural topsoils is usually about 10, make it possible to calculate the amount of nitrogen release (or immobilised) by a given quantity of plant material of a known nitrogen content. Figure 3 shows the net quantity of nitrogen immobilised or mineralised by one tonne of plant material one year after it had been incorporated into soil assuming:

(1) that $\frac{1}{3}$ of the plant carbon remains;

(2) that the C/N ratio of the residual material is 10.

These assumptions imply that 13 kg of nitrogen in organic form remains in the soil after the incorporation of one tonne of dry plant material, regardless of its initial composition. Figure 3 also shows the quantity of nitrogen immobilised or mineralised if the C/N ratio of the residual material is 15, implying that 9 kg of organic nitrogen remains in the soil one year after the incorporation of one tonne of dry plant material.

Figure 3 is based on approximations that are only relevant to arable soils from the temperate zones. It does not apply to strongly-acid soils, to waterlogged soils, or to situations where decomposition is held up for much of the year by drought or by low temperatures. It cannot be used without modification on pre-decomposed plant remains such as faeces or farmyard manure, where the retention of carbon is greater than $\frac{1}{3}$ (Sauerbeck, 1968; De Haan, 1977) or on highly lignified woody material like hardwood chippings. It must also be stressed that Figure 3 does not apply to the early stages of decomposition. Immature plant material initially decomposes much faster than mature material (Waksman and Tenney, 1927) and factors such as particle size (Stickler and Frederick, 1959) also influence the initial rate at which nitrogen is immobilised. Nevertheless Figure 3 does apply to the vast majority of temperate soils receiving plant residues from normal agricultural crops.

Release of nitrogen from plant residues that have been in the field for more than a year

Once the rapid phase is over, say after a year, decomposition continues at a much slower pace. This is reflected in the slow rate at which immobilised organic nitrogen is released during the second and subsequent years after immobilisation (Figure 4). The line drawn on this figure represents an exponential decay process of half-life 6.8 years and gives a close fit to the data for the uptake of immobilised ^{15}N by subsequent crops. It should be emphasised that the data in Figure 4 come from experiments where all, or nearly all, the ^{15}N originally added was present in organic form when the first crop was harvested. If appreciable quantities of inorganic nitrogen remain in the soil at the first harvest, some may survive the winter to be taken up by the second crop, and the curve in Figure 4 will fall much more sharply.

In a system under steady state conditions, where the input decays exponentially with a rate constant r and where annual additions are balanced by annual losses from the system, then $r = 0.693/t$, where t is the half-life. Under these conditions

$$n = r N$$

where n is the annual addition of organic nitrogen and N is the total organic nitrogen content of the soil. Taking n as 75 kg ha^{-1} year^{-1} of N (Figure 1) and r as 0.102 years^{-1} (= 0.693/6.8), then N is 736 kg ha^{-1}. The experimentally measured figure for the total organic nitrogen content of the soil (0–23 cm) is 3200, almost five times larger. It follows that much of the nitrogen immobilised each year has a half-life much greater than 6.8 years and that some of the organic nitrogen in soil decomposes very slowly indeed (Jenkinson and Rayner, 1977).

The nitrogen supplying capacity of a soil can thus be regarded as being in two parts. The first is associated with fresh additions of plant material; these will rapidly augment (or deplete, depending on the C/N ratio) the inorganic nitrogen

Fig. 4 The release of immobilised ^{15}N to subsequent crops. The ^{15}N was applied as inorganic fertiliser to the first crop: cumulative uptakes by the second, third and fourth crops are shown. All the data are from field experiments where < 150 kg ha^{-1} labelled N was applied to crops.

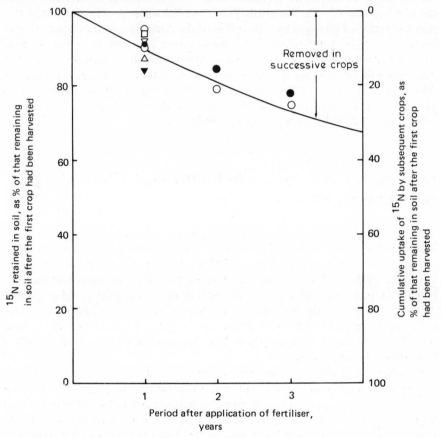

Period after application of fertiliser, years

•o Riga, Fischer and van Praag (1980); means of all treatments.
□ Dowdell and Crees (1980); mean of all treatments.
△ Westermann and Kurtz (1972); mean of urea treatments only.
▼ ▽ Hart, Jenkinson, Johnston, Powlson and Pruden (1982); mean for all rates of fertiliser nitrogen except the largest.
◖ Vaidyanathan and Leitch (1980); mean of direct drilled and ploughed treatments receiving 80 kg fertiliser N.

Data with open symbols show plant uptake of ^{15}N; solid symbols show the ^{15}N retained in soil. The curve represents an exponential decay process of half-life 6.8 years, fitted to the plant uptake data.

reserves of the soil. The second is from the older residues; there will be a small contribution from residues that have been in the soil one year, a slightly smaller contribution from residues two years in the field and so on. The formation of organic nitrogen, whether directly as organic nitrogen in roots and root exudates, or indirectly by immobilisation during the decomposition of these residues, is a rapid process, accomplished within a few months, whereas the subsequent remineralisation takes many years.

The remineralisation phase is strongly influenced by the soil environment –the greater the clay content, other things being equal, the slower the decomposition of organic matter and biomass (Jenkinson, 1977; Sorensen, 1981). Temperature also plays a role (Jenkinson and Ayanaba, 1977): the rate of decomposition during the slow phase was roughly four times as fast at Ibadan in the Nigerian rain forest (mean annual air temperature 26.1 °C) as at Rothamsted (mean annual air temperature 8.9 °C). Stanford, Frere and Schwaninger (1973) showed that mineralisation of nitrogen by soils followed the Arrhenius equation, and that an increase of 10 °C roughly doubled mineralisation rate over the range 5–35 °C. Mineralisation is slower under anaerobic conditions, although it is unlikely that aeration will be limiting for long periods in well-drained agricultural soils. Moisture also has an influence, although the response curve relating water content to rate of mineralisation of nitrogen is rather flat topped (Clement and Williams, 1962; Miller and Johnston, 1964).

Role of the soil microbial biomass in the cycling of nitrogen

About 3–5 per cent of the soil nitrogen is found in the soil microbial biomass (Ayanaba, Tuckwell and Jenkinson, 1976) – the living part of the soil. The top 25 cm of an arable soil can contain 200 kg ha[-1] of N in the microbial biomass (Figure 1), increasing to perhaps three or four times this level in old grassland. The biomass plays a double role: it is the agent of change – so far as we know, even the most stable fractions of the soil organic nitrogen are mineralised microbially. However, in addition, the biomass nitrogen is itself a small but labile fraction of the soil nitrogen.

Calculations based on steady state assumptions (Jenkinson and Ladd, 1981) suggest that, under temperate conditions, the turnover time of the soil biomass is of the order of two years. For a biomass containing 200 kg ha[-1] of N this would imply an annual flux of 100 kg ha[-1] year[-1] of N, The flux from the biomass to the soil inorganic nitrogen pool will be smaller, because a part of the microbial nitrogen will not be released into the soil but will be incorporated directly into new microbial tissue on cell division.

Although the soil microbial biomass is only 3–5 per cent of the total soil nitrogen, it makes up a larger fraction of recently immobilised nitrogen. Thus, of the 141 kg of ^{15}N labelled fertiliser applied to winter wheat in the spring, 17 per cent remained in the soil at harvest, almost all in organic form. Of this residual organic nitrogen, almost 30 per cent was present in the microbial biomass (Shen, Powlson, Pruden and Jenkinson, 1982).

The measurement of the nitrogen supplying capacity of soil

This subject has been reviewed so often (Harmsen and van Schreven, 1955; Bremner, 1965; Scarsbrook, 1965; Dahnke and Vasey, 1973; Campbell, 1978) and so recently (Stanford, 1982) that a further detailed review is superfluous. Instead, I will attempt to assess the relevance of the various proposed measurements to the practical problems of soil testing.

Mineral nitrogen in soil

The techniques for measuring inorganic nitrogen in soil are well established (Bremner, 1965; Dahnke and Vasey, 1973) and the mineral nitrogen contents of soil, usually sampled in spring, have been widely used as predictors of the nitrogen supplying capacity of the soil. However, it is only comparatively recently that the importance of deep sampling, particularly for nitrate, has been generally appreciated, although a few early workers did measure nitrate to depth (see Dahnke and Vasey, 1973 for references). Nitrate can be taken up by plants from depths of a metre and more, so that, if the soil nitrogen taken up by a crop comes mainly from nitrate present *at the time of sampling*, sampling must be deep. In this, it differs from potentially mineralisable organic nitrogen, which occurs predominantly in the plough layer of arable soils, where most of the soil organic nitrogen is located.

Numerous studies (Carter, Jensen and Bosma, 1974; Wehrmann and Scharpf, 1976; Soper and Huang, 1963; for other references see Stanford, 1982) have shown correlations between crop uptake (or fertiliser nitrogen requirement) and the nitrate content of the profile, sampling usually taking place in early spring.

Potentially mineralisable organic nitrogen

Tests for potentially mineralisable nitrogen can be separated into two groups: biological and chemical. Biological tests can be direct, in which the quantity of organic nitrogen mineralised by the soil is measured after an incubation done under standard conditions – which can be aerobic or anaerobic. Indirect biological methods have also been proposed – for example the quantities of carbon dioxide produced when cellulose was incubated with a range of soils is correlated with the amounts of mineral nitrogen produced when the same soils were incubated without cellulose (Cornfield, 1961). None of the indirect methods (for references see Dahnke and Vasey, 1973) have been widely used in advisory work.

All the biological methods suffer from two disadvantages. Firstly, an incubation period is required, which is inconvenient for laboratories engaged in predicting fertiliser requirements, particularly if large numbers of samples have to be processed. Secondly, the results obtained are very dependent on when the soil is sampled and how it is handled before incubation; for example, a period of drying prior to incubation greatly alters the results obtained.

Numerous chemical methods for assessing potentially mineralisable nitrogen have been proposed: Dahnke and Vasey (1973) list 58 papers on chemical tests that have been used over the first 70 years of this century and more have been studied since then (Stanford, 1982). It is intrinsically unlikely that any simple chemical method can measure the organic nitrogen about to be mineralised; this nitrogen is distributed through different fractions of the soil organic matter, the microbial biomass, partially decomposed plant material, the various humic materials, etc. In many of the chemical methods, the procedure used, for example refluxing the soil with alkaline permanganate, releases far more nitrogen than is released naturally in a growing season. The most successful tests are likely to be those that reflect the quantity of microbial biomass present, rather than the larger but relatively inert humus fractions. It must also be remembered that, in a set of soils all of which have attained steady state conditions, with annual inputs and outputs in balance, and in which the decomposition processes are similar, whatever the annual input of organic nitrogen, *any* fraction of the soil nitrogen will correlate with any other, including the potentially mineralisable organic nitrogen.

The most serious objection to chemical tests as distinct from biological incubation tests, is that no single chemical measurement is likely to give due weight to both the processes leading to mineralisation of nitrogen and those leading to immobilisation. A soil with a large mineralisation potential, as indicated by a chemical test, may in fact mineralise no nitrogen if immobilisation is vigorous. The highly significant correlations often obtained between the results of chemical tests and production of inorganic nitrogen are more likely to indicate that immobilisation is not very important in the soils used, rather than that the tests made allowance for the balance between mobilisation and immobilisation (Jenkinson, 1968).

The relative contributions of nitrate and potentially mineralisable organic nitrogen to the nitrogen supply

When a soil is sampled it contains some inorganic nitrogen that is immediately available to a plant and some potentially mineralisable organic nitrogen that will be mineralised in the period between sampling and harvest of the crop. One of the most intractable problems in assessing the nitrogen supplying capacity of soil is how to apportion the weight given to each of these components of nitrogen supply. There is unlikely to be any single solution to this problem.

It might be thought that the quantity of nitrate found in a soil at the time of sampling will be directly related to potentially mineralisable organic nitrogen, since the nitrate already in the soil is itself a product of mineralisation and there is no reason why the capacity to produce mineral nitrogen should be different before and after sampling. However, in many cases this is not so; the nitrate may have come from an external source, say fertiliser, rather than from the soil organic nitrogen by mineralisation. Furthermore, even if all the nitrate had come from mineralisation, it would not bear a directly proportional relationship to mineralisable organic nitrogen, if, for example, nitrate had been lost before sampling because of denitrification, leaching or plant uptake.

Whether measurements of nitrate or of potentially mineralisable organic nitrogen are the most important depends on the climate. Under conditions where nitrate from previous cropping is incompletely leached from the profile, nitrate measurement in the rooting zone by itself can give a good measure of the nitrogen supplying capacity of a soil (see above). Under more humid conditions, analyses for NO_3-N and NH_4-N had no value in predicting the response of winter wheat to nitrogen (Eagle, 1966). Often both make a significant contribution, and predictions of crop uptake are then best when an initial inorganic nitrogen measurement is combined with a measurement of potentially mineralisable nitrogen (Gasser, 1961; Jenkinson 1968).

Uptake of soil nitrogen by crops

Ultimately, the value of any measure of the soil nitrogen supplying capacity is tested by comparing the results it gives with the quantity of nitrogen taken up by the crop growing in the field, assuming that factors limiting uptake, such as plant disease, drought, etc., do not restrict nitrogen uptake. The nitrogen uptake by a control plot not receiving nitrogenous fertiliser can, in itself, be a useful guide to the fertiliser required in the following year, particularly if the soil has been exposed to the same nitrogen input and cropping for a number of years *and* conditions are such that nitrogen overwintering as nitrate is either completely lost or retained. In climates where the winter carry-over of nitrate varies greatly from year to year, control plot uptakes will be less useful.

Future developments in predicting nitrogen supply

Soil tests for nitrogen supplying capacity have never been as satisfactory as those for, say, available phosphorus or potassium and the complexity of the soil nitrogen supplying system makes it likely that they never will be. Incubation tests have not been used extensively in advisory work, apart from in the US Mid-West in regions of relative climatic and soil uniformity. Measurements of nitrate are more widespread and measurements of nitrate to depths of a metre or so are currently in use for advisory purposes in parts of Germany and France. However, recent unpublished ADAS work has shown that nitrate measurements to rooting depth have not been so satisfactory in the UK, with its wetter climate and less homogeneous soils. In addition, there are considerable practical difficulties in making these measurements; deep sampling is intrinsically difficult, particularly in stony or shallow soils. Sampling has to be done in early spring, only shortly before fertiliser recommendations are issued, leaving little time for analysing the samples and processing the data.

All this is tacitly admitted in the use of the ADAS N Index by advisors in this country. The N Index is based not on soil analysis but on past cropping. Fertiliser nitrogen recommendations are modified on the basis of the N Index and soil type. Soils are divided into three classes, 0, 1 and 2, usually on the basis of the last crop grown, although allowance is also made for the extra nitrogen released over a number of years when old pasture is ploughed up (ADAS Fertiliser Recommendations, 1979). One of the problems with the N Index system is that most fields fall into class 0, classes 1 and 2 being relatively rare. Another is its coarseness: with the increasing demand for more precise recommendations, a system with more categories is called for.

It seems to me that the way forward is through improving the N Index system, rather than through further development of soil testing. Computer-based systems for keeping field records are now being developed and these records contain the very information needed for an improved N Index system – soil type and depth, cropping history, and yields on a year-by-year basis. Such an improved N Index system could be extended to allow for winter leaching losses by a regular input of meteorological data, using one of the models now being developed (see Tinker and Addiscott, 1984) to predict leaching losses.

Soil nitrogen tests, particularly nitrate to rooting depth, will almost certainly be used in calibrating and validating such a system but the ultimate aim should be to predict the nitrogen supplying potential of the soil in a given field from our scientific knowledge of the behaviour of nitrogen in soil and from the history of the field, not from soil analyses. Such a system has the advantage that there is scope for continuous improvement – past differences between predicted and observed results can be used to improve future predictions.

References

AGRICULTURAL DEVELOPMENT AND ADVISORY SERVICE. 1979. *Fertiliser Recommendations* Booklet GF1, HMSO London.

ALLISON, F.E. 1973. *Soil Organic Matter and its Role in Crop Production,* Elsevier, Amsterdam.

ALLISON, F.E., SHERMAN, M.S. and PINCK, L.A. 1949. Maintenance of soil organic matter. I. Inorganic soil colloid as a factor in retention of carbon during formation of humus. *Soil Science* **68**, 463–478.

AYANABA, A., TUCKWELL, S.B. and JENKINSON, D.S. 1976. The effects of clearing and cropping on the organic reserves and biomass of tropical forest soils. *Soil Biology and Biochemistry* **8**, 519–525.

BARTHOLOMEW, W.V. 1965. Mineralisation and immobilisation of nitrogen in the decomposition of plant and animal residues. In: *Soil Nitrogen* (eds. W.V. Bartholomew and F.E. Clark) pp. 285–306. American Society of Agronomy, Madison.

BREMNER, J.M. 1965. Nitrogen availability indexes. In: *Methods of Soil Analysis* Part 2, (ed. C.A. Black) pp. 1324–1345. American Society of Agronomy, Madison.

CAMPBELL, C.A. 1978. Soil organic carbon, nitrogen and fertility. In: *Soil Organic Matter* (eds. Schnitzer and S.U. Khan) pp. 173–271. Elsevier, Amsterdam.

CARTER, J.N., JENSEN, M.E. and BOSMA, S.M. 1974. Determining nitrogen fertiliser needs for sugar beets from residual soil nitrate and mineralisable nitrogen. *Agronomy Journal* **66**, 319–323.

CLEMENT, C.R. and WILLIAMS, T.E. 1962. An incubation technique for assessing the nitrogen status of soils newly ploughed from leys. *Journal of Soil Science* **13**, 82–91.

CORNFIELD, A.H. 1961. Carbon dioxide production during incubation of soils treated with cellulose as a possible index of the nitrogen status of soils. *Journal of the Science of Food and Agriculture* **12**, 763–765.

DAHNKE, W.C. and VASEY, E.H. 1973. Testing soils for nitrogen. In: *Soil Testing and Plant Analyses* (eds. L.M. Walsh and J.D. Beaton) pp. 97–114. Soil Science Society of America, Madison.

DE HANN, S. 1977. Humus: its formation in relation to the mineral part of the soil, and its significance for soil productivity. In: *Soil Organic Matter Studies,* Vol. 1, I.A.E.A. Vienna, 21–30.

DOWDELL, R.J. and CREES, R. 1980. The uptake of ^{15}N-labelled fertiliser by winter wheat and its immobilisation in a clay soil after direct drilling or ploughing. *Journal of the Science of Food and Agriculture* **31**, 992–996.

EAGLE, D.J. 1966. Soil nitrogen analyses and their relation to nitrogen responses in winter wheat. *Journal of the Science of Food and Agriculture* **17**, 365–370.

FUHR, F. and SAUERBECK, D. 1968. Decomposition of wheat straw in the field as influenced by cropping and rotation. In: *Isotopes and Radiation in Soil Organic Matter Studies.* I.A.E.A. Vienna, 241–250.

GASSER, J.K.R. 1961. Soil nitrogen, IV. Correlations between laboratory measurements of soil mineral-N and crop yields and responses in pot and field experiments. *Journal of the Science of Food and Agriculture* **12**, 562–573.

HARMSEN, G.W. and VAN SCHREVEN, D.A. 1955. Mineralisation of organic nitrogen in soil. *Advances in Agronomy* **7**, 299–398.

HART, P.B.S., JENKINSON, D.S., JOHNSTON, A.E., POWLSON, D.S. and PRUDEN, G. 1982. The uptake *by wheat of fertiliser N applied to the preceding crop. Rothamsted Report for 1981* Part 1, 253–254.

JANSSON, S.L. 1958. Tracer studies on nitrogen transformations in soil with special attention to mineralisation-immobilisation relationships. *Kungliga Lantbrukshögskolans Annaler* **24**, 101–361.

JANSSON, S.L. and PERSSON, J. 1982. Immobilisation of soil nitrogen In: *Nitrogen in Agricultural Soils* (ed. F.J. Stevenson) pp. 229–252. American Society of Agronomy, Madison.

JENKINSON, D.S. 1968. Chemical tests for potentially available nitrogen in soil. *Journal of the Science of Food and Agriculture* **19**, 160–168.

JENKINSON, D.S. 1977. Studies on the decomposition of plant material in soil. V. *Journal of Soil Science* **28**, 424–434.

JENKINSON, D.S. 1982. The nitrogen cycle in long-term field experiments. *Philosophical Transactions of the Royal Society (London)* B. **296**, 563–571.

JENKINSON, D.S. and AYANABA, A. 1977. Decomposition of carbon-14 labelled plant material under tropical conditions. *Soil Science Society of America Journal* **41**, 912–915.

JENKINSON, D.S. and LADD, J.N. 1981. Microbial biomass in soil: measurement and turnover. In: *Soil Biochemistry* Vol. 5 (eds. E.A. Paul and J.N. Ladd) pp. 415–471. Marcel Dekker, New York.

JENKINSON, D.S. and RAYNER, J.H. 1977. The turnover of soil organic matter in some of the Rothamsted classical experiments. *Soil Science* **123**, 298–305.

JENSEN, H.L. 1929. On the influence of the C:N ratios of organic material on the mineralisation of nitrogen. *Journal of Agricultural Science* (Camb.) **22**, 1–25.

LADD, J.N. OADES, J.M. and AMATO, M. 1981 Microbial biomass formed from ^{14}C, ^{15}N-labelled plant material decomposing in soils in the field. *Soil Biology and Biochemistry* **13**, 119–126.

MILLER, R.D. and JOHNSTON, D.D. 1964. The effect of soil moisture tension on carbon dioxide evolution, nitrification and nitrogen mineralisation. *Soil Science Society of America Proceedings* **28**, 644–647.

MORTLAND, M.M. 1958. Reactions of ammonia in soils. *Advances in Agronomy* **10**, 325–348.

MYERS, R.J.K. and PAUL, E.A. 1971. Plant uptake and immobilisation of ^{15}N-labelled ammonium nitrate in a field experiment with wheat. In: *Nitrogen-15 in soil-plant studies* I.A.E.A. Vienna, 55–64.

NELSON, D.W. and BREMNER, J.M. 1969. Factors affecting chemical transformations of nitrite in soils. *Soil Biology and Biochemistry* **1**, 229–239.

NOMMIK, H. 1962. Mineral nitrogen immobilisation and carbon dioxide production during *Terrestrial Nitrogen Cycles* (eds. F.E. Clark and T. Rosswall) pp. 273–279. Ecological Bulletin *Scandinavica* **12**, 81–94.

NOMMIK, H. 1981. Fixation and biological availability of ammonium in soil clay minerals. In: *Terrestrial Nitrogen Cycles* (eds. F.E. Clark and T. Rosswall pp. 273–279. Ecological Bulletin (Stockholm) 33.

OBERLANDER, H.E. 1973. The fate of organic manures in soil as traced by means of radiocarbon. *Pontificiae Academiae Scientiarum Scripta Varia* **38**, 1001–1071.

RIGA, A., FISCHER, V. and VAN PRAAG, H.J. 1980. Fate of fertiliser nitrogen applied to winter wheat as $Na^{15}NO_3$ and $(^{15}NH_4)_2 SO_4$ studied in microplots through a four-course rotation. *Soil Science* **130**, 88–99.

RUBINS, E.J. and BEAR, F.E. 1942. Carbon:nitrogen ratios in organic fertiliser materials in relation to the availability of their nitrogen. *Soil Science* **54**, 411–423.

SAUERBECK, D. 1968. Comparison of plant material and animal manure in relation to their decomposition in soil. In: *Isotopes and Radiation in Soil Organic Matter Studies,* I.A.E.A. Vienna, 219–224.

SCARSBROOK, C.E. 1965. Nitrogen availability. In: *Soil Nitrogen* (eds. W.V. Bartholomew and F.E. Clark) pp. 451–502. American Society of Agronomy, Wisconsin.

SHEN, S.M., POWLSON, D.S., PRUDEN, G. and JENKINSON, D.S. 1982. Residual fertiliser nitrogen and nitrogen mineralisation in Broadbalk soils. *Rothamsted Report for 1981* Part I, 253.

SIEGEL, O. 1940. Mehrjährige Beobachtungen über den Abbau und die Humifizierung organischer Stoffe im Bodem. *Bodenk. u. Pflanzenernahr* **21–22**, 455–473.

SOPER, R.J. and HUANG, R.M. 1963. The effect of nitrate nitrogen in the soil profile on the response of barley to fertiliser nitrogen. *Canadian Journal of Soil Science* **43**, 350–358.

SORENSEN, L.H. 1981. Carbon-nitrogen relationships during the humification of cellulose in soils containing different amounts of clay. *Soil Biology and Biochemistry* **13**, 313–321.

STANFORD, G. 1982. Assessment of soil nitrogen availability. In: *Nitrogen in Agricultural Soils* (ed. F.J. Stevenson) pp. 651–688. American Society of Agronomy, Madison.

STANFORD, G. FRERE, M.H. and SCHWANINGER, D.H. 1973. Temperature coefficient of soil nitrogen mineralisation. *Soil Science* **115**, 321–323.

STEVENSON, F.J. 1982. *Nitrogen in Agricultural Soils.* American Society of Agronomy, Crop Science Society of America and Soil Science Society of America Monograph 22, Madison.

STICKLER, F.C. and FREDERICK, L.R. 1959. Residue particle size as a factor in nitrate release from legume tops and roots. *Agronomy Journal* **51**, 271–274.

TANJI, K.K. and GUPTA, S.K. 1978. Computer simulation modelling for nitrogen in irrigated croplands. In: *Nitrogen in the Environment* (eds. D.R. Nielson and J.C. MacDonald) pp. 79–162. Academic Press, New York.

TINKER, P.B. and ADDISCOTT, T.M. 1984. Modelling of the nitrogen requirement of cereals. Ministry of Agriculture, Fisheries and Food, Reference Book 385, *The Nitrogen Requirement of Cereals*, pp. 265–281

VAIDYANATHAN, L.V. and LEITCH, M.H. 1980. Use of fertiliser and soil nitrogen by winter wheat established with and without soil cultivation prior to drilling. *Journal of the Science of Food and Agriculture* **31**, 852–853.

WAKSMAN, S.A. and TENNEY, F.G. 1927. The composition of natural organic materials and their decomposition in the soil. *Soil Science* **24**, 317–333.

WEHRMANN, J. and SCHARPF, H.C. 1976. Fertiliser nitrogen requirements of winter wheat as affected by the mineral nitrogen content of the soil in spring. *Proceedings of the VIIIth International Fertilizer Congress,* Vol. II, 182–191.

WESTERMAN, R.L. and KURTZ, L.T. 1972. Residual effects of ^{15}N-labelled fertilisers in a field study. *Soil Science Society of America Proceedings* **36**, 91–94.

Discussion

Dr Gasser asked if there was any role for periodic testing to monitor possible changes in the nitrogen supply from the soil. Dr Jenkinson replied that there were two cases where monitoring would be useful. Firstly at the beginning, to provide more information, and secondly to act as a check on the calculated nitrogen supply. This would involve the calibration of soil tests, for example aerobic incubation, with the calculated amounts of nitrogen released each year from the soil. This would be a time consuming operation and unfortunately it could not be done on a regular basis.

Dr Greenwood applauded Dr Jenkinson's opportunity for periodic testing for nitrogen down the profile. This would add to the knowledge at a particular site, e.g. the amounts of nitrogen uptake by the crop from applied fertiliser and fertiliser residues remaining in the soil. Dr Jenkinson replied that the ^{15}N work measured the amount of fertiliser nitrogen left in the soil in the organic form. This can vary according to the amount applied, for example 30 per cent can remain in the soil with small applications but with larger nitrogen applications only about 15 per cent may remain since a greater proportion of nitrogen is taken up by the crop.

Dr Batey commented that better field correlations would be achieved by reporting results on a volumetric basis or in kg/ha rather than as a concentration. Dr Jenkinson agreed with this.

Mr Wadsworth thought that a refined soil nitrogen Index would not be sufficient. For example, two fields can be similar both in soil type and previous cropping but have different optimum nitrogen requirements. Dr Jenkinson said that these differences could be due to differences in the inorganic nitrogen reserves, soil depth and cropping history. If there were differences in the long-term cropping history then this would account for considerable differences in the amount of soil nitrogen supplied.

Dr Holmes asked how summer rainfall affected the availability of both fertiliser nitrogen and organic nitrogen. Dr Jenkinson said that the efficiency of nitrogen use depended upon the weather conditions after application. Until there were reliable long-term weather forecasts, there would always be an element of risk in choosing the correct nitrogen application. The risk would be reduced if the farmer was given a range of nitrogen requirements based on expected yield. However, the farmer must decide on what level of yield to aim for, depending upon the yield potential of the land. The farmer would also have the opportunity to apply extra nitrogen following periods of adverse weather conditions. This approach is justified because there are only small variations in nitrogen losses (ranging from 15 per cent in a good year to 25 per cent in a poor year) and it would, therefore, lead to a better efficiency of use of nitrogen.

Mr George commented that nitrogen prediction methods should be based on cropping history. He said that large effects could still be seen in the field eight to ten years after there had been a major change in cropping.

Estimation of annual variations in leaching of residual nitrate under deep-rooted crops during winter

I G Burns
National Vegetable Research Station, Wellesbourne, Warwick

Summary

The influence of winter rainfall on annual variations in the amounts of residual nitrate retained within the rooting zone of deeper rooting crops in spring has been analysed for different soils and regions of England and Wales using a simple leaching model. The calculations show that the amount leached depends on soil type and winter rainfall, which varies from year to year and from region to region over the country. It was estimated that mean losses during the winter averaged from 85 kg/ha of N for light soils in the wet western regions to 15 kg/ha of N for heavy soils in the east, where rainfall is less. The largest annual variations were predicted for sandy soils in the east and the smallest for sandy soils in the west. Annual variations in leaching from heavier clay and peat soils were similar for all regions of the country.

Introduction

Although considerable quantities of nitrate can be leached from UK soils during the winter, there is still uncertainty about the influence of these losses on the growth of crops in the following spring. Experimental results have shown that residual effects are dominated primarily by the nature of the previous crop (Eagle, 1971). The full effects of winter rainfall on spring N levels can therefore only be distinguished by comparisons of individual measurements at representative sites with the same cropping history over many years (van der Paauw, 1963; Lidgate, 1978). However, a widespread programme of experiments of this type is both impractical and expensive.

The development of simple models of leaching has provided an alternative method for assessing the importance of winter rainfall. This method has been used by Burns and Greenwood (1982) for calculating the losses of residual nitrate from various soils in different regions of England and Wales using information on soil properties and weather conditions. The results for the average rainfall for each region over a period of 20 years were compared with similar calculations for the extreme wettest and driest year over the same period. Their results show that losses of nitrate vary greatly with depth, soil type and amount of rainfall, which also varies from region to region. It was calculated that extreme differences in the extent to which residual nitrate is leached by winter rains may cause the amounts of nitrate retained in the spring to vary between 9 and 100 per cent of the autumn levels in the top metre of individual fields in different years.

This study has provided useful estimates of how regional variations in rainfall and differences in soil type are likely to influence the amounts of residual nitrate retained in the spring. Information on the effects of annual variations in winter rainfall was, however, limited to a comparison of results for the wettest and driest years. Although this allowed estimation of the maximum variation in leaching it gave little indication of the likely deviation from the mean in any one year. The object of this paper is to extend the previous study in an attempt to quantify the effects of year-to-year variations in rainfall on the spring levels of residual nitrogen available for deeper rooting crops (such as cereals) for various soils in different parts of the country.

Methods

The methods used have been described in detail by Burns and Greenwood (1982). The calculations were made assuming that there was 100 kg/ha of residual nitrate-N in the top metre of all soils at their return to field capacity in the autumn and that this was uniformly distributed with depth (Needham, 1976). Losses of nitrate during the winter were calculated by the model of Burns (1976):

$$f = \left(\frac{P}{P + 10\,\theta} \right)^{h/2} \tag{1}$$

where f is the fraction of nitrate leached below a depth h cm in the soil of volumetric field capacity θ after P mm of excess rainfall over evaporation. The model assumes there are no gains or losses of nitrate by mineralisation or dentrification during the winter. The value of h was fixed at 100 cm (a typical value for cereal crops), on the assumption that all of the nitrate retained within this depth in the spring will be available to the crop during subsequent growth (Burns, 1980).

Table 1 Regions of England and Wales

Region	Abbreviation	Counties
Northwest	NW	Cumbria, Lancs., Merseyside, G. Manchester, N. Yorks (west).
Northeast	NE	Cleveland, Durham, Humberside (north), Northumberland, Tyne & Wear, N. Yorks (east) S. Yorks, W. Yorks.
West Midlands	WM	Cheshire, Gloucs., Hereford & Worcester, Oxon (west), Salop, Staffs, Warwicks., W. Midlands.
East Midlands	EM	Bucks., Derbyshire, Humberside (south), Northants, Notts., Oxon (east), Leics., Lincs.
East	E	Beds., Cambs., Essex, Lincs. (south east), Norfolk, Suffolk.
Southeast	SE	Berks, Hants. (east), Herts., Kent, G. London, Surrey, E. Sussex, W. Sussex.
Far Southwest	FSW	Cornwall, Devon, Somerset (west).
Mid Southwest	MSW	Avon, Dorset, Hants. (west), Wilts., Somerset (east).
Wales	W	All counties.

96

Separate estimates of leaching were made for five different soils (with $\theta = 0.15$, 0.25, 0.35, 0.45 or 0.55) corresponding uncritically to the average values for sands, sandy loams, loams, clays and peats respectively.

Excess rainfall data for a typical sample decade were calculated for each of nine separate regions in England and Wales from information given by Smith (1971) and were used to assess the year-to-year variability in leaching in different parts of the country. Details of the regions are given in Table 1, and the corresponding mean excess rainfall data at the bottom of Table 2.

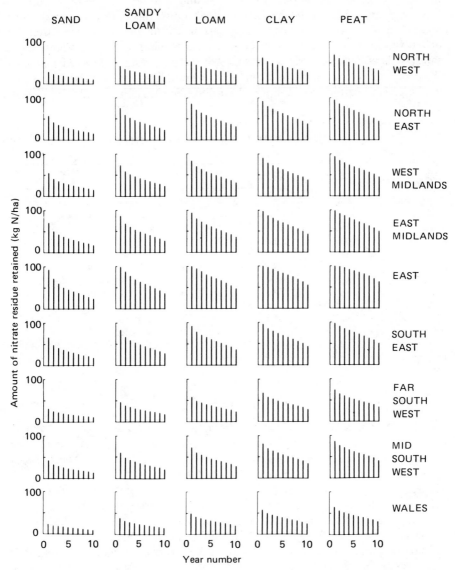

Fig. 1 Calculated amounts of residual nitrate retained in spring in various soils in different regions of England and Wales over a sample decade with years ranked in order of increasing rainfall (1 = driest, 10 = wettest), assuming that 100 kg/ha of nitrate-N was present in the autumn; the regions are tabulated on the right and the soils at the top.

97

Results and discussion

The calculated amounts of nitrate retained in spring within the top 100 cm of various soils in different regions over a typical ten year period are summarised in Figure 1. The values have been ranked in order of increasing rainfall to aid comparison. The results show that in each region the amount of residual nitrate retained is consistently smaller in light soils than in heavy ones by a factor which varies from *ca* 1.5 after the driest winters to *ca* 3 after the wettest. An average of *ca* 40 kg/ha more residual nitrate-N is calculated to be retained in soils of the Eastern Region than in those of the west, although this difference increases to more than 90 kg/ha of N when the amounts of residual nitrate retained after the driest winters in the peat soils of the east are compared with those remaining in sandy soils after the wettest winters in Wales. These results are consistent with those of the previous study in which leaching estimates for extremes of rainfall over a 20 year period were compared for different sites (Burns and Greenwood, 1982).

Table 2 Calculated amounts of nitrate retained in various soils in different regions of England and Wales

Soil type	Value	Region								
		NW	NE	WM	EM	E	SE	FSW	MSW	W
sands	mean	17	30	29	35	48	34	19	24	15
	s.d.	5	13	12	16	21	14	6	9	5
sandy loams	mean	27	43	43	50	64	49	29	36	24
	s.d.	8	16	15	18	20	17	9	12	7
loams	mean	35	54	53	61	74	60	38	46	32
	s.d.	10	17	16	18	17	17	10	13	9
clays	mean	42	62	62	68	80	68	45	54	39
	s.d.	11	16	16	17	15	16	12	14	10
peats	mean	49	69	68	75	85	75	52	61	45
	s.d.	11	16	15	16	12	15	12	14	11
Excess winter rainfall (mm)	mean	440	251	254	209	138	211	402	310	490
	s.d.	146	112	111	102	76	97	138	121	159

Means and standard deviations of the data in Figure 1 are given in Table 2, together with corresponding excess winter rainfall data for each region. The standard deviations are particularly useful for assessing annual variability as not only are they calculated using all of the data (and not just the two extremes), but they can also be used to estimate the probability of spring nitrate residues falling within given limits. Table 2 shows that year-to-year variations in the amounts of nitrate retained in the spring are greatest in the Eastern Region, with standard deviations of up to ± 20 kg/ha of N for sandy and sandy loam soils. This means that there is about a one in three chance of the spring nitrate levels in these soils deviating by more than ± 20 kg/ha of N from the mean. In extreme conditions, however, maximum variability can increase to almost 70 kg/ha of N when the wettest and driest years are compared. The year-to-year differences are consistently smaller in the wetter western regions (e.g. Wales and the Northwest) where the largest standard deviations occur in the heavier clay and peat soils. Here there is a one in three chance of spring levels deviating by more than ± 11 kg/ha of N from the mean, and a deviation of more than ± 22 kg/ha can only be expected about once every 20 years. In regions of intermediate rainfall (e.g. Northeast and West Midlands) the standard deviation is similar (at about ± 15 kg/ha) for all soils.

Comparison of estimates of the residual amounts retained after a winter of average rainfall (Burns and Greenwood, 1982) with the mean data in Table 2, shows that in almost all cases the mean amount retained in spring exceeds that for the year of average rainfall by a small but consistent amount (up to 5 kg/ha). The only exceptions are for clay and peat soils in the Eastern Region where there is little difference between the two values. This means that if spring nitrogen fertiliser dressings are to be adjusted for leaching on the basis of deviation from the mean excess winter rainfall, the reductions in dressing recommended after a dry winter will on average always be larger than the increases in dressing required after a wet one. Similar deductions may be made from the experimental study of residual effects by van der Paauw (1963).

The reason for this discrepancy can be seen from Figure 2 which compares the frequency distributions for excess winter rainfall and for the amount of winter leaching for each of the soils over the country as a whole. The rainfall distribution has a slight positive skew so that the mean value exceeds the mode. However, because of the approximately exponential form of the relation between rainfall and leaching in equation (1) (Burns, 1976), transformation of rainfall data into leaching data often introduces a slight negative skew, which is particularly pronounced for the lighter soils. Thus the amount leached in a winter of average rainfall is invariably more than the mean winter leaching losses over the decade and this difference is mirrored in the nitrate residues retained in spring. Examination of Figure 2 suggests that the amount leached in a year of average rainfall often falls closer to the median value than to the mean. Separate analysis has shown that a similar pattern of results is observed when data for each of the regions is analysed separately, although there is a greater variability in the shapes of the frequency distributions for the amounts of nitrate leached, particularly for heavier soils in the dry eastern regions.

In conclusion, it must be emphasised that the results in this paper are only as good as the model on which they are based. Burns and Greenwood (1982) have discussed in some detail the limitations of the methods used here. Suffice it to say that the greatest errors are likely to be introduced where deviations from uniform vertical movement of water and nitrate occurs during leaching (particularly in structured soils or those with impermeable layers within a metre of the surface), and where the amounts and distribution of nitrate present in the soil in the autumn differ considerably from those used here. Furthermore, as the model does not take account of mineralisation of organic nitrogen in the spring, the results should be used only for assessing the *variability* in spring nitrate levels rather than their absolute values. Despite these limitations, the model has given good estimates of the average concentrations of nitrate emerging from field drains, (Burns and Greenwood, 1982) and it seems likely, therefore, that the overall pattern of the predictions is correct. At the very least, the data presented here should provide valuable information about where and when the largest variations in winter leaching can be expected for use in future experimental work.

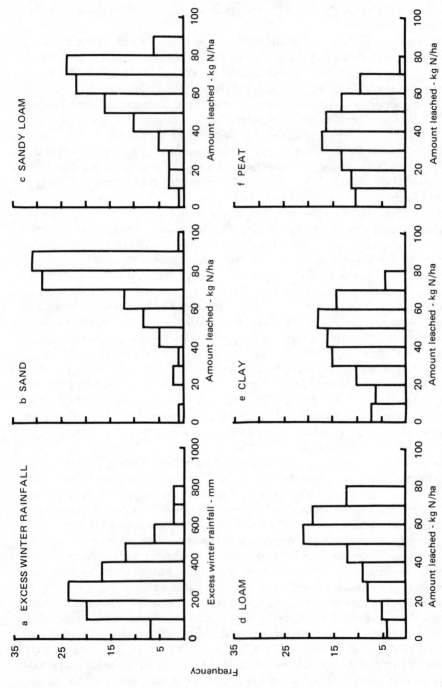

Fig. 2 Frequency distributions for excess winter rainfall (a) and for amount of nitrate leached during winter from sands (b), sandy loams (c), loams (d), clays (e) and peats (f) over the whole country.

100

Acknowledgement

The author wishes to thank Mr G E L Morris for helpful discussion during the preparation of this work.

References

BURNS, I.G. 1976. Equations to predict the leaching of nitrate uniformly incorporated to a known depth or uniformly distributed throughout a soil profile. *Journal of Agricultural Science, Cambridge* **86**, 305–313.

BURNS, I.G. 1980. Influence of the spatial distribution of nitrate on the uptake of N by plants: A review and a model for rooting depth. *Journal of Soil Science* **31**, 155–173.

BURNS, I.G. and GREENWOOD, D.J. 1982. Estimation of the year-to-year variations in nitrate leaching in different soils and regions of England and Wales. *Agriculture and Environment* **7**, 35–45.

EAGLE, D.J. 1971. Effect of winter rainfall on residual nitrogen. Ministry of Agriculture, Fisheries and Food, Technical Bulletin No. 20, HMSO, London, pp. 145–158.

LIDGATE, H.J. 1978. Nitrogen requirements of winter wheat. *Journal of Science of Food and Agriculture* **29**, 650.

NEEDHAM, P. 1976. Survey of residual nitrogen in soils, 1973–75. *ADAS: Experiments and Development in the Eastern Region, 1975.* pp. 45–47.

PAAUW, F. VAN DER, 1963. Residual effect of nitrogen fertiliser on succeeding crops in a moderate marine climate. *Plant and Soil* **19**, 324–331.

SMITH, L.P. 1971. The significance of winter rainfall over farmland in England and Wales. Ministry of Agriculture, Fisheries and Food, Technical Bulletin No. 24, HMSO, London, pp. 69.

Field measurements of the leaching of fertiliser nitrate

J A Nicholsby and A Wild
University of Reading

Summary

On a soil kept under bare fallow, ^{36}Cl and $^{15}NO_3$ under irrigation and winter rainfall leached at the same rate. The vertical distribution was well described by an analytical equation which assumes piston displacement with dispersion.

At a site cropped successively to winter wheat and winter barley 7.5 per cent of the ^{15}N applied (150 kg/ha of N) as ammonium nitrate to the winter wheat crop was leached out of the root zone. There was evidence that a small proportion of the ^{15}N that was leached had been mineralised after incorporation into the soil organic matter.

Leaching losses can be measured with least ambiguity by using ^{15}N enriched fertilisers. Because of the expense of such experiments rates of leaching should be used to improve models or equations to try to give them universal application.

Introduction

Gregory *et al.* (1979) have shown that a good crop of winter wheat takes up about 2 kg of N per day during its period of most rapid growth in May and June. In most soils this uptake rate cannot be met by mineralisation of soil organic matter, and fertiliser nitrogen is, therefore, used. Fertiliser nitrogen may also be needed at earlier stages of crop growth. The fate of fertiliser nitrogen applied at different stages of crop growth, on different soils, and under different climatic conditions, is still largely unresolved. It could be resolved by using ^{15}N labelled fertiliser, but a very large number of expensive field experiments would be needed if all combinations of soil, climate and crop were to be included. Instead, if the processes that determine the fate of fertiliser nitrogen could be quantified, a mechanistic model would be developed which could be used for all circumstances.

The account that follows describes two experiments to measure the rate of nitrate leaching. The measured rates are compared with those predicted by leaching models. The experiments differ in that Experiment I measures short-term leaching on a soil kept bare of vegetation, whereas Experiment 2 measures leaching over a period of 31 months during which a crop of winter wheat was followed by winter barley. Both were sited at Bridgets EHF, Martyr Worthy, Hampshire.

103

Methods and results

Experiment 1

The site was on Andover series soil. Leaching rates of $^{15}NO_3$, ^{36}Cl and HTO were measured under (a) irrigation and (b) winter rainfall. Before imposing treatments the soils were brought to field capacity ($\theta = 0.35$). For (a), 40 mm water was applied by overhead sprinklers and soil cores were taken 60 h after the end of irrigation, when the water content of the soil had returned to its initial value. A further addition of 40 mm water was then made and the soil was again sampled. For (b), the treatments were applied to plots after the water content of the soil had reached field capacity, and soil samples were taken after 80 and 180 mm rainfall.

The vertical distribution of nitrate down the soil as a mean for all sampling occasions was only slightly skewed from normal, with a weak leading edge. The rate of leaching of nitrate, as assessed from the peak depth, was approximately 3 centimetre per centimetre of added water (effective rainfall or irrigation). The peak depth was a little higher than that expected from piston displacement when expressed as Q/θ where Q is added water (see above) and θ is the volumetric water content of the soil. The ratio of peak depth to that expected from Q/θ varied from 1.0 to 1.3.

The measured distributions of nitrate were compared with those predicted by three models. The best fit was obtained with the analytical equation of Rose *et al.* (1982). The results of this experiment, including a comparison of the leaching rates of $^{15}NO_3$, ^{36}Cl and HTO, and the appraisal of the leaching models are given by Cameron and Wild (1982a, b). One important conclusion was that under the conditions of this experiment the leaching rates of ^{36}Cl and $^{15}NO_3$ were the same.

Experiment 2

As part of a larger experiment to assess the size of the various sinks for fertiliser nitrogen, a 3×3 m plot received the equivalent of 150 kg/ha of N as ammonium nitrate with 10 per cent enrichment of ^{15}N on both N atoms. The plot was on a flinty silt loam (Coombe series). The fertiliser was applied in April 1979 to a crop of winter wheat (Huntsman) which followed winter wheat. Apart from some protection to avoid cross contamination with non-labelled areas, this area received normal agricultural management. The above-ground crop was harvested in August, as was the succeeding winter barley crop in 1980 (which received 135 kg/ha of N as unlabelled fertiliser) and analysed for labelled nitrogen.

In November 1981, thirty-one months after the labelled fertiliser was applied, a single 10 m core was taken from the centre of the plot by percussion auger in increments of 30 cm. The core samples were immediately heat-sealed in polythene bags and transported back to the laboratory, where they were stored at 4 °C prior to analysis for nitrate-nitrogen and $^{15}N/^{14}N$ ratio.

A single 600 g subsample of the core from each depth was extracted by high-speed centrifugation (Young *et al.*, 1976) and the extracted soil solution analysed for nitrate by an automated method (Litchfield, 1967). Following reduction with Devarda's alloy the extracts were made alkaline with magnesium oxide and steam distilled into dilute (0.025M) sulphuric acid. The distillates were then dried and analysed for $^{15}N/^{14}N$ ratios on a Vacuum Generator 602E isotope-ratio mass spectrometer. Additional subsamples from each depth of the core were used for the determination of moisture content and bulk density.

Results

Figure 1 shows the soil nitrate profile together with the atom per cent ^{15}N of the nitrate nitrogen. The figure clearly indicates that the modal depth of leaching of the labelled fertiliser is 3.3 to 3.6 m. It is also evident that it is not possible to associate any clear peak in the nitrate profile with the labelled nitrate, indicating

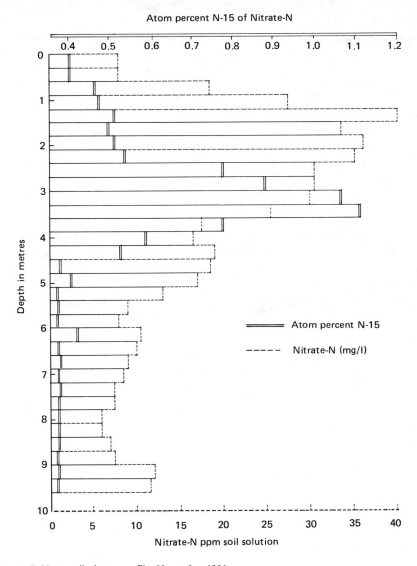

Fig. 1 Bridgets soil nitrate profile, November 1981.

that, under these conditions, loss of fertiliser nitrogen by leaching can be measured with the least ambiguity by labelling the fertiliser with ^{15}N.

Below 4.5 m the $^{15}N/^{14}N$ ratio is close to background except in two samples at about 5 m and just below 6 m depth. In these two samples the ^{15}N enrichment might be the result of a small amount of fissure flow. Above the peak ^{15}N concentration at 3.3 to 3.6 m, the distribution shows a pronounced shoulder at 0.6 to 2 m. It is probable that this slow nitrate leaching is the result of ^{15}N incorporation in the soil organic matter followed by mineralisation. The shoulder represents only 1.2 per cent of the total ^{15}N excess in the profile present as nitrate. The total ^{15}N excess as nitrate equalled 7.5 per cent of the applied fertiliser, which is thus the per cent of the fertiliser nitrogen lost by leaching. There will be very small additional amounts lost by leaching as more ^{15}N incorporated in the soil organic matter is mineralised.

References

CAMERON, K.C. and WILD, A. 1982a. Comparative rates of leaching of chloride, nitrate and tritiated water under field conditions. *Journal of Soil Science* 33, 649–657.

CAMERON, K.C. and WILD, A. 1982b. Prediction of solute leaching under field conditions: an appraisal of three methods. *Journal of Soil Science* 33, 659–669.

GREGORY, P.J., CRAWFORD, D.V. and McGOWAN, M. 1979. Nutrient relations of winter wheat. I. Accumulation and distribution of Na, K, Mg, P, S and N. *Journal of Agricultural Science, Cambridge* 93, 485–494.

LITCHFIELD, M.H. 1967. The automated analysis of nitrite and nitrate in blood. *Analyst* 92, 132–136.

ROSE, C.W., CHICHESTER, F.W., WILLIAMS, J.R. and RITCHIE, J.T. 1982. Application of an approximate analytic method of computing solute profiles with dispersion in soils. *Journal of Environmental Quality* 11, 151–155.

YOUNG, C.P., HALL, E.S. and OAKES, D.B. 1976. Nitrate in Groundwater Studies of the Chalk near Winchester, Hampshire. *Water Research Centre Technical Report* 31. Medmenham.

Soil and fertiliser nitrogen use by winter wheat

L V Vaidyanathan
ADAS, Cambridge

Summary

Soil and fertiliser nitrogen offtakes by twenty-one winter wheat crops were studied using small applications of ^{15}N. The crops were grown during 1979–1980 on clay loam or silty clay loam soils overlying boulder clay in the ADAS Eastern Region. They were all commercial field crops under farmers' own management, including spring fertiliser nitrogen additions ranging between 108 and 210 kg/ha.

Total above ground crop weights at harvest ranged between 13 and 19 t/ha and grain between 5.6 and 10.3 t/ha both at 85 per cent dry matter, grain contributing 41.5 to 54.7 per cent depending apparently on variety.

Nitrogen concentration in the total crop ranged between 1.0 and 1.6 per cent. Nitrogen content of the total crop ranged between 139 and 238 kg/ha, roughly three-quarters being in grain. About a fifth to two-thirds of the total nitrogen was from fertiliser nitrogen, and this accounted for 30 to 72 per cent of the total amount of fertiliser added in the spring. The 13 wheat crops which followed another wheat contained an average of just over 51 per cent fertiliser nitrogen while the eight first wheats after a break crop contained an average of 47 per cent. Each tonne of grain harvested (85 per cent DM) was associated with an average total offtake of 23 kg nitrogen with a range of 16.1 to 27.4. These values were not related to variety, cultivation, previous crop or added fertiliser. Empirical relationships between fertiliser offtake and a function of (i) soil nitrogen use and (ii) crop growth attributable to fertiliser use, could be derived which accounted for up to three-quarters of the variance.

Growth and nitrogen offtake by two of the crops were measured frequently from early spring. The evidence clearly demonstrated that most of the dry matter and nitrogen stored in shoots which were not 'destined' to produce grain was transferred and used by those with developing ears.

Introduction

National average winter wheat yields have been increasing by about 0.15 t/ha annually from under 4.3 t/ha in 1973 to nearly 5.6 t/ha in 1981 (MAFF, 1982). Average use of fertiliser nitrogen during this period has been increasing almost proportionally (Vaidyanathan, 1984) from 85 kg/ha in 1974, at a steady annual rate of just under 10 kg/ha (Figure 1a). The area receiving more than 100 kg/ha nitrogen has risen from under 60 per cent in 1974 to over 90 per cent in 1981

107

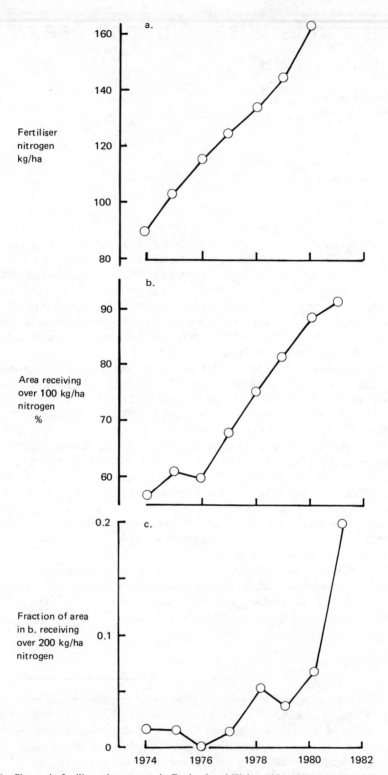

Fig. 1 Change in fertiliser nitrogen use in England and Wales, 1974–1981 (MAFF, 1982).

(Figure 1b). Almost all of these areas received under 200 kg/ha nitrogen until 1977, but nearly a fifth of these areas was given more than 200 kg/ha in 1981 (Figure 1c).

Although the apparent efficiency of this increasing fertiliser nitrogen usage is very comparable to the median value of 16–18 kg grain per kg nitrogen estimated from recent trials (Sylvester-Bradley et al., 1984) there is concern that increasing amounts of the nitrogen applied to crops may be entering sources of public water supply.

Information on the contribution of soil and fertiliser nitrogen to crop offtakes and the fate of added fertiliser nitrogen is therefore required, and these are best estimated through the use of ^{15}N-labelled fertiliser.

This paper discusses soil and fertiliser nitrogen offtakes by several winter wheat crops grown during 1979–80 in the ADAS Eastern Region.

Experimental

Twenty-one winter wheat crops were selected on farms in the Eastern Region of UK. All crops were grown during 1979–1980 on clay loam or silty clay loam soils overlying chalky boulder clay and were all under the farmers' own husbandry which varied from crop to crop and included spring fertiliser nitrogen additions ranging between 108 and 210 kg/ha (Table 1). Thirteen of the crops were following a wheat crop, seven being direct drilled and six sown after some soil cultivations. Seven of the other eight crops drilled into cultivated soils followed a break crop of winter oilseed rape and one followed dried peas. Eight varieties, four tall and four semi dwarfs, were involved. The only special treatment was the establishment of nine microplots (about 1 m^2) in each field by applying a small, known amount (2–3 kg/ha in 19 and about 9 kg/ha in two) of ^{15}NH$_4$ ^{15}NO$_3$ (50 per cent ^{15}N) a few days before or after the main farm top dressing at GS 30–31 (Zadoks et al., 1974). The labelled fertiliser, added as solution between rows, was sufficient to give about 0.8 per cent or 2.5 per cent of ^{15}N in the total (farmers' + labelled) by presumed in situ dilution.

Ears per m^2 in the unlabelled crops were assessed on four occasions, once after anthesis and thrice before and at harvest; the anthesis assessment and one harvest assessment were by destructive sampling and the others by in situ counting.

Grain yields were means of six separate strips (60–70 m^2) harvested by plot-combine at each site. Spikelet number, grain number and weight, and harvest index were determined by hand threshing 50 individual ears collected randomly at harvest from each site.

Crop samples from 0.6 × 0.6 m areas in the middle of each of the nine microplots were taken at harvest and bulked by groups of three to obtain three replicate samples for analysis.

Total nitrogen in above ground dry matter was measured by Kjeldahl digestion of six separate samples. Three of these were from unlabelled areas. The other three were from the nine ^{15}N labelled microplots which were also used for triplicate ^{15}N/^{14}N ratio determinations.

Results and discussion

Plant populations at the time of the main fertiliser nitrogen additions in mid April, were around $350/m^2$ in fourteen sites; five were between 235 and 275 and two were less than $200/m^2$. These were, however, unrelated to yields.

Total crop weights at harvest ranged between 13 and 19 t/ha and grain between 5.6 and 10.3 t/ha (both at 85 per cent dry matter). Grain contributed between 41.5 and 54.7 per cent of total weight, apparently depending on variety (Table 1). Nitrogen concentration in whole tops ranged between 1.0 and 1.6 per cent (oven dry). Total nitrogen content of whole tops ranged between 139 and 238 kg/ha, roughly three-quarters being in the grain (Table 1).

Table 1 Site and crop growth observations on 21 winter wheat fields in 1980. Harvest data are means of six measurements.

Site	Variety	Fertiliser nitrogen including ^{15}N		Plant population	Harvest data			
					Total crop weight	Grain weight	Total crop nitrogen	Nitrogen offtake
		kg/ha	$\%^{15}N$	per m^2	t/ha 85% DM		% oven dry	kg/ha
	Wheat after wheat – direct drilled							
C	Mardler	161	0.866	310	13.7	7.12	1.36	158
D	Bounty	213	0.808	359	14.9	7.39	1.60	202
E	Kador	204	2.443	336	13.7	5.97	1.21	141
F	Huntsman	178	0.795	238	12.8	5.57	1.28	139
I	Armada	199	2.494	325	18.7	8.36	1.26	200
Q	Armada	175	0.868	327	18.6	7.71	1.14	180
T	Mardler	201	0.865	235	18.6	9.79	1.38	218
	Wheat after wheat – cultivated							
A	Hustler	193	0.857	351	19.0	10.30	1.03	166
J	Hobbit	199	0.728	270	16.0	8.28	1.24	168
L	Hobbit	212	0.640	379	16.3	8.93	1.52	211
O	Flanders	140	0.877	382	16.5	7.11	1.14	158
S	Hobbit	152	0.808	273	18.1	8.87	1.19	184
U	Armada	131	0.770	313	15.0	6.72	1.14	146
	First wheat after dried peas* or Winter oilseed rape – cultivated							
B*	Hobbit	143	1.153	314	19.2	9.84	1.03	169
G	Kador	129	0.782	316	15.5	7.44	1.22	161
H	Mardler	178	0.795	342	15.3	7.51	1.35	176
K	Armada	182	0.797	306	19.5	8.60	1.35	224
M	Hustler	150	0.540	256	18.4	9.67	1.52	238
N	Huntsman	110	0.917	165	13.1	6.74	1.39	154
P	Hobbit	151	0.814	381	13.9	7.12	1.31	155
R	Hobbit	137	0.749	192	15.1	8.24	1.53	194

Ears per m^2 was poorly related to grain yield ($r^2 = 0.037$) but represented total harvested dry weight very well ($r^2 = 0.85$; $F = 113$, 20 df) as follows: Harvest weight (t/ha 85 per cent DM) = $0.4746 + ears/m^2 \times 0.0328$.

Ears per m^2 was less well associated with nitrogen offtake ($r^2 = 0.62$; $F = 33$, 20 df):

Nitrogen offtake (kg/ha) = 20.726 + ears/m² × 0.327

Fertile spikelets (14–18/ear) and grain size (40–53 mg/grain 85 per cent DM) varied unsystematically, but grain number was markedly less in long-strawed cultivars (35.3/ear, nine sites) than short-strawed cultivars (45.1/ear, 12 sites). This may have had some influence on the yield differences.

Each tonne of grain harvested (85 per cent DM) was associated with an average total offtake of 23 kg nitrogen. The range was from 16.1 to 27.4 kg (Table 2) and was not related to variety, cultivation, previous crop or added fertiliser. The relationship between nitrogen offtake and grain yield is shown in Figure 2.

Table 2 Components of harvested growth and yield of 21 winter wheat crops in 1980

Site	Ears	Fertile spikelet number	Grain number	Mean grain weight	Harvest index	Ear weight Total g/fertile stem 85% DM	Ear weight Grain g/fertile stem 85% DM	Total nitrogen offtake
	(a)	(b)	(b)	(b)				
	per m²	per ear	per ear	mg 85% DM	%	85% DM		kg/t grain 85% DM
C	433	17.2	46.7	50.5	52.0	3.33	1.73	22.2
D	482	15.7	43.0	44.8	49.8	3.05	1.52	27.4
E	437	18.0	34.5	40.7	43.7	3.27	1.43	23.6
F	379	15.3	38.3	50.3	43.7	3.34	1.46	25.0
I	562	16.7	35.6	44.1	44.8	3.30	1.48	24.0
Q	568	15.9	34.8	43.5	41.5	3.24	1.35	23.4
T	483	16.8	42.5	46.2	52.7	3.70	1.95	22.3
A	543	15.4	46.7	50.9	51.7	4.08	2.11	16.1
J	509	16.6	43.2	46.4	51.7	3.75	1.94	20.3
L	427	16.1	47.9	46.6	54.8	4.36	2.39	23.6
O	546	14.2	30.7	46.4	43.3	2.70	1.17	22.2
S	481	16.4	43.3	43.4	48.9	3.95	1.93	20.7
U	505	16.4	34.5	46.0	44.8	2.86	1.28	21.7
B	452	15.8	40.0	52.6	51.1	4.03	2.06	17.2
G	462	17.0	37.9	48.6	47.8	3.72	1.78	21.6
H	453	17.2	45.7	49.7	49.0	2.43	1.19	23.4
K	569	16.3	30.3	47.6	44.2	3.64	1.61	26.0
M	480	16.8	44.3	45.0	52.6	3.33	1.75	24.6
N	411	16.7	41.6	51.9	51.6	3.53	1.82	22.9
P	480	17.5	48.8	39.9	51.5	2.74	1.41	21.7
R	448	17.3	55.0	42.7	54.7	3.64	1.99	23.9

(a) Means of over 30 counts.
(b) Means of 50 measurements.

About a fifth to two-thirds of the nitrogen offtake was from fertiliser nitrogen, accounting for 30 to 72 per cent of the total amount of fertiliser added in the spring (Table 3). The 13 wheats following wheats, both direct drilled and cultivated, contained an average of just over 51 per cent while the eight first wheats after a break crop contained an average of 47 per cent.

Coefficients of variation of the means of isotope ratios were generally less than 10 per cent; sites J and N were more variable with 19.5 and 24.7 per cent respectively. The major part (95–98 per cent) of the fertiliser nitrogen was applied

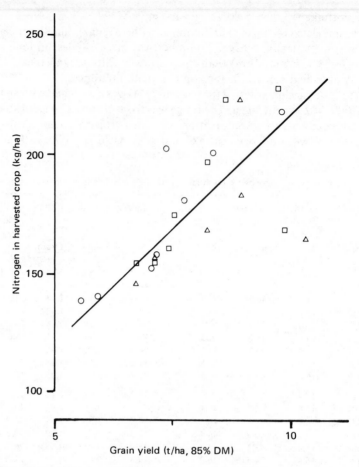

Fig. 2 Winter wheat nitrogen offtake as a function of grain yield, 1980. Wheat after wheat – cultivated (△); first wheat – cultivated (□); wheat after wheat – direct drilled (○). Nitrogen offtake, kg/ha = 19.984 + 19.824 × (grain t/ha 85% DM); r^2 = 0.773.

in divided doses, some as solid prills of ammonium nitrate and some as liquid nitrogen fertiliser (half or more as urea), using farm equipment. The measurements thus incorporate several sources of variability, due both to fertiliser and soil nitrogen supply. The farmers' estimates of amounts applied in the different doses and the uniformity of spread by farm equipment are subject to errors (MAFF, 1980), perhaps larger than those of the isotope ratios. The labelled nitrogen was given at times different from the divided farm applications, but was assumed to be used in exactly the same way as all the farm-applied nitrogen. The effect of time on addition of fertiliser nitrogen in the spring is expected to be small; large differences are likely only when some is given in the autumn (Leitch and Vaidyanathan, 1979 and unpublished). Uncertainty in the amount of farmer-applied fertiliser affects only the calculation of the amount of fertiliser nitrogen harvested in the crop and not the proportion. Thus, provided effects of method, timing and uniformity of spreading on the behaviour of added fertiliser are small, the technique seems to offer a simple means of assessing nitrogen use by commercial field crops.

Table 3 Fertiliser and soil nitrogen recovery at harvest in 21 winter wheat crops, 1980. (Data derived from Table 1)

Site	Fertiliser nitrogen in crop		Fertiliser nitrogen		Soil nitrogen in crop
			harvested	not harvested	
	%	kg/ha	%	kg/ha	kg/ha
C	40.1	63.5	38.3	102.5	94.7
D	47.0	95.0	44.6	115.0	107.3
E	61.1	85.9	42.1	118.1	54.6
F	67.4	93.6	52.6	84.4	45.3
I	49.7	99.5	50.0	99.5	100.8
Q	58.6	105.8	60.5	69.2	74.6
T	66.6	145.2	72.2	55.8	72.9
A	58.7	97.2	50.4	95.8	68.5
J	35.7	60.1	30.2	138.9	108.2
L	52.5	117.3	55.3	94.7	93.6
O	42.6	67.1	47.9	72.9	90.4
S	58.3	107.0	70.4	45.0	76.6
U	49.8	72.7	55.5	58.3	73.4
B	41.5	70.1	49.0	72.9	98.7
G	29.7	47.8	37.1	81.2	112.9
H	46.7	82.1	46.1	95.9	93.9
K	52.5	117.3	64.5	64.7	106.3
M	20.8	49.5	33.0	100.5	188.3
N	28.8	44.4	40.4	65.6	109.8
P	43.4	67.1	44.4	83.9	87.6
R	43.6	85.7	62.6	51.3	110.8

Figure 3 shows that, in general, fertiliser nitrogen not harvested in the crop is less than the soil nitrogen removed by crops; instances of residues accumulating in excess of soil nitrogen depletion are infrequent. As implied in the ADAS soil nitrogen Index system, the first wheats after a break crop show a considerable depletion of soil nitrogen. Thus, there will not be much fertiliser nitrogen contributing to sources of public water supply in fields receiving the range of doses encountered here.

The proportion of fertiliser nitrogen harvested could be explained by either of two functions:

1) Crop growth notionally attributable to fertiliser nitrogen use, defined as the product of total crop weight and the fraction of crop nitrogen derived from fertiliser ($r^2 = 0.75$, Figure 4 on page 115).

2) Soil nitrogen use, defined as the fraction of crop nitrogen derived from soil ($r^2 = 0.58$, Figure 5 on page 116).

These factors, i.e. growth response to fertiliser nitrogen and soil nitrogen use, will obviously influence fertiliser nitrogen use, the former positively and the latter negatively, but the definitions proposed here are arbitrary and debatable. The relationships are merely taken as indicators of directions to pursue in later studies.

Total weights at 85 per cent DM of the two crops were measured frequently (sites L and A) and increased from 0.2 to 3.5 t/ha in Hustler and 0.7 to 5.6 t/ha in Hobbit from GS21 in early February to GS31 in early May; corresponding changes in total nitrogen contents were 11 to 72 kg/ha and 34 to 78 kg/ha.

113

Proportion of crop weight in axillary shoots during this period increased from 19 per cent to 51 per cent in Hobbit and decreased from 55–60 per cent to 43 per cent in Hustler; total nitrogen on the other hand increased from 21 per cent to 44 per cent and then decreased to 16 per cent in Hobbit and changed from 59 per cent to 70 per cent to 35 per cent in Hustler. Once the crops reached booting stage (GS45–50), proportions of dry weight and total nitrogen in infertile and senescent or dead shoots dropped to less than 7 per cent and then steadily declined to below 1.5 per cent at a fortnight before harvest (Table 4 in page 117). The evidence clearly demonstrates that most of the dry matter and nitrogen stored in shoots not 'destined' to produce grain was transferred in sufficient time to be used by those with developing ears.

Acknowledgements

I am grateful to all the farmers for facilities provided. Several colleagues in ADAS helped with various aspects of the study. Ms Karin E Nest, who had a Research Assistantship supported by the Agricultural Research Council through

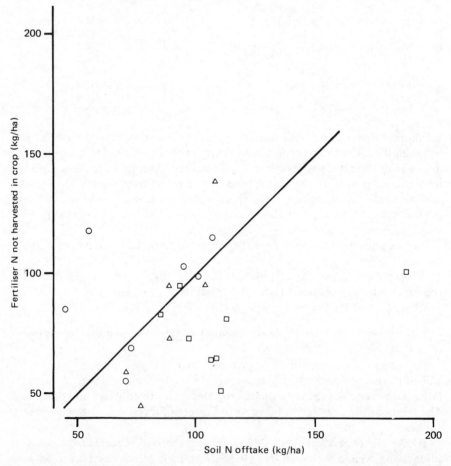

Fig. 3 The relationship between soil nitrogen offtake and fertiliser nitrogen not harvested in crops of winter wheat. The lime represents an exact balance between both quantities. Symbols as in Figure 2.

the University of Reading, Department of Soil Science, did much of the experimental work, with assistance from trainee undergraduates of Trent Polytechnic in Nottingham, Lanchester Polytechnic in Coventry, and the Universities of Salford and Reading. Mr T M Bloom, also supported by the Agricultural Research Council, though the Soil Science Department of Reading University, helped complete some of the chemical analyses.

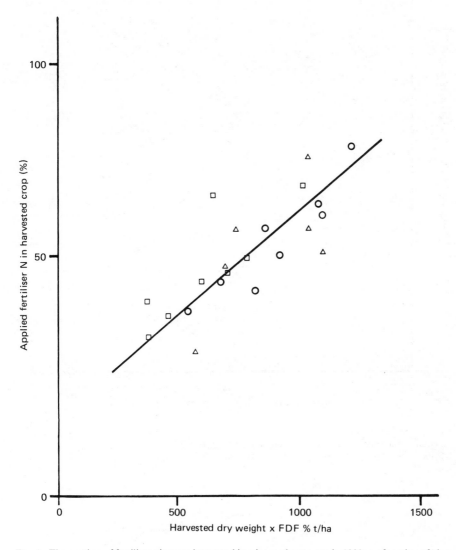

Fig. 4 The portion of fertiliser nitrogen harvested in winter wheat crops in 1980 as a function of 'dry weight due to fertiliser'. Symbols as in Figure 2.
Fertiliser nitrogen offtake % = 13.5749 + 0.0455 × (total dry weight × fraction of crop nitrogen derived from fertiliser); $r^2 = 0.747$.

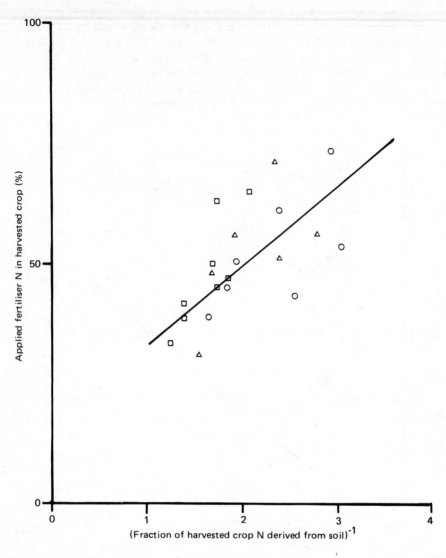

Fig. 5 The portion of fertiliser nitrogen harvested in winter wheat crops in 1980 as an inverse function of the fraction of crop nitrogen derived from soil. Symbols as in Figure 2.
Fertiliser nitrogen offtake % = 16.475 + 0.1512 × (fraction of crop nitrogen derived from soil) $^{-1}$; $r^2 = 0.574$.

Table 4 Change in dry weight and nitrogen held in axillary, senescent, and dead shoots of winter wheat at two sites in 1980. (Values are means of 10 measurements on each date of sampling)

Date of sampling	Site A total g/m²	Site A axillary* g/m²	Site A axillary* % total	Site L total g/m²	Site L axillary* g/m²	Site L axillary* % total
Dry weight						
12/11 February	72	40	55	21	4	19
25 February	83	47	57	26	7	27
18 March	115	69	60	41	15	37
31 March	168	100	59	68	29	43
7 April	287	156	54	116	43	37
6 May	558	241	43	346	75	22
25 May	1132	80	7	756	49	6
11/16 June	1371	63	5	1071	37	4
2 July	1601	71	4	1383	72	5
11 July	1757	100	6	1425	49	3
29 July	2156	42	2	1605	22	1
Nitrogen						
12/11 February	3.4	2.2	59	1.1	0.2	21
25 February	3.6	2.2	61	1.3	0.4	30
18 March	5.1	3.3	64	2.3	0.9	39
31 March	7.4	4.5	61	3.1	1.4	44
7 April	9.3	5.1	55	5.5	1.5	27
6 May	13.8	4.2	31	9.2	1.4	15
25 May	18.4	1.4	7	15.0	1.0	7
11/16 June	17.2	0.7	4	17.1	0.4	3
2 July	16.3	0.6	4	19.7	1.1	6
11 July	17.8	0.9	5	20.8	0.6	3
29 July	21.4	0.3	1	21.1	0.2	1

*Includes senescent and dead shoots.

References

LEITCH, M.H. and VAIDYANATHAN, L.V. 1979. Winter wheat – comparison of drilling methods – Nitrogen subplots using labelled nitrogen 1977. In: *ADAS Experiments and Developments in the Eastern Region 1978*, 75–97. Cambridge.

MAFF. 1980. *Study of fertiliser application.* Farm mechanisation study No. 35, Booklet 2292. London: HMSO.

MAFF. 1981. Agricultural Statistics, England and Wales.

MAFF. 1982. *Fertiliser use on farm crops in England and Wales. 1974–1981.*

SYLVESTER-BRADLEY, R., DAMPNEY P.M.R. and MURRAY, A.W.A. 1984. The response of winter wheat to nitrogen. Ministry of Agriculture, Fisheries and Food, Reference Book 385, *The Nitrogen Requirement of Cereals,* pp. 151–174. HMSO, London.

VAIDYANATHAN, L.V. 1984. Winter wheat yield variability. Ministry of Agriculture, Food, Reference Book 385, *The Nitrogen Requirement of Cereals,* pp.69–77. HMSO, London.

ZADOKS, J.C., CHANG, T.T. and KONZAK, C.F. 1974. A decimal code for the growth stage of cereals. *Weed Research* **14**, 415–421.

Discussion

Dr Gasser asked if residual soil ^{15}N measurements had been made, and whether Dr Vaidyanathan agreed with Dr Jenkinson on the amount of nitrogen returned to the soil. Dr Vaidyanathan said that the ^{15}N analyses were under way but not yet completed. He agreed with Dr Jenkinson on the amounts of nitrogen returned to the soil and added that similar results had been obtained from other ^{15}N experiments.

Mr Nicholsby said that if the first year fertiliser uptake is included, then the overall efficiency of nitrogen use would probably be about 80 per cent. Dr Vaidyanathan replied that in some cases it could be. However, he was concerned with the efficiency of nitrogen use in the season of application. Some of the nitrogen would be lost, the remainder if not used would be immobilised. He was trying to determine how much of the nitrogen was recovered, how much was not being used and why it was not being used.

M. Viaux commented that roots were very high in nitrogen and should be included in the model for nitrogen efficiency.

Dr Dilz said that ^{15}N measurements were always complicated, because of the effect of organic matter. The higher the organic matter content the more ^{15}N may be immobilised in the first year. Dr Vaidyanathan did not agree entirely because a soil with high organic matter would have a larger nitrogen supply. Therefore, fertiliser nitrogen may be used to less advantage since the plant could obtain sufficient nitrogen from the soil, and would not discriminate between ^{15}N and ^{14}N.

Dr Addiscott asked if any experiments had been carried out to determine whether the plant discriminates between ^{14}N and ^{15}N. Dr Vaidyanathan said that in highly controlled experiments one would expect discrimination between ^{15}N and ^{14}N if volatile nitrogen compounds were involved, for example the ammonium ion. However, in the field the many biological processes prevent the study of isotope immobilisation or the plants' discrimination between ^{15}N and ^{14}N.

Recovery of ^{15}N-labelled fertiliser by winter wheat

D S Powlson; G Pruden and D S Jenkinson
Rothamsted Experimental Station, Harpenden

Summary

When ^{15}N-labelled fertiliser was applied to winter wheat, recoveries in soil and crop were 71 per cent in 1980 and between 82 and 87 per cent in 1981. The lower recoveries in 1980 were associated with wetter conditions after fertiliser application in 1980 than in 1981.

Introduction

In 1980 and 1981 ^{15}N-labelled fertiliser was applied to early sown plots within the Rothamsted multifactorial winter wheat experiment and the recovery of fertiliser N in crop and soil measured. For details of these experiments see Thorne *et al.* (1981,1982).

Experimental procedures

Winter wheat (var. Hustler) was drilled in September after early potatoes. A solution containing equal amounts of NH_4-N and NO_3-N at 2 atom per cent excess ^{15}N was applied to 2 m $\times$ 1 m microplots in spring. The solution was applied using a spreader designed to give accurate and even application (Woodcock *et al.*, 1982). The seedbed was treated with aldicarb and the crop was sprayed with fungicide ('Cosmic' and 'Sanspor') and aphicide (pirimicarb); dates of sowing, application of ^{15}N, etc., are given in Table 1.

Table 1 Experimental details of the ^{15}N experiment on winter wheat

Season	1979–80	1980–81
Sowing date	20 September	15 September
Date of ^{15}N application	4 March	20 March
^{15}N applied, kg ha^{-1}	194	114 or 231
Date of final harvest	19 August	12 August

Results

The ^{15}N microplots were situated within plots given optimum pest and disease control and grain yields of above 8 t ha^{-1} were obtained in both years (Table 2). Table 2 also shows the recovery of labelled fertiliser N by crop and soil in the two years. In 1981 about two-thirds of the N applied was recovered in the above ground parts of the crop and less than 20 per cent could *not* be accounted for in the crop and soil. In 1980 N was used less efficiently and 30 per cent of the labelled fertiliser N was unaccounted for. Fertiliser application was earlier in 1980 than in 1981 (Table 1) and was followed by a period of higher rainfall (Table 2). As a result, losses by leaching and/or denitrification were greater in 1980 than in 1981 and hence the recovery of N was lower.

Table 2 Recovery of fertiliser nitrogen by winter wheat in 1980 and 1981.

Season	1979–80	1980–81	
^{15}N-labelled fertiliser applied, kg ha^{-1}	194	114	231
Grain yield, t ha^{-1} (15% moisture)	8.9	9.1	8.3
Rainfall in month following N application, mm	97	46	
	Recovery of fertiliser N, %		
In grain	37	44	31
In straw	12	16	24
In chaff	3	5	6
In stubble	3	4	5
In soil (0–23 cm)	16	18	16
Recovered in above ground crop	55	69	66
Recovered in crop + soil	71	87	82

Conclusions

Well grown wheat, protected from pests and diseases, can use nitrogen very efficiently. However, losses of fertiliser nitrogen can be large if soil conditions between application and uptake favour leaching and/or denitrification.

References

THORNE, G.N., DEWAR, A.M., WILLIAMS, T.D., LACEY, J., PLUMB, R.T., PREW, R.D., PENNY, A., CHURCH, B.M. and TODD, A.D. 1981. Factors limiting yield of wheat. *Rothamsted Report for 1980,* Part 1, 18–23.

THORNE, G.N., DEWAR, A.M., WILLIAMS, T.D., LACEY, J., PLUMB, R.T., PREW, R.D., PENNY, A., CHURCH, B.M. and TODD, A.D. 1982. Factors limiting yield of wheat. *Rothamsted Report for 1981* Part 1, 19–25.

WOODCOCK, T.M., PRUDEN, G., POWLSON, D.S. and JENKINSON, D.S. 1982. Apparatus for applying ^{15}N-labelled fertiliser uniformly to field micro-plots. *Journal of Agricultural Engineering Research* **27**, 369–372.

Uptake of fertiliser nitrogen by arable crops

R J Dowdell, R Crees and D Christian
ARC Letcombe Laboratory, Wantage

The efficient utilisation of nitrogen fertiliser is a matter of great economic importance. Our work aims to discover not only how much is used by the crop (the subject of this paper) but also the fate of the remainder, so that with better understanding of the processes involved, most effective use can be made of the fertiliser applied. In our experiments we use fertiliser labelled with nitrogen-15 so that we can distinguish between fertiliser nitrogen and nitrogen already present within the soil; this is essential because plants derive nitrogen from both sources.

Many agronomic experiments (Allison, 1966) have suggested that crops typically use only about half of the applied fertiliser nitrogen in creating harvestable dry matter. The remainder may be temporarily retained in roots, immobilised into soil organic matter by soil micro-organisms or lost by leaching or denitrification. The vigour of the crop, however, interacts with these processes and directly or indirectly alters their magnitude. Unfavourable growing conditions (e.g. drought or waterlogging) or major changes in the management of the crop–soil system (e.g. improvements in drainage, use of simplified cultivation systems or adjustments in the rate and timing of application of fertiliser nitrogen) can profoundly affect the inter-relationships of the nitrogen cycle.

Results from a number of field and lysimeter experiments at Letcombe Laboratory (Dowdell, 1982) show that the efficiency of nitrogen fertiliser use, expressed as the percentage recovery of applied nitrogen-15 in the above ground parts of the plants, averaged around 45–50% with a range of 41–72%. The 'apparent' recovery of nitrogen by the plants in the same experiments always exceeded the recovery estimated by nitrogen-15, being in the range 51–111 per cent. These estimates differ because in the 'apparent' recovery calculation, the nitrogen used by the crop is taken to have come only from the fertiliser applied, and no allowance is made for the contributions from other sources. The changes in the proportion of fertiliser nitrogen to soil nitrogen used by the plants could result from increased vigour of the crop and extent of exploration of the soil by roots. Stimulation of the activity of soil micro-organisms by the supply of fertiliser nitrogen and by readily metabolisable exudates from plant roots may also be important. However, these results should be interpreted cautiously because dilution of the labelled mineral nitrogen part by turnover of unlabelled soil organic nitrogen could also result in apparent increases in uptake of soil nitrogen (Hauck and Bremner, 1976).

Adverse environmental conditions for crop growth can markedly affect the efficiency of nitrogen fertiliser utilisation. On a spring barley crop growing on shallow soil overlying chalk, drought conditions imposed during the 10 weeks immediately after sowing diminished yield of total dry matter and grain to 74 and 80 per cent respectively of controls (11.8 t ha^{-1} dry matter, 4.4 t ha^{-1} grain) receiving the average rainfall distribution. However, the efficiency of nitrogen fertiliser uptake into the whole droughted crop (50 per cent) and grain (53 per cent) was greater than the controls (48 per cent and 50 per cent respectively). This was due to the greater nitrogen content of the droughted plants (23.3 mg g^{-1} dry weight in grain and 8.1 mg g^{-1} dry weight in straw) compared with control plants (17.6 mg g^{-1} dry weight in grain and 4.4 mg g^{-1} dry weight in straw). In a comparative experiment with permanent pastures (Dowdell, 1982), drought conditions together with defoliation diminished the plant's ability to recover nitrogen applied at the beginning of a short period of precipitation to 80 per cent of the control treatment (the nitrogen-15 recovery was 49 per cent of the nitrogen applied).

Waterlogging has also been shown to depress the nitrogen content of the plants. Midwinter waterlogging of winter wheat on a clay soil diminished the nitrogen content in shoots in the spring to 66 per cent of that in unwaterlogged controls, but by harvest these differences had disappeared (Cannell *et al.,* 1980). Plants waterlogged before emergence contained as much nitrogen per unit of soil area as on other treatments, but as final shoot populations were much smaller the concentration of nitrogen in the grain was significantly greater. In another experiment on a sandy soil where winter wheat was waterlogged for six weeks in midwinter, 54 per cent of the labelled fertiliser was recovered in the crop compared to 63 per cent in unwaterlogged controls (Cannell *et al.,* 1977). There was an indication, however, that the proportion of the total nitrogen in the crop that had been derived from the labelled fertiliser was greater in the crop that experienced the midwinter waterlogging. In contrast on a clay loam, the waterlogged crop recovered more fertiliser (54 per cent) than the controls (39 per cent) (Cannell *et al.,* 1980).

Experiments elsewhere (Davies and Cannell, 1975; Hodgson *et al.,* 1977) have indicated that the nitrogen requirement of direct-drilled crops may be different from that of crops grown on ploughed land, but results have varied from season to season. The content of organic matter increases within the root zone of crops in direct-drilled soil (Fleige and Baeumer, 1974) and this is associated with increased soil biomass (Lynch and Panting, 1980) and smaller rates of mineralisation (Dowdell and Cannell, 1975). Thus it may be anticipated that net immobilisation of applied mineral nitrogen could be greater in these circumstances and by changing the availability of mineral nitrogen, diminish the efficiency of nitrogen fertiliser use. In our experiments (Dowdell and Crees, 1980) where uptake of spring applied nitrogen by winter wheat was compared in a clay soil subjected to five or six years of continuous direct drilling or ploughing or one and two years of direct drilling after four years of deep tined cultivation, 60–67 per cent of the applied nitrogen-15 was recovered in the crop, but there were no significant differences between cultivation histories. The extreme contrast in the amount of soil disturbance caused by different cultivation methods in the autumn had little effect upon the uptake of fertiliser N by the crop or upon retention of nitrogen in the upper layers of the soil. It must be concluded that by the date of the spring top dressings plants grown in soils after contrasting autumn cultivations were able to compete satisfactorily for the applied fertiliser nitrogen, and there were no constraints imposed on this activity by use of direct drilling to establish the crop.

The effect of varying the rate of nitrogen applied to winter barley and also of early and late dressings on the efficiency of nitrogen recovery has been examined in a field experiment on a winter barley crop established by direct drilling on a shallow soil overlying chalk. Nitrogen (labelled with nitrogen-15) was applied at five tillers (20 March) and at the detection of the second node (23 April) in rates from 0–140 kg ha^{-1} of N with different proportions between the two applications. Preliminary results indicate that 56 per cent of the fertiliser nitrogen applied in the split dressing of 140 kg ha^{-1} of N was recovered in the crop. When the nitrogen was applied as early or late dressings of 100 kg ha^{-1} of N, the crop recovered 67 and 63 per cent of the fertiliser respectively.

References

ALLISON, F. E. 1966. The fate of nitrogen applied to soils. *Advances in Agronomy* **18**, 219–258.

CANNELL, R. Q., BELFORD, R. K. and BEETLESTONE, G. R. 1977. Uptake of fertiliser nitrogen by winter wheat and loss of nitrogen by leaching. In: *Agricultural Research Council Letcombe Laboratory Annual Report 1976*, pp. 88–90.

CANNELL, R. Q., BELFORD, R. K., GALES, K., DENNIS, D. W. and PREW R. D. 1980. Effects of water-logging at different stages of development on the growth and yield of winter wheat. *Journal of the Science of Food and Agriculture* **31**, 117–132.

DAVIES, D. B. and CANNELL, R. Q. 1975. Review of experiments on reduced cultivation and direct drilling in the United Kingdom, 1954–1974. *Outlook on Agriculture* **8**, 216–220.

DOWDELL, R. J. 1982. Fate of nitrogen applied to agricultural crops with particular reference to denitrification. *Philosophical Transactions of the Royal Society, London,* B 296, 363–373.

DOWDELL, R. J. and CANNELL, R. Q. 1975. Effect of ploughing and direct drilling on soil nitrate content. *Journal of Soil Science* **26**, 53–61.

DOWDELL, R. J. and GREES, R. 1980. The uptake of ^{15}N-labelled fertiliser by winter wheat and its immobilisation in a clay soil after direct drilling or ploughing. *Journal of the Science of Food and Agriculture* **31**, 992–996.

FLEIGE, H. and BEAUMER, K. 1974. Effect of zero-tillage on organic carbon and total nitrogen content and their distribution in different nitrogen fractions in loessial soils. *Agro-Ecosystems* **1**, 19–29.

HAUCK, R. D. and BREMNER, J. M. 1976. The use of tracers for soil and nitrogen research. *Advances in Agronomy* **28**, 219–266.

HODGSON, D. R., PROUD, J. R. and BROWNE, S. 1977. Cultivation systems for spring barley with special reference to direct drilling (1971–1974). *Journal of Agricultural Science, Cambridge* **88**, 631–644.

LYNCH, J. M. and PANTING, L. M. 1980. Cultivation and the soil biomass. *Soil Biology and Biochemistry,* **12**, 29–33.

The effect of sowing date and of leaching on soil nitrogen supply for winter wheat, at Rothamsted and Woburn, 1981

F V Widdowson, A Penny, R J Darby and E Bird
Rothamsted Experimental Station, Harpenden

Introduction

The causes of differences in yield on different soils are being examined in experiments with winter wheat on clay-with-flints (Batcombe series) soils at Rothamsted and on light sandy loams (Cottenham series) at Woburn (Welbank *et al.*, 1982). In 1981 thirty-two plots of an experiment at Woburn were given the same treatments, in a half-replicate of a 2^6 design, as 32 of the plots in the Factors Limiting Yield of Winter Wheat experiment at Rothamsted. All plots in this comparison were given basal fungicides, aphicide and growth regulator, and crop and soil samples were taken and treatments applied on successive days in the two experiments. These experiments were used for a detailed examination of how soil nitrate varied with time, and how this related to the uptake of nitrogen by wheat, and the NO_3-nitrogen concentration in the plants.

Method

The soils were sampled by auger to 90 cm depth on five occasions during winter and spring and their NO_3-nitrogen contents were measured, after extraction with 2M KC1 (soil solution ratio 1:2.5), by the method of Litchfield (1967). NH_4-N was also measured, but is not presented here.

The crops on the two fields were sampled on six occasions, beginning in December, by removing a 0.75 m^2 sample. Total fresh and dry weights were measured. Percentages of nitrogen in dry matter were measured and used to calculate nitrogen uptakes. Ten wheat stems were cut at ground level from the same plots and at the same time as the soils were sampled and the NO_3-nitrogen content of the sap in the lower parts of the stems was measured colorimetrically using diphenylamine as the indicator (Williams, 1969).

Results

Date of sowing affected the amount of nitrogen taken up, both at Rothamsted on the clay soil and at Woburn on the sandy soil (Figures 1a and b). The supply of nitrogen was entirely from the soil until April, but afterwards it was from both soil and fertiliser nitrogen. At Rothamsted the larger uptakes by the early-sown wheat were clearly related to the smaller amounts of 'residual' NO$_3$-nitrogen in soil measured at successive samplings, but this was less evident at Woburn because of the very much greater susceptibility to leaching of the sandy Woburn soil (Widdowson, Darby and Bird, 1982). On both sites, but especially at Rothamsted, the early-sown wheat contained much more nitrogen in April than the later sown. As soil NO$_3$-nitrogen was almost zero at this time all the rest of the mineral nitrogen originally found in the soils must have been lost by leaching

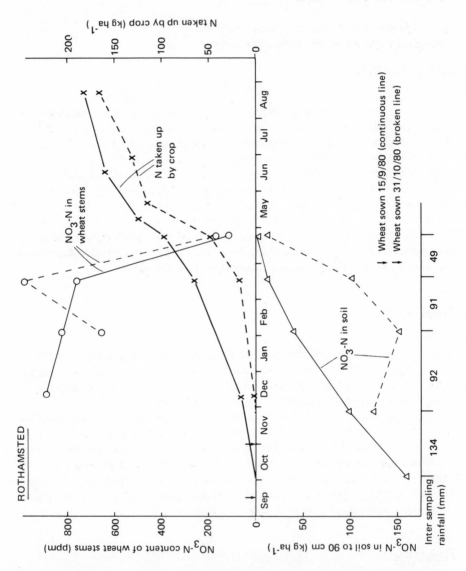

Figs. 1a and 1b (opposite) The effects at Rothamsted and at Woburn of sowing winter wheat either in September or in October on (a) The amount of N taken up (kg ha^{-1}) by the wheat from emergence to harvest ×, (b) the amount of NO$_3$-N (kg ha 1) in the soil (to 90 cm) during winter and spring (△) and (c) the concentration of NO$_3$-N in the wheat stems during winter and spring (O). Final values of (b) and (c) coincided with the application of 80 kg N ha^{-1} at Rothamsted and 150 kg N ha^{-1} at Woburn (as 'Nitro-Chalk') on 22/21 April respectively.

126

and possibly denitrification. Early sowing can thus save appreciable amounts of soil nitrogen from loss.

The NO_3-nitrogen values in wheat stems and in soil declined rapidly in spring and approached zero at about the same time (Figures 1a and 1b). There was thus close agreement between soil and plant measurements for NO_3-nitrogen. It appears, therefore, that NO_3-nitrogen in stems can be used to determine whether

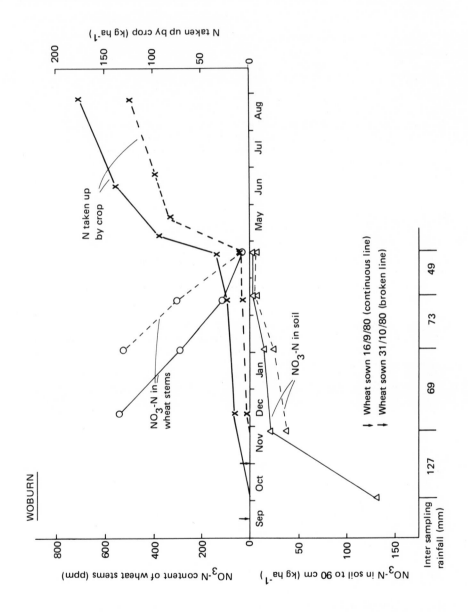

or not early top-dressings are needed in spring, i.e. before the main dressing of nitrogen, needed for grain production, is given at the beginning of stem extension, usually in April.

The data in Table 1 shows that the benefits from early sowing were reflected not only in larger nitrogen uptakes, but also in larger grain yields at harvest.

Table 1 The effect of sowing date on the yield of, and nitrogen uptake by, winter wheat at Rothamsted and Woburn in 1981

	Yields of grain (t ha⁻¹ at 85% DM)		Uptake of N by grain plus straw (kg ha⁻¹)	
	Rothamsted	Woburn	Rothamsted	Woburn
Early sowing (15–16/9/80)				
N_2	80* 9.53	150* 9.41	183	176
N_4	150* 9.37	220* 9.39	231	198
Later sowing (30–31/10/80)				
N_2	80* 8.77	150* 7.45	166	124
N_4	150* 8.82	220* 8.23	208	166

*kg ha⁻¹ of fertiliser-N applied.

References

LITCHFIELD, M. H. 1967. The automated analysis of nitrite and nitrate in blood. *Analyst* **92**, 132–136.

WELBANK, P. J., TAYLOR, P. J., WIDDOWSON, F. V., PENNY, A., DARBY, R. J. and HEWITT, M. V. 1982. Growth and yield of winter wheat on contrasting soils: Rothamsted and Woburn. *Rothamsted Report for 1981* Part I pp. 25–28.

WIDDOWSON, F. V., DARBY, R. J. and BIRD, E. 1982. Nitrogen in soils under winter wheat during winter and spring. *Rothamsted Report for 1981* Part I pp. 250–251.

WILLIAMS, R. J. B. 1969. The rapid determination of nitrate in crops, soils, drainage and rain water by a simple field method using diphenylamine or diphenylbazidene with glass fibre paper. *Chemistry and Industry* 1735–1736.

Uptake of nitrogen by barley in Scottish climatic conditions

K A Smith, A Elmes and R S Howard
The Edinburgh School of Agriculture

Field experiments have been carried out since 1978 using ^{15}N-labelled nitrogen fertiliser to investigate how the uptake of fertiliser nitrogen and soil nitrogen is affected by soil type and tillage practices. The study began on the long-term cultivation experiment at Bush Estate, near Penicuik, Midlothian, where spring barley has been grown continuously since 1968 on Macmerry series (stagnogleyic brown earth) and Winton series (cambic stagnogley) soils (Holmes, 1976; Pidgeon, 1980). The work has now been extended to include other sites with contrasting soil and climatic conditions, and winter and spring barley are also being compared at a site at Aberlady, East Lothian on a brown sand soil.

Calcium nitrate fertiliser containing ca. 0.7 atom per cent ^{15}N (i.e. about twice the natural abundance) was applied to 2 m $\times$ 1.5 m microplots within larger plots treated with unlabelled fertiliser at rates up to 180 kg ha^{-1}. Plant samples were taken on five or six occasions during the growing season for ^{15}N and total nitrogen analysis. The atom per cent ^{15}N in the plants was determined by mass spectrometry, thus enabling the fraction of nitrogen in the plant derived from fertiliser to be calculated.

At Bush Estate in 1978 and 1980, late uptake of soil-derived nitrogen significantly reduced the proportion of nitrogen in the plants derived from fertiliser; this did not occur in 1979. Differences between years were also seen in the effects of tillage. In 1978 and 1980, uptake of nitrogen in the earlier stages of growth was generally greater from ploughed than from direct-drilled soil, but this was reversed in 1979. The relative contributions from soil nitrogen and fertiliser nitrogen varied considerably between years, both at anthesis and at final harvest. These variations are correlated with differences in rainfall distribution. In 1979 there was a much higher rainfall in March–May, but less in June and July, than the other years. Uptake of nitrogen was generally greater from the lighter Macmerry soil, particularly in the earlier part of the season, but differences between soils were usually less than those between tillage treatments.

In 1981, the first year of the comparison between winter and spring barley, on the brown sand at Aberlady, yields of grain were much higher from the winter crop at all rates of fertiliser applied up to 90 kg ha^{-1}. In general, the uptake of soil nitrogen remained fairly constant, while that of fertiliser-derived nitrogen increased, with increasing rates of fertiliser, but absolute quantities of nitrogen from both sources were significantly higher in the winter than in the spring barley. The constant uptake of soil nitrogen contrasts with the results for Bush Estate, where uptake increased significantly with level of fertiliser nitrogen in all three years for which results are available.

References

HOLMES, J. C. 1976. Effects of tillage, direct-drilling and nitrogen in a long-term barley monoculture system. *Edinburgh School of Agriculture Annual Report 1976*, pp. 104–112.

PIDGEON, J. D. 1980. A comparison of the suitability of two soils for direct drilling of spring barley. *Journal of Soil Science* **31**, 581–594.

Effects of nitrogen on the growth and development of winter wheat

V B A Willington and P V Biscoe
Broom's Barn Experimental Station, Higham, Bury St. Edmunds, Suffolk

Avalon winter wheat was sown on 18th September 1981 and three very different treatments were applied in terms of the amount and timing of nitrogen fertiliser. These are summarised in Table 1. The crop was kept free of weeds, pests and diseases throughout by the appropriate use of chemical sprays.

Table 1   Timing and amounts (kg/ha) of fertiliser nitrogen applied

| Crop | Dates | | | | |
	26 Feb.*	19 Mar.	9 Apr.**	17 May	Total
N_1	–	–	90	–	90
N_2	30	–	150	–	180
N_3	60	60	150	60	330

* $\frac{1}{2}$ spikelet primordia formed on apex.
** Terminal spikelet primordium forming on apex.

The growth and development of the three crops were measured by taking samples at regular intervals during the season; every two weeks during the winter and weekly from March until maturity. The green area index (GAI), the ratio of green laminae and sheath to ground area, and dry matter production were measured and used to describe the growth of the crop. Crop development was measured in terms of the production of leaf and spikelet primordia, determined by apical dissections.

Total dry matter production, grain yield and the amount of nitrogen taken up by the crops all increased as more nitrogen fertiliser was applied (Table 2). While

Table 2   Total dry matter production, grain yield and amount of nitrogen taken up by the three crops

Crop	Total dry matter production (t/ha)	Dry matter grain yield (t/ha)	Nitrogen uptake (kg/ha)
N_1	13.8	6.5	119.6
N_2	15.9	7.8	215.0
N_3	18.9	8.7	282.8

these data clearly indicate that nitrogen fertiliser stimulates crop growth the underlying reasons are less obvious. However, using the framework for analysing the effects of environmental factors on dry matter production that we described earlier (Biscoe and Willington, this publication, pages 53–65) we will try to explain the reasons for the larger crops.

The efficiency with which intercepted radiation was converted to dry matter was the same in all crops, about 1.9 g/MJ. Therefore, the nitrogen fertiliser must have influenced the amount of radiation that was intercepted. In cereals more than 80 per cent of the incident radiation is being intercepted once GAI exceeds about four. There was no difference in GAI until March, when crops that received nitrogen fertiliser had larger GAIs and the differences between the crops was largest at anthesis, when maximum GAI was reached (Table 3). Table 3 also

Table 3 Effect of nitrogen fertiliser on the maximum GAI and the duration of GAI above 4

Crop	Maximum GAI	Duration of GAI>4 (days)
N_1	5.6	39
N_2	7.7	70
N_3	9.1	88

shows that nitrogen fertiliser increased persistence of the GAI, there being a two-fold difference in the duration of GAI above four between the well-fertilised and poorly fertilised crops. As the amount of incident radiation was the same for all crops, the effect of the nitrogen fertiliser was to increase the total amount of radiation intercepted by the crops.

Having identified that the main effect of the nitrogen fertiliser was to increase GAI, is it possible to identify which processes in leaf area production and persistence were affected? The rates at which leaf primordia were initiated on the apex (64 °C days/leaf) and the rate of leaf appearance (104 °C days/leaf) were the same for all three crops and not influenced by nitrogen fertiliser. However, the area of the last four leaves to appear on the mainstem was increased with

Table 4 Effect of nitrogen fertiliser on the size of the last four leaves to appear on the main stem; leaf 14 was the flag leaf

Crop	Area of leaf (cm²/leaf)			
	11	12	13	14
N_1	14.6	19.8	27.0	27.8
N_2	16.1	20.5	22.7	32.3
N_3	18.2	26.1	31.2	33.3

increasing nitrogen fertiliser (Table 4). Leaf area production was also increased because the number of tillers surviving to produce an ear at anthesis increased from 0.2 tillers/plant for N_1 to 1.1 tillers/plant for N_3.

These results clearly show that the major effect of nitrogen fertiliser on cereal growth and yield is to increase the total amount of radiation intercepted by the crop and not the efficiency with which it is converted to dry matter. This is achieved not by increasing the rate at which leaves emerged nor the number of leaves produced on individual stems, but by increasing the area of individual leaves and the number of ear-bearing stems, via tillering.

Design and interpretation of nitrogen response experiments

B J George
Rothamsted Experimental Station, Harpenden

Summary

The investigation of response to nitrogen application may be undertaken at the fundamental, descriptive or predictive level. Fundamental investigation is considered inappropriate for field experiments. The descriptive approach, summarising and discussing results, has been useful in the past but serves only to indicate broad trends. The predictive approach implies the assumption of a model. The parameters of this model are estimated from the data and used to predict future results or to compare experiments. Earlier work in this field is reviewed, and the exponential function modified by the addition of a linear term is proposed as a convenient working model. The properties of this model are discussed and some examples of its use are given. A possible generalisation to a modified logistic function is also suggested. The implications for the conduct of future experiments are considered and it is shown that the rigid approach appropriate for analysis of variance is no longer necessary.

Introduction

In some branches of science and engineering experimental results may be obtained with high precision and repeatability. It is then possible to formulate a law for the process under observation based on the data, and to deduce from this the underlying mechanism. Unfortunately, in agricultural research the results from similar experiments may differ widely, and the formulation of a law is seldom possible. Some of the causes of this variation are obvious, but their effects may be very patchy, even within quite closely adjacent and apparently similar areas. In addition, the response to nitrogen may be highly dependent on other applied treatments or background factors such as previous cropping.

The investigation of crop response to nitrogen application is considered below at three levels, described broadly as fundamental, descriptive and predictive. Models used by previous workers are briefly reviewed, and the modified exponential function is proposed as a useful working model. The merits of this model and the implications for future experiments are then considered.

133

Fundamental investigation

At the fundamental level the objective is to determine the detailed mechanism of the response. Because of the wide variability of field experiments there is little hope of achieving this objective. Some information may be available from field experiments using the same, or closely adjacent, plots over a long period, but these are still subject to much uncontrolled and local variation. Closely controlled experiments in laboratory conditions will normally be required.

Descriptive analysis

The descriptive level of analysis aims to summarise results, possibly from a wide range of experiments, and to describe empirically the relationship between chosen measures of response and the known features of the experiments. Typical of this approach are the papers by Lessels and Webber (1965) on the effect of nitrogen on spring and winter cereals. These take the yield with zero applied nitrogen as a basis for classifying the results, and discuss the increase in yield resulting from the application of nitrogen at a standard level (usually 0.30 and 0.60 cwt/acre). No model is considered and the quoted values are the average increases in yield over several sites and years. Not surprisingly, the results show many inconsistencies and few clear trends. This may be attributable partly to the rather small number of results involved in most of the averages, and partly to the rather arbitrary division of the data by region, presence or absence of lodging, etc. A further source of difficulty is probably the use of zero applied nitrogen as the reference standard. This is discussed further below.

Analysis of variance

A common adjunct to the descriptive approach is the use of analysis of variance. In its basic form this tests the hypothesis that the applied treatment factors have no effect, by means of the ratios of appropriate mean squares. A significantly large ratio implies that the variation in the observed means of the factor levels is greater than might reasonably be expected to arise by chance. The hypothesis of no real differences is, therefore, untenable and one concludes that real differences do exist. A significant result says nothing about their size or nature, only that on average there are appreciable differences in the effects of the levels of the factor. It may be that yields at all levels differ appreciably from each other, or that yields at most levels are similar but a few differ considerably. The identification of any pattern is a separate matter.

The occurrence of a mean square ratio too small to be considered significant does not imply that the levels of the factor are equal in effect, only that in the conditions of the experiment the observed differences were not unduly large. There may be differences in effects which are masked by the average nature of the test, particularly if most of the levels are similar in effect and only one effect differs appreciably. This one difference may be of considerable interest even though the average difference is relatively small. In addition, if several factors are

134

involved the main effects are averages over all levels of the other factors. The main effects may then be small even though there are large, but possibly varying, effects at some levels of these other factors. This situation would normally be detected by the occurrence of significantly large interaction terms, provided that the design and analysis permit the separation of such terms.

Very small mean square ratios are an indication of a failure of some part of the model assumptions. The assumed distributional properties may not be valid, the treatment effects may not be additive, or the random components may not be independent, i.e. there may be unsuspected correlations between the observed values of some experimental units. Failures such as this may be evident on inspection of the residuals, particularly when arranged in field order.

Example

As an example of the interpretation of a fairly simple experiment consider the wheat yields of the organic manuring experiment 79/W/RN/12 published in, *Yields of the Field Experiments, 1979,* by Rothamsted Experimental Station and reproduced in Table 1. Organic matter residues from six manuring treatments had been built up over several years in plots, with two sets of plots given inorganic fertilisers equivalent to two of the organic manures. From 1971 the plots had been in an arable rotation with inorganic fertilisers used on all plots. The experiment was arranged in two blocks, each containing eight plots to which the early manuring treatments had been applied. Each plot was divided into eight sub-plots to which a range of nitrogen dressing was applied. The tabulated values are the mean yields over the two blocks.

Examination of the data shows that for all manures the grain yield increased rapidly with increasing applied nitrogen to about 120 kg/ha, and then decreased rather erratically. Mean yields for the manuring treatments ranged from 4.26 to 5.59 t/ha, and the differences between manures were fairly constant over the range of applied nitrogen. The apparently simple conclusion that yield varied considerably with both manures and nitrogen levels, with little interaction, is belied by the analysis of variance given in Table 2.

Table 1 Yields of grain in tonnes/hectare from organic manuring experiment 79/W/RN/12

Nitrogen (kg/ha)	0	30	60	90	120	150	180	210	Mean
Manure									
FYM	1.82	3.82	5.77	6.06	6.88	5.64	6.18	5.89	5.26
Straw	1.72	3.90	5.48	6.68	6.42	6.58	6.48	6.00	5.41
Peat	1.38	3.83	5.52	6.42	6.50	7.13	5.89	6.21	5.36
Green manure	1.63	3.58	5.16	5.81	4.99	4.76	5.87	5.08	4.61
Fert=FYM	1.16	3.45	4.73	5.83	5.01	4.76	4.44	4.71	4.26
Fert=straw	1.81	3.69	5.44	6.49	6.87	6.33	5.99	5.81	5.30
Clover ley	2.29	4.28	6.11	6.55	6.98	6.17	6.17	6.13	5.59
Grass ley	1.57	3.60	5.19	6.52	6.25	5.79	6.52	6.29	5.22
Mean	1.67	3.77	5.42	6.29	6.24	5.90	5.94	5.77	5.13

Table 2 Analysis of variance of the yields of grain in experiment 79/W/RN/12

	df	MS	MSR
Blocks	1	23.78	130.66
Manures (whole plots)	7	3.23	0.88
Residual for whole plots	7	3.69	20.25
Nitrogen (subplots)	7	41.39	227.43
Manures × nitrogen	49	0.27	1.50
Residual for subplots	56	0.18	—

While the large and small mean square ratios for nitrogen and manures by nitrogen interaction respectively are as expected, the very small mean square ratio for manures is not. The simple conclusion from this analysis would be that yields for the various manures were closely similar. The clue to the contradiction between the analysis and common sense is in the very large mean square ratio for the whole plot residual compared with the subplot residual. One would expect whole plots to be the more variable but not to this extent. Only by examining the original data can the reason be found. For most manures the yields in block 2 exceed those in block 1 by less than 1 t/ha. The difference is a little larger for green manure, and considerably so for fertiliser equivalent to FYM (almost 3 t/ha). For grass ley there is a difference of about $\frac{1}{4}$ t/ha in the opposite direction. It is this large variation in manure effects between blocks which inflates the whole plot residual mean square, and causes a difference in yield of about $1\frac{1}{2}$ t/ha to be declared statistically non-significant.

General interpretation

Overall, the interpretation of an analysis of variance is far from simple and is subject to a number of strong assumptions. Judicious inspection of tables of means may be much more informative. Standard errors provide a useful yardstick here but should not be allowed the status of automatic decision makers. One should beware also of the temptation to try to explain away every minor fluctuation in the data. This has led in the past to much unwarranted speculation and to the coining of meaningless phrases such as 'responsive sites' and 'crops able to utilise nitrogen efficiently'.

Subdivision of sums of squares

A common criticism of analysis of variance is that it fails to answer any specific questions. This is not a valid criticism of the technique, only of the experimenters for not posing specific questions. Any linear combination of levels of a factor may be extracted and tested if one wishes. The only provisos are that the questions generating the combinations should be based on features of interest to the experimenter and not as a result of inspection of the data, that multiple questions should not overlap, and that the number of questions that may be examined is, therefore, limited by the information available in the factor.

When the levels of the applied factor are quantitative, e.g. various rates of applied nitrogen, the detection of significant differences in yield does not imply any particular functional form. Partitioning the sum of squares further into polynomial contrasts may indicate the existence of a general trend, simple curvature, or appreciable deviation from a smooth curve, but does not provide a useful working model for further study. The use of polynomials as approximations to other functions was valuable when computations had to be done by hand. With computers and good software now available it is possible to fit much more general functions. This is the basis of the predictive approach to the analysis of response data.

Predictive analysis

Here, the experimental data are used to estimate the values of the parameters in a model of chosen form. Ideally, the model would be based on a comprehensive theory of crop response, but it should at least accord with the known general form of response and be compatible with available theory. It should also be as simple as possible in form, and preferably be based on parameters with direct physical interpretation. Although one would naturally prefer a function which fits well to a particular set of data, it is more important that the model be capable of fitting reasonably well to a number of related sets of data with the same or a related set of parameters. In the long term it may be important that the model behave in a biologically sensible way when extrapolated but at the present stage of model development this is not crucial. However, given a choice between otherwise acceptable models with similar success in fitting to current data it is preferable to choose a model which is capable of generalisation with little change of functional form.

Review of models

Exponential equations

In a classic paper, Crowther and Yates (1941) reviewed all published results of fertiliser experiments from 1900 to 1940 in Great Britain and other northern European countries. The model used was the asymptotic exponential or Mitscherlich equation in the form

$$y = y_0 + d(1 - 10^{-k\overline{x}})$$

where y is the predicted yield in tons/acre with nitrogen applied at the rate of x cwt/acre, y_0 is the yield with zero applied nitrogen, d is the asymptotic limit of yield and k is a constant.

Despite earlier criticisms of this model, they were apparently satisfied with its performance in this study but do not state how well the model fitted the data. The average value for the constant k is given as 1.1.

Bullen and Lessells (1957) used a similar technique on the results of a further 270 cereal experiments. They found that k varied from 0.13 to 1.68 for winter wheat, but that the average over experiments was again about 1.1. They were careful to point out that there was no question of this form of response curve having the status of a universal law, but that the use of other curves is likely to be much less convenient in practice. Some of the force of this argument has now been lost with improvements in computing power but the law of diminishing returns aspect of the model is still attractive. The main shortcoming of the model is the lack of any descending portion at high levels of applied nitrogen. This may not have been a serious problem in these earlier experiments with relatively low levels of nitrogen dressing.

A common modification of the asymptotic exponential model is the addition of a linear term. The model is then usually written as

$$y = a + br^x + cx$$

where a, b, c and r are constant, $a > 0$ and b, $c < 0$; $0 < r < 1$.

Inverse polynomials

A totally different type of model was proposed by Nelder (1966). He argued that the response function should be capable of asymmetry, be non-negative and bounded, i.e. remain finite whatever level of applied nitrogen be considered. A family of models with these properties is the inverse polynomials of the general form

$$\frac{x}{y} = P_n(x)$$

where $P_n(x)$ is a polynomial of order n with non-negative coefficients. A problem arises in fitting such models due to the unknown amount of nitrogen available to the crop in addition to that applied. It is necessary to estimate this base level first and then to estimate the polynomial coefficients.

Inverse polynomials were proposed by Nelder as a convenient addition to the range of models, and have been shown to fit well to data from many sources. Inverse linear functions had been proposed earlier by Balmukand (1928). Greenwood et. al., (1971) developed a rather simplified theory which led to a model of modified inverse linear form.

Split lines

Boyd (1972) noted that quadratic or exponential curves fitted to sugar beet data with five or six levels of applied nitrogen showed disturbingly similar residuals on different sites. He suggested that two straight lines would provide a good fit to many sets of experimental data. Anderson and Nelson (1975) took this idea further and allowed the possibility of three intersecting straight lines

Comparison of models

Boyd et al. (1976) compared a variety of models for the nitrogen response of cereals in 41 experiments and concluded that split lines performed best as judged by the average residual variances. Sparrow (1979) also compared a range of models for fitting to 83 spring barley experiments. The best model on the basis of the residual mean square varied from one experiment to another but, overall, split lines were considered to be the best. It is interesting to note that he discarded two experiments because of the lack of any clear relationship between adjacent yields, but accepted all the other data as sufficiently reliable to provide an adequate comparison of models.

Multiple inputs

Some of the above single variable models may be generalised readily to cope with several nutrients, others have no simple generalisations. Since single nutrient response functions are not yet agreed it is premature to expect much progress with multi-dimensional functions.

The popularity of response surface designs in industry in the early 1960s prompted some interest in agricultural applications. The best known designs are 3^n factorials, possibly in fractional replication, and composite designs based on 2^n factorials with additional points for rotatability or to improve the accuracy of estimation in some directions. Inkson (1966) gave some examples and hinted at the use of sequential experimentation over several years. Since the optimum combination of nutrients may change considerably from year to year, and the designs concentrate on the fitting of quadratic surfaces, they are of limited value.

Yates (1966) briefly reviewed non-factorial designs and concluded that broader experimentation was still necessary.

Choice of model

General form of model

As demonstrated by the data in Table 1, experimental data over a sufficiently wide range of nitrogen dressing generally show a rapid increase followed by a slow decrease in yield with increasing applied nitrogen. Not all data follow this form. Some experiments show continuously increasing yields, others are continuously decreasing. Either of these is compatible with the more general form. More difficult to reconcile are experiments in which the yield fluctuates. These are often discarded as being unreliable or uninformative but they should not be dismissed too lightly. The fact that some experiments can produce such erratic results throws doubt on the reliability of others, and on the validity of discrimination between alternative models on the basis of small differences in the residual sums of squares.

Inspection of a large number of experiments showing both rising and descending portions of the response curve suggests that the variance is much larger at high levels of nitrogen than at low levels. The data given in Table 1, and plotted in Figure 1, are typical. The variance appears to increase sharply at, or perhaps a little below, the maximum value of the response curve. This is borne out by the variance components at the successive nitrogen levels, based on the differences between blocks adjusted for manure effects. The values obtained are 0.18, 0.05, 0.26, 0.19, 0.48, 0.36, 0.51 and 0.31; the ratio of the mean variance estimates for nitrogen levels of 120 to 210 and 0 to 90 kg/ha is 2.44. This is approximately equal to the 1 per cent probability point for the F distribution with 28 and 28 degrees of freedom, so the difference is unlikely to have arisen by chance.

It seems likely that this increased variability at higher nitrogen levels is associated with the well-known increased risks of fungal attack and lodging. Both of these are catastrophic phenomena, i.e. even when conditions produce enhanced risk the crop sometimes escapes wholly or partly, but the affected part of the crop may suffer a serious reduction in yield. This sporadic loss of yield creates both an increase in variance and, more importantly, a net reduction of yield at the higher nitrogen levels. This not only distorts the shape of the response

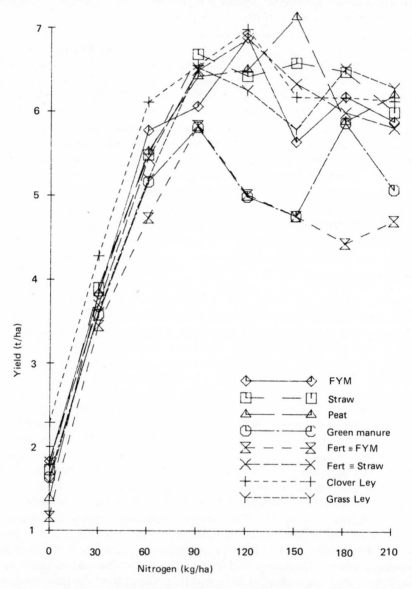

Fig. 1 Grain yields for the eight treatments in the long-term manuring experiment 79/W/RN/12.

function, to produce a sharp change of slope, but also poses a difficult problem in estimating the 'true' shape of the curve. The estimation method needs to be such that at lower levels of nitrogen positive and negative discrepancies about the fitted curve are equally likely, but at higher nitrogen levels low yield points are largely discounted in favour of a curve passing close to any high yield points. Although techniques exist to achieve this it is not easy to justify the use of such an asymmetric and irregular method. The difficulty may be eased by modern cereal varieties and the more widespread use of fungicides.

Previous experimentation

Many early experiments used only a few levels of applied nitrogen with the highest being too low to produce maximum yield. In addition, there was often inadequate control and recording of other factors, such as disease or level of other nutrients. More recent experiments have tried to span the maximum but have often been unduly complicated by the inclusion of too many other factors. In consequence, the exponents of the various models have been able to find data to support their cases, and no clear conclusion has been reached.

Two major red herrings have confused the issue. The first is the lack of recognition of the relative unreliability of data at higher nitrogen levels. The second is the emphasis on good numerical fit to individual sets of data, which both Yates (1966) and Nelder (1966) queried. In different ways, they stressed the need to seek confirmation from series of experiments. Nelder advocated the use of general parameters, with values remaining constant for experiments in similar conditions and varying in relation to changes in the conditions. The criterion of success of a model would then be that it fitted well to a series of related experiments, with changes in the parameters reflecting the differences between the experiments in the series. This criterion appears to have been overlooked by subsequent workers who have concentrated on producing the best possible fit to each individual experiment. As Nelder pointed out, a high value of R^2, or equivalently a low residual mean square, in a single experiment is no guarantee of a good model.

A convenient working model

Wimble (1980), in a paper published after his death, described the four important features of a fertiliser response model as the slope of the rising part, the slope past the peak, the yield near the optimum dressing, and the location of the optimum dressing. To permit flexibility in matching four such characteristics a four parameter model is needed, and he listed the most popular models as the inverse quadratic, modified inverse linear, modified exponential and two straight lines. The latter model is unique in having a sharp break of slope and agrees well with many sets of experimental data. The break of slope found in the data may, however, be an indication of the onset of a limiting condition which may not remain in force in the future. The split-line model then accurately represents history but does not provide a basis for the estimation of the potential response of the crop. For this purpose, a smooth curve is preferable. The other three models

141

are all capable of representing the more general shape of a response curve, but the modified exponential has several advantages.

The law of diminishing returns interpretation of exponential curves has already been mentioned, and the addition of a linear term, with a negative coefficient, provides a simple way of allowing for reduced yields at higher nitrogen levels. Clearly, the linear term cannot be strictly valid since extrapolation of the curve will eventually produce negative values. In practice, few observations are normally made at nitrogen levels above the maximum and the linear term is a sufficiently good approximation, particularly in view of the doubtful reliability of these points.

With any multiparameter function, estimates of the parameters based on a moderate number of distinct nitrogen levels will be correlated. For the modified exponential model the estimates of c and r are quite highly correlated. This means that when the model is fitted to experimental data any divergence of one of these parameters from its optimum value may be largely offset by a corresponding change in the value of the other. Since the major practical difficulty in fitting the model is the estimation of the non-linear parameter r, it would be advantageous if this could be fixed at some value close to its optimum. Fitting the model would than be very simple since all terms would be linear. Determination of the optimum value of r for a number of cereal experiments gave estimates varying from about 0.985 to just over 0.99. Varying the value of r from 0.98 to 0.995, and estimating the best corresponding values of a, b and c, was found to produce negligibly different values of R^2 for individual experiments. It has subsequently been found that fixing r at 0.99 allows a wide range of experiments to be adequately fitted. It is of interest to note that the value of k = 1.1 found by Crowther and Yates is equivalent to r = 0.98, allowing for the change in the units of measurement.

The remaining two parameters in the modified exponential model, a and b, correspond essentially to the vertical and horizontal location of the curve. If two curves, with the same value of c, have the equations

$$y_1 = a_1 + b_1 r^x + cx \text{ and } y_2 = a_2 + b_2 r^x + cx$$

the second may be rewritten as

$$y_2 = a_1 + \Delta a + b_1 r^{x+\Delta x} + c (x + \Delta x)$$

where $\Delta x = \ln (b_2/b_1)/\ln (r)$ and $\Delta a = a_2 - a_1 - c\Delta x$

The second equation is then seen as being the same as the first, but with a horizontal shift of Δx and a vertical shift of Δa. As response curves, the interpretation is that the second function has a maximum yield Δa units higher than the first, attained at an applied nitrogen level Δx units higher. The principle extends to more than two curves. If a family of curves be fitted to a series of related experiments, with c held constant, but estimated from the data, and both a and b allowed to vary from experiment to experiment, the differences between the experiments may be summarised in simple terms as the differences in maximum yield and the differences in nitrogen level at which the maxima are attained.

Families of curves have been fitted in this way to several series of experiments. Details will be published elsewhere, but the percentage variation explained over series of 30 to 40 experiments has generally been about 95 to 99 per cent. This is not perhaps as impressive as it might appear since it is usually possible to account for 50 to 60 per cent of the variation by fitting a single curve to the whole series.

In some cases it has been possible to find simple interpretations of the vertical and horizontal shifts. In a series of experiments with four cropping sequences over nine years, differences in yield were related largely to years while differences in nitrogen level were related largely to cropping sequences.

The maximum of the modified exponential curve occurs when

$$x = \ln\left\{-c/[b\ln(r)]\right\} \Big/ \ln(r).$$

Although easily calculated the value is not very reliable since the curve is relatively flat around the maximum.

The economic optimum for a price ratio of p:1 is at

$$x = \ln\left\{(p-c)/[(b\ln(r)]\right\} \Big/ \ln(r).$$

Since c is generally small (about -0.01 to -0.03) and p is constant at about 0.003 to 0.004 (with the grain yield measured in t/ha and nitrogen application in kg/ha), this is determined largely by the value of c/b.

One useful mathematical property of modified exponential curves with a constant value for r is that the average of two curves is of the same form. If c is also constant, the x value at the maximum of the average of two such curves is as above but with b replaced by the average value $\bar{b}$. The average of the x values at the two separate maxima is again as above but with b replaced by the geometric mean $\sqrt{b_1 b_2}$, with the appropriate sign. If the separate values of b are similar, the simple average and the geometric mean will be little different; e.g. if $b_1 = -9$ and $b_2 = -10$, then $\bar{b} = -9.5$ and $\sqrt{b_1 b_2} = -9.487$. Many experiments are replicated in blocks and the curve is then fitted to the average values of yield over the blocks. Although the yields may differ appreciably between blocks, the nitrogen level at the maximum is generally almost constant. The fitted curve then estimates the optimum nitrogen dressing accurately, and the differences between the blocks provides a valid estimate of experimental error.

When two or more sets of data differ appreciably in location their average is of no interest. If the shape of the curves may be assumed to be the same, fitting a family of curves differing only in the values of a and b allows the fitted curves to be superimposed by suitable horizontal and vertical shifts. The deviations of the adjusted data about this common curve are then the appropriate measure of experimental error. Fitting a family of curves in this way to the data in Table 1, with r = 0.99, gave an estimated common value of c = -0.33 and the values of a and b given in Table 3. The calculated maximum yields and corresponding nitrogen levels are also tabulated, together with the horizontal and vertical shifts required to bring the fitted curves into coincidence with that for FYM. The adjusted data are plotted in Figure 2, where the values marked on the axes are those for FYM. The good fit of the common curve at low levels of applied nitrogen, and the general increase in variability at higher levels, are easily seen.

Table 3 Fitted parameters and differences in yield and N level for data in Table 1

Manure	a	b	Y Max	N Max	ΔY	ΔN
FYM	14.030	−12.196	6.47	131.3	—	—
Straw	14.405	−12.710	6.71	135.4	0.24	4.1
Peat	14.512	−13.065	6.73	138.1	0.26	6.8
Green manure	13.017	−11.361	5.69	124.2	−0.78	−7.1
Fert=FYM	12.567	−11.129	5.30	122.2	−1.17	−9.1
Fert=straw	14.185	−12.446	6.56	133.3	0.09	2.0
Clover ley	14.209	−11.857	6.74	128.5	0.27	−2.8
Grass ley	14.286	−12.877	6.55	136.7	0.08	5.4

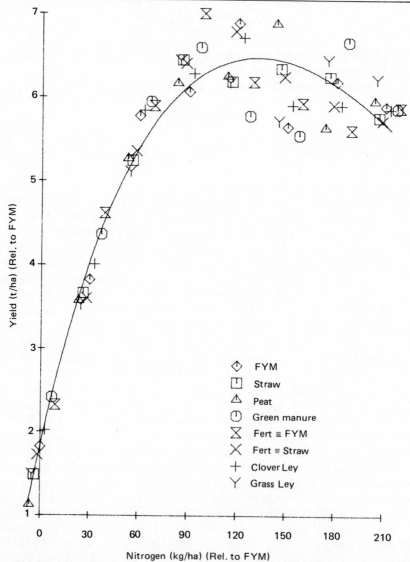

Fig. 2 Grain yields in experiment 79/W/RN/12 adjusted relative to FYM to bring the fitted curves into superposition.

In this example the maximum yields are all attained at similar applied nitrogen levels. In other cases this may not be so and the gradient of the response function at zero applied nitrogen may be appreciably different from one treatment to another. Description of response in terms of the rate of increase in yield between zero applied nitrogen and the maximum, or the yield at some arbitrarily chosen level of applied nitrogen, will reflect this gradient. It will indicate the response per unit applied nitrogen at low levels but this is a combination of the nitrogen available in the site and the shape of the response curve for the particular crop. What is really required is the separation of these two terms, as afforded by the estimation of the maximum yield and the level of nitrogen application at which this is attained.

Development of the model

Although the modified exponential curve is mathematically convenient and provides a good fit to many series of experiments, the model is only a first approximation to biological reality. Extrapolation in either direction produces negative yield values. A more realistic model would level off to zero yield at low levels of nitrogen (negative values of applied nitrogen), and would also level off at high levels of nitrogen to a possibly non-zero yield. A possible function with these characteristics might be the modified logistic

$$y = \frac{a + br_1^x}{1 + cr_2^x}$$

where a, b and c are all positive, and r_1 and r_2 both lie between 0 and 1. For low and moderate levels of x this will be dominated by the denominator, and at high values of x by the numerator. For suitable values of the parameters it can be closely approximated by a modified exponential function over a wide range of values of x.

The modified logistic model contains five parameters. To determine these, or a similar set of parameters for other general models, would require experimentation at very low levels of nitrogen, obtainable only on seriously impoverished sites, and at very high levels of applied nitrogen on similar sites. The results might be of academic interest but would have little practical value.

Experimental requirements

Single experiment

In order to fit a four parameter model it is clearly necessary to have at least four data points. With only four points the fitted model may pass through them precisely. With only a few additional independent points there will be little information available to determine the variability about the fitted line, and it will be quite impossible to recognise whether this variability is random or systematic. The least squares principle normally used to estimate the parameters will tend to produce similar positive and negative errors about the fitted curve. Only if these show a distinct pattern, for example positive for high and low nitrogen levels and negative for intermediate levels, will there be any suggestion of lack of fit, and even then it will be only an unprovable suggestion. To fit and adequately test a model many points are needed, with replicate observations at some or all of a number of distinct nitrogen levels, which must be appreciably more than four.

With n replicate observations at k nitrogen levels, the best fitting line will be determined effectively by the averages of the k groups of yields. The deviations of these averages from the line will provide a measure of the lack of fit of the model, and the deviations of individual yields from their corresponding averages will provide a measure of pure error. The ratio of the mean squares for lack of fit to that for pure error may be compared with the appropriate F distribution to test if the lack of fit is significantly large. If not so, the model is an adequate fit to the data.

Since four parameters have to be estimated, the lack of fit mean square has $\nu_1 = k-4$ degrees of freedom. The pure error mean square has $\nu_2 = k(n-1)$ degrees of freedom. The F test is more sensitive to changes in ν_2 than in ν_1, and ν_2 should be reasonably large. As a general rule of thumb one should aim for $\nu_2 = 12$, and $\nu_1 = 3$. Reasonable values for this single experiment would then be k = 7 and n = 3, so that $\nu_1 = 3$ and $\nu_2 = 14$.

It is not necessary to have the same number of replicates at each nitrogen level. With n_1, n_2, ... replicates at the various levels, $\nu_2 = \Sigma (n_i - 1)$. This gives a little more freedom, and one might choose to set k = 8 and allow n_i to alternate between 2 and 3, to obtain $\nu_1 = 4$ and $\nu_2 = 12$, from a total of 20 experimental units.

The optimum spacing of the nitrogen levels is less easily defined. There is a natural tendency to use equally spaced levels but this is not necessary and is certainly not optimum for a non-linear model. In theory, for any assumed form of model it would be possible to calculate the optimum spacing but this would involve some further assumption such as the position of the maximum. The computations would be laborious and the gain in precision over the use of equally spaced levels would probably be quite small.

The lowest possible value of applied nitrogen is, of course, zero. Since the precision of the parameter estimates increases with the increasing range of nitrogen levels it is clearly advantageous to set the lowest level of application at zero, but this does not imply that this provides any special information. It is only the zero level of applied nitrogen. The actual nitrogen level will depend on the site. Since there is evidence that the grain yield is erratic at nitrogen levels much above the maximum yield value, the mathematical advantage of setting the highest level of applied nitrogen as high as possible may be offset by a breakdown of the model. The practical limit is, therefore, only a little above the expected maximum yield point.

The major determinants of the nitrogen levels to be used in an experiment are practical rather than theoretical, but some advantage may be taken of the relative stability of the response at lower nitrogen levels. Few points are required on the steeply rising part of the curve, compared with the number around the maximum.

Although the descending portion of the curve is of little practical interest, the relative instability of the yields here requires a disproportionate number of points, or replicates, to avoid the risk of serious error in the parameter estimates.

The shape of the fitted curve will be particularly sensitive to the yields at these high levels of nitrogen.

Series of experiments

When data are available from a series of related experiments, or possibly when a range of nitrogen dressings has been applied at several levels of some other factor, it may be reasonable to assume that the shape of the response function is the same for each experiment in the series. Only two independent parameters are then required for each individual experiment, with two further general parameters. Sufficient degrees of freedom to test the fit of the model adequately may then be obtained with much smaller numbers of both applied nitrogen levels and replicates.

If, in a series of s experiments, each experiment has k nitrogen levels and n replicates of each level, the degrees of freedom for fitted parameters, lack of fit and pure error are $2(s + 1)$, $sk - 2(s + 1)$ and $sk(n - 1)$ respectively. With $s = 4$ it would be possible, but not advisable, to have $k = 4$ and $n = 3$, giving 6 and 32 degrees of freedom for lack of fit and pure error. A better arrangement for the same total number of experimental units would be $k = 6$ and $n = 2$, giving 14 and 24 degrees of freedom.

As in the single experiment, it is not necessary to have equal replication of each nitrogen level. In addition, it is not necessary to have the same nitrogen levels in a series. This allows considerable flexibility in arranging the experiments. Provided that the assumption of constant shape were secure, it would be possible to include some experiments in the series with very few experimental points. Estimates of lack of fit and error would then rely on the more intensive experiments in the series.

The strong dependence on the assumption of constant shape is reduced if the experiments in the series are similar and each contains enough distinct nitrogen levels to be capable of fitting a curve independently with some degrees of freedom left for estimating the lack of fit. The lack of fit term in the composite analysis can then be subdivided into components representing the lack of fit in each individual experiment and the overall lack of fit in the series. In the above example with $k = 6$ and $n = 2$, the 14 degrees of freedom for lack of fit may be partitioned into 8 degrees of freedom (two from each of the four experiments) for individual experiments and 6 degrees of freedom for overall lack of fit. The alternative arrangement with $k = 4$ and $n = 3$ supplies only the 6 degrees of freedom for overall fit, i.e. for general agreement of the model with the data. It does not provide any means of testing the differences in fit for the individual experiments.

Conclusions

The response of cereal yields to applied nitrogen generally follows a steeply rising followed by a less steeply falling curve. Extra sources of variation apply at higher nitrogen levels causing erratic results and decreased yields. This may have misled previous workers into proposing response functions with sharp breaks of slope. The modified exponential function, having a linear term with negative

147

coefficient, has been found to fit reasonably well to many sets of data. The exponential term appears to differ little in a range of experiments and may be fixed at r = 0.99, for nitrogen applications in kg/ha and yields in t/ha, with little loss of generality. The modified exponential function is particularly convenient for fitting to series of experiments when the response function is roughly constant in shape but varies in location. A possible underlying model is the modified logistic function. Current experimental data is inadequate to test this. A curve fitting approach to the examination of response data allows much more flexibility than does an analysis of variance approach, and does not contain the same implication of constant horizontal location of the response function. In addition, it allows the response function to be described in terms of a limited number of parameters with possible biological interpretation. Differences between fitted response functions for experiments in a series may be expressed simply in terms of the maximum yield and the corresponding level of applied nitrogen, or similar quantities for any required economic yield criterion. Series of experiments intended to be examined by curve fitting may be arranged in a flexible way. Ideally, each experiment should be capable of analysis independently, should span the expected maximum for the site, and should contain direct replication of some applied nitrogen levels. The residual error term may then be partitioned to provide tests of lack of fit of the model.

References

ANDERSON, R.L. and NELSON, L.A. 1975. A family of models involving intersecting straight lines and concomitant experimental designs useful in evaluating the response to fertiliser nutrients. *Biometrics* **31**, 303–318.

BALMUKAND, Bh. 1928. Studies in crop variation. V The relation between yield and soil nutrients. *Journal of Agricultural Science* **18**, 602–627.

BOYD. D.A. 1972. Some recent ideas on fertiliser response curves. Proceedings of the 9th International Congress of the Potash Institute, 461–473.

BOYD, D.A., YUEN, L.T.K. and NEEDHAM, P. 1976. Nitrogen requirement of cereals. I. Response Curves. *Journal of Agricultural Science* **87**, 149–162.

BULLEN, E.R. and LESSELS, W.J. 1957. The effect of nitrogen on cereal yields. *Journal of Agricultural Science* **49**, 319–328.

CROWTHER, E.M. and YATES, F. 1941. Fertiliser policy in war-time. *Empire Journal of Experimental Agriculture* **9**, 77–97.

GREENWOOD, D.J., WOOD, J.T., CLEAVER, T.J. and HUNT, J. 1971. A theory for fertiliser response. *Journal of Agricultural Science* **77**, 511–523.

INKSON, R.H.E. 1966. Field experiments to estimate optimum fertiliser levels. *Plant and Soil* **24**, 447–453.

LESSELS, W.J. and WEBBER, J. 1965. The effect of nitrogen on spring cereals. *Experimental Husbandry* **12**, 62–73.

LESSELS, W.J. and WEBBER, J. 1965. The effect of nitrogen on winter wheat. *Experimental Husbandry* **12**, 74–88.

NELDER, J.A. 1966. Inverse polynomials, a useful group of multi-factor response functions. *Biometrics* **22**, 128–141.

SPARROW, P.E. 1979. Nitrogen response curves of spring barley. *Journal of Agricultural Science* **92**, 307–317.

WIMBLE, R.H. 1980. Theoretical basis of fertiliser recommendations. *Chemistry and Industry* **17**, 680–683.

YATES, F. 1966. A fresh look at the basic principles of the design and analysis of experiments. *Proceedings of the Fifth Berkeley Symposium of Mathematical Statistics and Probability*, 770–790.

Discussion

Dr Hughes said that the 'catastrophic zone' was evident in many of the results of the recent cereal trials. He asked if there was more replication within each block, would this show that the points above the curve were subject to a greater degree of error. Mr George replied that catastrophes would occur on all replicates. However, with more replication of the high nitrogen treatments it would be possible to estimate variance directly. Unfortunately the higher nitrogen treatments were unstable figures, and in excess of the general nitrogen recommendations, but it would be desirable to have replication of the high rates within each block.

Dr Jenkinson asked if there were different types of catastrophe, for example, pests or lodging. He also asked if local variations in soil fertility were important. Mr George replied that it was unlikely that catastrophe was due to different levels of fertility within a trial site. Catastrophe or erratic behaviour is not noticeable on the lower part of the response curve. Erratic behaviour is only noticed on the part of the curve above the optimum, and therefore unlikely to be due to changes in soil fertility.

Dr Batey asked if the same sort of catastrophe occurred in other crops, for example grass where only vegetative growth was measured. The lower part of the curve was associated with vegetative growth and therefore a direct response to nitrogen. Mr George replied that he had no experience as to the response of grass to nitrogen. However, the results quoted in the paper were part of a rotational experiment, involving sugar beet, potatoes and spring barley. The sugar beet showed similar response characteristics to wheat.

Mr Lidgate asked if catastrophe was too strong a word. He also stated that on the part of the curve above the optimum, nitrogen was no longer the limiting factor to yield. Mr George replied that he has tried to define catastrophe as a naturally occurring phenomenon, not as a disaster.

Dr Tinker asked if the response curve to other nutrients had been studied. Mr George replied that as yet he had not studied the effect of other nutrients and obviously this required further work.

Mr Whitear said that in an analysis of variance each plot contributes an equal amount of error. From this approach, did the amount of error increase at higher yields. Mr George said that the changes in variance were not smooth. Values for variance were quoted in the paper, and there was an abrupt change in the variance at or above the optimum nitrogen level. The variance values were much less at the lower nitrogen rates.

Mr Wadsworth asked if shapes of the response curve would be same from trials carried out on apparently similar sites, where there were differences in both yield and optimum nitrogen level. Mr George replied that if experiments were conducted on similar sites then one would expect similar shapes in the response curve.

The response of winter wheat to nitrogen

R Sylvester-Bradley, P M R Dampney
ADAS Wolverhampton

A W A Murray
Rothamsted Experimental Station, Harpenden

Summary

In order to assess the nitrogen requirement of winter wheat 142 experiments were considered in which grain yields had been measured over a range of nitrogen levels. The experiments were conducted throughout England and Wales between 1977 and 1981. A curve was fitted to the yields from each trial, and where possible the level of nitrogen (N-opt) beyond which additional nitrogen would not repay its cost, was calculated. This level is taken to be the nitrogen requirement to obtain maximum returns from fertiliser nitrogen.

There was no response to applied nitrogen in 11 trials and in 46 trials extrapolation showed N-opt to be greater than the maximum level tested (normally 200 kg/ha). A method of estimating the standard error of N-opt is presented. Confidence in N-opt was found to be low in some trials, especially where N-opt approached the maximum level tested.

The ranges of both N-opt and rate of response to nitrogen were large in all years and variation cannot be adequately explained by estimates of residual soil nitrogen (N Index), or seasonal differences in weather. Estimates of N-opt tend to be higher in trials where the yield without any nitrogen (Y_0) was low. There are also indications that N-opt tends to be higher on sandy or shallow soils than on other types of soils. The values of N-opt indicate that, over all N Indices and soil types, an application of 175 kg/ha of nitrogen would have been economic on about half the crops tested.

The trials also compared a number of timing regimes for application of the nitrogen. Applying 40 kg/ha of the total nitrogen during tillering rarely resulted in a yield reduction and showed a good chance of a yield increase, especially where Y_0 was low. Applying 40 to 50 kg/ha of the total nitrogen at flag leaf emergence or later resulted in few yield increases and often led to a reduction in yield, especially where the estimate of N-opt was above the range of dressings which were split. Division of the total amount of nitrogen between three applications never showed a clear yield advantage over two applications or a single application.

In a further 31 trials, carried out between 1975 and 1976 to measure the effects of foliar urea sprays applied at or after flowering, statistically significant yield effects were infrequent and small.

Introduction

Economic returns from applying nitrogen to winter wheat are usually large. However, the response of winter wheat to nitrogen fertiliser is notoriously variable. This variation has been attributed to differences in weather, soil, variety, yield and husbandry factors but has so far eluded accurate prediction.

For many years field experiments on commercial crops have been carried out by ADAS Soil Science Departments and Experimental Husbandry Farms in England and Wales. Most of these experiments have formed parts of national series which have identical treatments and design. The experiments were intended to identify the optimum level and timing of application of nitrogen and the major factors causing variation in response between different sites and different seasons. Advice on nitrogen fertiliser use (MAFF, 1981) given by ADAS is largely based on the results of such experiments. Recommendations are currently adjusted according to soil type and nitrogen Index. The nitrogen Index of a soil is based on previous cropping and use of organic manures (MAFF, 1981); see also Needham (1984) in this volume (pages 245–254).

This paper summarises the results of three series of experiments carried out between 1975 and 1981. The variation between sites in yield response to applied nitrogen is discussed and an attempt made to identify the major factors causing this variation. None of the experiments considered in this paper were conducted in the same field in successive years so direct assessment of seasonal variation is not possible. The experiments were set up to examine effects on grain quality as well as yield. However, only the effects on yield are considered in this paper.

Design of experiments

The object, treatments and design of the four series of experiments reported are given below. Table 1 shows the seasons in which experiments were carried out. All growth stages are according to the system of Zadoks *et al.* (1974).

Table 1 Number of trials per year in each series of experiments

| | | Harvest year | | | | | | | |
		1975	1976	1977	1978	1979	1980	1981	Total
SS.68	Late foliar urea sprays for winter wheat	11	11	9	–	–	–	–	31
SS.76	Late nitrogen top-dressing for winter wheat	–	–	21	26	2	–	–	49
'Marathon series'	Nitrogen for winter wheat	–	–	–	–	–	–	12	12
SA.92	Timing of nitrogen	–	–	–	–	21	32	28	81

SS.68 – Late foliar urea sprays for winter wheat

This series of experiments was designed to examine the effects of late foliar sprays of urea nitrogen. Treatments consisted of all combinations of:
1. three levels of granular nitrogen (selected to span the expected optimum) applied at GS 31
2. four levels of foliar urea (0, 20, 40, 60 kg/ha urea N in 500 litres/ha water)
3. two times of application of foliar urea – GS 65 (anthesis) and GS 75 (milky ripe)

At each site there were two replicates of each treatment arranged in randomised blocks.

This series of experiments was not designed to determine the optimum level of nitrogen top-dressing.

SS.76 – Late nitrogen for winter wheat

This series of experiments was designed to determine the optimum level of nitrogen top-dressing and the effect of late applications of nitrogen. Treatments consisted of nine levels of nitrogen (0 to 200 kg/ha in increments of 25 kg/ha) applied as a single dressing at GS 31; additionally the upper five levels were applied as two different two-way split applications as follows:
1. 50 kg/ha at GS 37 to 39 (flag leaf emergence) and the balance at GS 31
2. 50 kg/ha at GS 45 to 50 (booting) and the balance at GS 31

At each site there were two replicates of each treatment arranged in randomised blocks.

'Marathon series' – Nitrogen for winter wheat

This series of experiments was designed to determine the optimum level of nitrogen top-dressing. Treatments consisted of seven levels of nitrogen (0, 80, 120, 160, 200, 240 and 280 kg/ha) applied as a single application at GS 31. There were three replicates of each treatment. These trials were carried out in 1981 in East Anglia.

SA.92 – Timing of nitrogen for winter wheat

This series of experiments was designed to determine the optimum level of nitrogen top-dressing and the effect of single, two-way and three-way split applications of nitrogen. Treatments consisted of a range of nitrogen levels (either 0 to 200 kg/ha in 25 kg/ha increments or 0 to 240 in 40 kg/ha increments) applied as a single application at GS 31 (first node detectable); additionally the upper five levels of nitrogen (100 to 200 kg/ha or 80 to 240 kg/ha) were each applied as different split applications as follows:
1. 40 kg/ha at GS 21 to 25 (tillering) and the balance at GS 31
2. 40 kg/ha at GS 39 (flag leaf visible) and the balance at GS 31
3. 40 kg/ha at GS 21 to 25, 40 kg/ha at GS 39 and the balance at GS 31

At each site there were two replicates of each treatment arranged in randomised blocks.

153

Experimental technique

With the exception of trials carried out at Experimental Husbandry Farms, all trials were carried out with the co-operation of farmers and were superimposed on commercial farm crops. Because of the need to select sites where the farmer was able to accommodate trial work it is likely that a high proportion of the trials were located on farms of better than average management. Many of the results are presented as frequency distributions and it must be borne in mind that these are not from an unbiased selection of wheat crops. This should be taken into account before any recommendations are made. Sites were selected to be of uniform soil type and plant establishment. Plot size was usually between 50 and 100 m². All nitrogen fertiliser was applied by hand and yields assessed either by farm or small plot combine harvester and adjusted to 85 per cent dry matter. Weed, disease and pest control measures at most sites were usually carried out by the farmer, according to his normal practice.

Soil type

The soil type at each experimental site was described and at most sites classified according to soil series. The trials covered a wide range of soils and to simplify analysis of the data these have been divided into five broad groups. These are:
Heavy clay soils
Shallow or sandy soils
Alluvial soils
Loamy soils with permeable subsoil
Loamy soils with relatively impermeable subsoil

Rainfall

Rainfall data were provided by the Meterological Office and are from the nearest available rain gauge to each site. This was usually within 8 kilometres of the trial.

Statistical methods

For the purposes of this investigation, the nitrogen requirement, or economic optimum (N-opt), is that level of applied nitrogen at which the rate of response reaches 3 kg of grain per kg of nitrogen applied. This arbitrary cut-off point was chosen because, at present prices 3 kg of grain would purchase about 1 kg of fertiliser nitrogen. In order to estimate such an optimum, the yield must be expressed as some smooth function of the applied nitrogen. This function can then be differentiated to give its slope at any point and the level of applied nitrogen for which the slope is equal to the chosen cut-off value of 3:1 can be found.

Choice of function

In summarising the results of large series of experiments, such as those reported here, it is desirable to adopt a consistent procedure for the analysis of each separate experiment. Therefore, the same form of function has been chosen to model the response of yield to nitrogen at each site. Inspection of a large number of scatter diagrams of yield against applied nitrogen suggested the need for a response function which is concave downwards and need not be symmetric about its maximum. For the latter reason, the popular quadratic polynomials which are necessarily symmetrical are clearly unsuitable models for these data.

In view of the large number of sites involved in this study and limitations on the computing resources available, an important consideration in the choice of model was speed and simplicity of computation. Thus, it was not feasible to make use of non-linear models requiring iterative methods of solution. For this reason, the otherwise attractive inverse polynomials (Nelder, 1966) could not be fitted.

The chosen form is an exponential plus linear function of applied nitrogen, giving the model

$$Y = a + br^N + cN$$

where Y is the yield of grain in t/ha, N is the applied fertiliser nitrogen in kg/ha, r is a predetermined constant, and a, b and c are parameters of the model whose values are found by a least squares fit for each site. This modified exponential model has been extensively used in similar investigations (Boyd *et al.,* 1976 and Sparrow, 1979) and is discussed also by George (1984) in a paper elsewhere in this volume (pages 133–148). Fixing the value of r avoids problems of non-linear fitting. The value of r has been set at 0.99 as, in a large number of data sets with a range of values for r, this value gives consistently good fits for cereal yield responses to nitrogen and is close to the best value for many data sets of this type. The shapes generated by fitting this model are illustrated in Figure 1 for negative values of b, (the coefficient of the exponential term). A negative value of c (the coefficient of the linear term) gives a descending asymptote and a clearly defined maximum, whereas a positive value for this parameter gives a continuously increasing function. If the slope of a positive asymptote exceeds the 3:1 ratio then no optimum, in the sense defined above, will be reached.

Ten trials had very low yields or variable data and were omitted from further consideration. Of the remaining 132 trials, 121 were fitted by a function with negative values of b; of these the majority had negative values of c. Table 2 shows the categories of fit obtained and the number of trials in each. Other than the trials with extremely variable data, only 11 trials gave curves which were either flat, through lack of response to nitrogen, or had ever increasing slope (that is positive b).

The value of applied nitrogen which gives the optimum yield is found from the expression

$$\text{N-opt} = \frac{\ln (k - c) - \ln (b\ln r)}{\ln r}$$

where k is the arbitrary cut-off point; here k = 0.003 (since yield is in t/ha).

Because N-opt is a non-linear function of b and c, it is a biased estimator for the true economic optimum in the sense that the average value of the difference between N-opt and the true optimum is not zero. Using Taylor series approximations (Cox and Hinkley, 1974), estimators for the bias and the variance of N-opt were calculated. To do this certain assumptions must be made

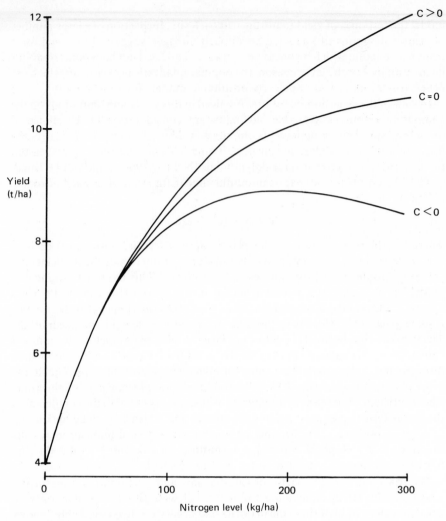

Fig. 1 Typical exponential plus linear response curves.

regarding the distributions of $\hat{b}$ and $\hat{c}$, the estimators for b and c. If the errors were normally distributed then $\hat{b}$ and $\hat{c}$ would also be normal, but a true normal distribution would involve very large values that would invalidate the Taylor series approximation. It is therefore assumed that the distributions of both $\hat{b}$ and $k-\hat{c}$ are normal, but truncated on either side at the points three standard deviations from the mean. It is also assumed that for both distributions the ratio σ/μ is small enough for $(\sigma/\mu)^4$ to be ignored.

Under these assumptions an unbiased estimator of the economic optimum is

$$\text{N-true} = \text{N-opt} + \left[\frac{s_c^2}{(k-c)^2} - \frac{s_b^2}{b^2} \right] \bigg/ 2 \ln r$$

and an unbiased estimator of the variance of both N-opt and N-true is

156

$$V = \left[\frac{s_c^2}{(k-c)^2} + \frac{s_b^2}{b^2} + \frac{2s_{bc}^2}{(k-c)^b} \right] \bigg/ (\ln r)^2$$

Here s_c^2, s_b^2, s_{bc}^2 respectively denote the variance of c, variance of b, and covariance of b and c, as estimated from the data. The formula for V is plausible since it shows that V increases when s_c^2, s_b^2, s_{bc}^2 increase (that is where the data are more variable) and when (k–c) becomes small (that is where the slope of the curve is changing very slowly in the region of the economic optimum).

Table 2 Number of trials in various categories of model fit (SS.76 and SA.92)

Fit	Location of N-opt	Number of trials
Yield very low (max.<4.5 t/ha)	–	3
Data too variable for fitting model	–	7
No response to applied N	0	9
Positive b and positive c	>maximum level tested	2
Negative b and:	(estimated from curve by expression for N-opt)	
c>0.003	>maximum level tested	33
0<c<0.003	estimate within range	4
	>maximum level tested	10
c<0	estimate within range	72
	>maximum level tested	1
	0	1

If either of the distributions for $\hat{b}$ and $k-\hat{c}$ were to have $|\sigma/\mu| > 1/3$, then negative values of b ln r or (k–c) could theoretically occur. Since the ln function is defined for positive values only, N-opt would not be defined for such values. Hence, the above formulae for N-true and V are not really appropriate if either of $S_c / (k-c)$ or $S_b /-b$ be greater than 1/3. This occurred at only a small number of trials.

In the analysis of each experiment the degrees of freedom for the nitrogen treatment effect were partitioned into 1 degree of freedom for a constant (a), 2 degrees of freedom for the curve (b and c) and the remainder, which was considered to be a measure of the lack of fit of the model. Trials with a serious lack of fit have not been considered further. The SS.76 and SA.92 series of experiments included treatments intended to explore the effects of different timing of fertiliser application. For both series, curves have been fitted to the mean over timing treatments and blocks at each level of nitrogen.

In the SS.76 experiments, the timing treatment involved delaying 50 kg/ha of applied nitrogen from the time of the main application until May or June, or applying all the nitrogen at the usual time. This has been analysed to give two contrasts: (i) single dressing vs. mean of split dressings and (ii) May vs. June (within split dressings). Interactions of these effects with nitrogen level were also examined.

In the SA.92 experiments, the timing treatments are best considered as a 2×2 factorial combination of (i) 0 or 40 kg/ha (out of the total nitrogen) applied early, hereafter called 'early split nitrogen' and (ii) 0 or 40 kg/ha (out of the total nitrogen) applied late, hereafter called 'late split nitrogen'. This enables the data to be analysed to give single degree of freedom sums of squares for main effects (that is average over the presence and absence of the other factor) of early or late split nitrogen and for the interaction between early and late split nitrogen (that is any non-additivity in their effects). Again, interactions of the timing factors with nitrogen level were examined. Appropriate standard errors were calculated from the residual mean square at each trial.

At this stage in our investigation no attempt has yet been made to fit separate curves at the different levels of timing factors as might be suggested in the presence of nitrogen $\times$ timing interactions at some sites. The results presented here are the effects of the timing treatments averaged over the levels of nitrogen, together with an indication of where this procedure may be misleading.

Analysis of SS.68 trials

The SS.68 foliar urea trials have been examined by analysis of variance to determine the effects of timing and rate of application of urea. To this end the 6 degrees of freedom for timing $\times$ urea have been broken down to give 1 degree of freedom each for linear, quadratic and cubic orthogonal components of level of application, 1 degree of freedom for timing and 2 degrees of freedom for timing $\times$ level interactions. The components for level of application can be interpreted as characterising the shape of the response to urea rather than as providing a predictive equation. Mean squares for main effects of solid nitrogen fertiliser at (usually) three levels and the interactions of this nitrogen with the timing $\times$ urea factor were also obtained from the analysis-of-variance table.

Precision of nitrogen requirements

In any determination of nitrogen requirement, estimates of N-opt should be treated with reserve where: the data are very variable, the rate of change of slope is small in the region of N-opt, or N-opt lies close to the ends of the range of nitrogen levels tested.

The experimenter has only partial control over these conditions. Hence, values of N-opt are subject to varying degrees of confidence. The standard error calculated for each N-opt in this investigation reflects the first two sources of uncertainty (Figure 2). Highly variable trials were excluded from the investigation altogether, but in Figure 2 a few trials remain which have a standard error of similar size to their N-opt. In these trials, although the model is a good fit, the shape of the curve is very flat.

Standard errors for many trials are acceptable but for optima close to 200 kg/ha (the usual maximum level in these trials) they are often over 20 kg/ha. Most of the low standard errors in this area relate to the 'Marathon' trials which tested levels up to 280 kg/ha. In future experiments it would be desirable to be

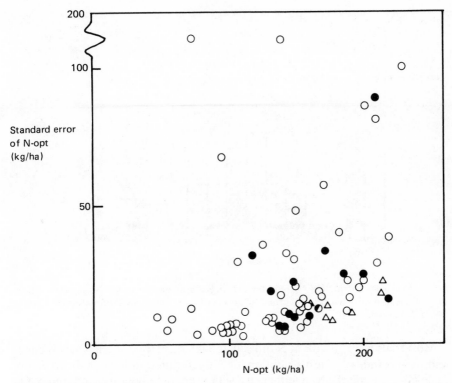

Fig. 2 Standard errors of estimates of nitrogen requirement (N-opt) for trials with maximum applied nitrogen levels of 200 (O), 240 (●) and 280 (Δ) kg/ha.

able to distinguish differences in N-opt of 40 kg/ha or less. It will therefore be necessary to alter the designs of future trials, especially where optima are likely to be high.

It has already been mentioned that the model has been fitted to the means of all timings. Where there are real interactions between timing and level of nitrogen, the effect of fitting to means is to distort the curve from the shape which would be obtained were the timing effects constant over all nitrogen levels. Consequently, the distortion alters the estimate of N-opt from that given by a fit to one timing regime only. There are 18 trials out of 120 which show statistically significant interactions and several more which show a similar pattern of response, though the interaction terms were not judged significant. These effects will be discussed in more detail later, but it must be recognised when considering estimates of N-opt that the 16 examples of interaction with late split nitrogen tend to cause overestimation of N-opt compared with the nitrogen requirement for the best timing treatment, and in the two trials showing interactions with early split nitrogen the tendency is for underestimation.

Variation in nitrogen requirements

The values of N-opt vary widely between trials (Figure 3) and in a third of the trials the requirement apparently exceeded the maximum level tested.

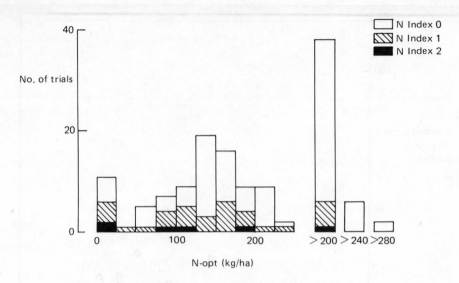

N-opt (kg/ha)

Fig. 3 Frequency distribution of N-opt for 132 trials according to N Index. N-opt values greater than 200 kg/ha were derived from the small number of trials (35) which included nitrogen levels up to 240 or 280 kg/ha.

Most trials were on soils at N Index 0, though there were 32 trials at N Index 1, and six at N Index 2. The distributions of N-opt for these different indices (Figure 3) do not differ markedly and there is a wide range of N-opt for each N Index. On a quarter of trials at N Index 1 and 2, N-opt apparently exceeded 200 kg/ha, compared with a half of trials at N Index 0. Eleven trials do not show any statistically significant effect of nitrogen on yield and only half of these were at N Index 1 or 2.

For trials where N-opt can be estimated the mean slope of the response curve between zero applied nitrogen and N-opt varies (Figure 4) but most are between 12 and 24 kg grain per kg nitrogen, demonstrating that the use of nitrogen fertiliser is usually very profitable.

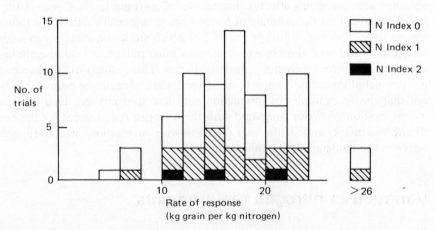

Rate of response
(kg grain per kg nitrogen)

Fig. 4 Frequency distribution of the mean slope of the response curve between N-zero and N-opt from trials where N-opt was estimated.

160

In order to distinguish among trials in which N-opt exceeds the maximum level of nitrogen tested, the mean slope between 160 and 200 kg/ha for each trial is shown in Figure 5. Most trials have a slope considerably greater than the 'break even' slope of 3 kg grain per kg of nitrogen and for some the slope is almost 20 kg/kg.

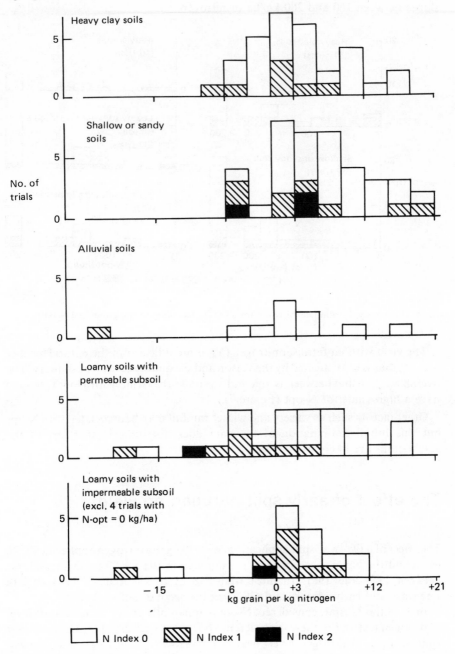

Fig. 5 Frequency distribution of the mean slope of response curve between 160 and 200 kg/ha nitrogen for all trials, according to soil groups and nitrogen Index.

Examination of the relationship between soil group and N-opt (Figure 6) or slope of the response curve between 160 and 200 kg N/ha (Figure 5) shows a distinction between shallow or sandy soils and the other soil groups. The shallow or sandy soils in these trials appear to be the soils on which there was most response to nitrogen, with a high proportion of such trials having steep positive slopes between 160 and 200 kg/ha of nitrogen.

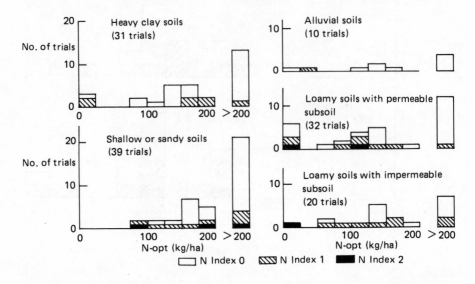

Fig. 6   Frequency distributions of N-opt for all trials according to soil group and N Index.

The yield without fertiliser nitrogen (Y_0) is an indicator of the natural fertility of a site, but is also affected by the season and the quality of crop husbandry. The overall relationship between N-opt and Y_0 shows that trials with a low Y_0 tend to have a high value for N-opt (Figure 7).

Other factors such as variety and winter rainfall may be associated with N-opt but this initial examination of the data does not indicate that any of the associations are likely to be close.

The effect of early split nitrogen on yield

The effect of a two-way split application, with 40 kg/ha nitrogen applied at GS 21 to 25 and the balance at GS 31, was examined in the SA.92 series carried out between 1979 and 1981. In most trials GS 21 to 25 occurred between late February and early March, and GS 31 in the second half of April.

In 32 of the 72 trials considered, N-opt is apparently above the maximum level of nitrogen tested. For these trials, it is not possible to be sure of the effect of early split nitrogen at nitrogen levels near N-opt. However, only two trials show a significant nitrogen timing × level interaction, though both show a higher rate of response where early nitrogen was applied. Therefore, in the following

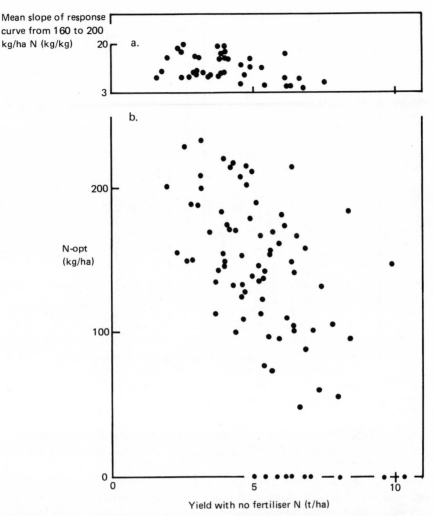

Mean slope of response curve from 160 to 200 kg/ha N (kg/kg)

N-opt (kg/ha)

Yield with no fertiliser N (t/ha)

Fig. 7a Mean slope of response curve from 160 to 200 kg/ha nitrogen according to grain yield without fertiliser nitrogen for trials where N-opt was in excess of the maximum level tested.
Fig. 7b N-opt according to grain yield without fertiliser nitrogen.

discussion, it is assumed that the effect of early split nitrogen below the maximum level tested was the same below and in the vicinity of N-opt.

Statistically significant effects ($P<0.05$ for all and $P<0.01$ for many) were detected in 30 trials. Of these effects 22 are yield increases from early split nitrogen and eight are yield decreases. In the remaining 42 trials any effect which might have existed could not be distinguished from random error, the inference being that there was no effect in these trials.

At several sites a visible effect from early nitrogen application was noted though this did not necessarily result in a yield increase. At a few sites where lodging occurred it was also noted that the lodging was worse where early nitrogen had been applied. The magnitude of the yield difference is generally small (Figure 8) and usually less than 0.5 t/ha. With one exception all yield increases of more than 0.5 t/ha occurred in 1980.

163

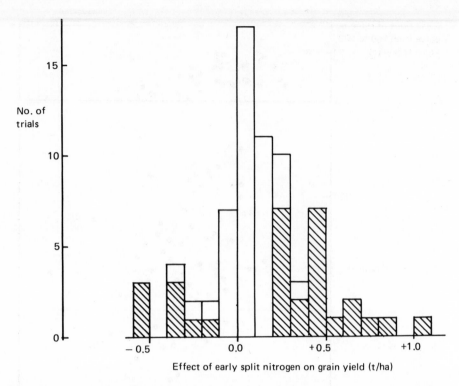

Fig. 8 Frequency distribution of the yield differences due to early split nitrogen. Differences significant at the level $P = 0.05$ are shaded.

Figure 9 shows the effect of early split nitrogen in each year, and according to the N Index of each trial. Yield increases were more common in 1980 and 1981 than in 1979. For trials at N Index 0, substantial positive responses were especially frequent in 1980. This was very likely due to the dry April and May in this year, with less than 25 mm rain at many sites over the two months. At many trials there was less than 10 mm rain between the main nitrogen application at GS 31 and mid-May. It may be that some of the yield increases resulting from early split nitrogen in 1980 were due to the delayed activity and reduced effectiveness of the main nitrogen application rather than to any characteristic of the site or crop causing a direct benefit from early split nitrogen. This effect illustrates that the application of early nitrogen may reduce any yield loss resulting from dry spring weather. With one exception, all yield increases were from crops grown at N Index 0. In 21 out of 58 trials at N Index 0 there was a yield increase from early split nitrogen compared with only one out of 14 trials at N Index 1 and 2. Of the eight trials where a yield decrease was recorded, five were at N Index 0 and 3 at N Index 1 or 2.

Examples of yield increase can be found in all soil groups (Figure 10), though more frequently on heavy clay soils and shallow or sandy soils. The shallow or sandy soils also tend to give larger responses to applied nitrogen than any other group of soils. However, six of the eight trials where a yield decrease was recorded were also on shallow or sandy soils. Of these, three trials were at N Index 0 and their early nitrogen was applied between late February and early

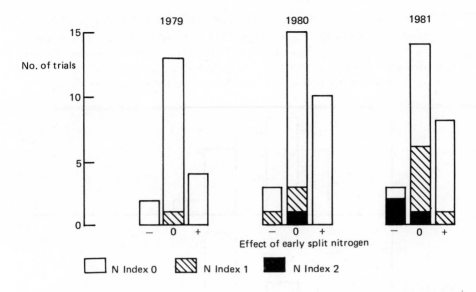

Fig. 9 Frequency distribution of trials showing yield increases, (+) and decreases (–) from early split nitrogen, and these where effects are not statistically significant (0), according to year and N Index.

March, followed by between 100 and 145 mm rain in March. It is possible that leaching of the early applied nitrogen occurred, resulting in a yield decrease compared with an equivalent single application in April. There were other trials, however, on these soil types and with similar amounts of early spring rainfall after application of early nitrogen, where no yield decrease was recorded. Of the eight trials that showed a yield decrease, optima in two were below 100 kg/ha and in five were above 200 kg/ha. Hence, yield reduction from use of early split nitrogen dressings can occur where a large response to nitrogen would be expected.

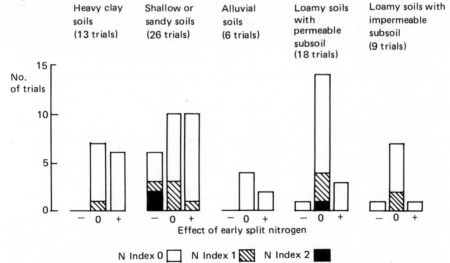

Fig. 10 Frequency distribution of trials showing yield increases (+) and decreases (–) from early split nitrogen and those where effects are not statistically significant (0), according to soil group and N Index.

165

The response to early split nitrogen is apparently related to Y_0 (yield when no nitrogen fertiliser was applied, see Figure 11). More sites gave a yield increase to early split nitrogen where Y_0 was low, and those sites where a yield decrease was recorded generally had a higher Y_0. This relationship provides further evidence linking response to applied nitrogen with Y_0 as suggested also by Figure 7.

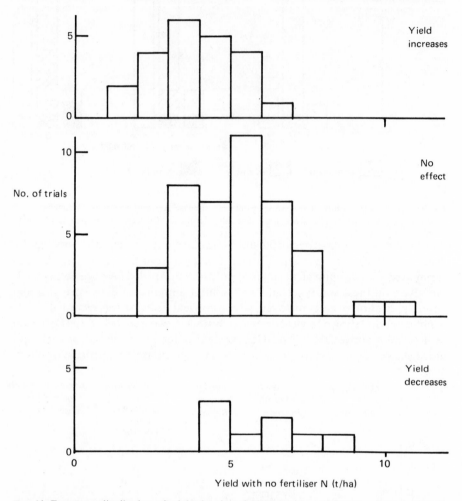

Fig. 11 Frequency distribution of trials showing yield increases and decreases from early split nitrogen and those where effects are not statistically significant, according to yield without fertiliser nitrogen.

The effects of late split nitrogen on yield

Late split applications of nitrogen were tested in the SA.76 and SA.92 series of experiments, covering the years 1977 to 1981, giving in total 120 trials. In SA.76 two late applications were tested, one at GS 37 to 39 and the other at GS 45 to 50. These were normally applied in May and June. Effects have been assessed by comparing the single dressing in April with the mean of both split dressings (late

166

split nitrogen). Comparisons between the two split dressings (delay of late split nitrogen) are described in a subsequent section, but statistically significant differences are rare.

In SA.92 only one late application, made at full emergence of the flag leaf (GS 39), was tested. This normally occurred in either late May or early June. Effects of late split nitrogen seldom interacted significantly with effects of early split nitrogen. Where such interactions occurred the effect of late split nitrogen has been assessed by comparison with the single dressing only but, in the absence of any interaction, the effect of late split nitrogen is the average over both levels of early split nitrogen.

The frequency of detectable yield effects of late split nitrogen depends on the position of N-opt relative to the range of dressings which were split (Figure 12).

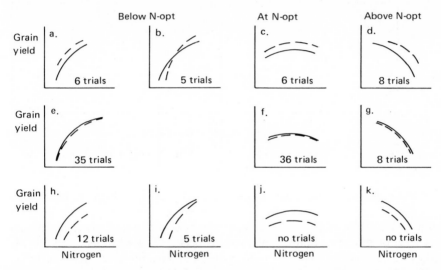

Fig. 12 Diagrams of different responses to nitrogen with (---) and without (—) late split nitrogen according to whether the range of split dressings was below, near or above N-opt. The number of trials showing yield increases (a, b, c, d) and decreases (h, i, j, k) to late split nitrogen and those where effects are not statistically significant (e, f, g) is given for each category. The trial at Bedworth in 1978 is included in both i and d (see Figure 13).

Of the 63 trials where split dressings were tested at nitrogen levels less than N-opt in total, 17 gave reductions in yield, and 11 showed increases. Split dressings tested at nitrogen levels close to optimum seldom give statistically significant effects; there were no reductions and six increases in yield from 42 trials. In trials where split dressings were tested at nitrogen levels greater than N-opt in total, eight out of 16 gave yield increases with late split nitrogen; no decreases were detected. However, the levels of yield attained in these circumstances never exceeded the yield from a single dressing at the optimum level: the effect was rather to maintain yield which otherwise declined from any single dressing in excess of N-opt.

Most effects, both above and below N-opt, appear to be due to a reduction in the quantity applied in April rather than to any direct effect of nitrogen applied late. A good example of this effect of late split nitrogen occurred at Bedworth, Warwickshire in 1978 (Figure 13).

167

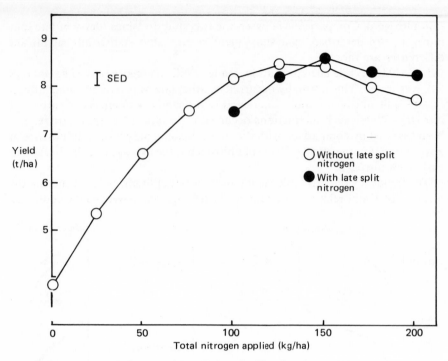

Fig. 13 Response curves from a trial at Bedworth, Warwickshire in 1978 showing a typical nitrogen × timing interaction from late split nitrogen.

In this trial the late split nitrogen caused a reduction in yield below N-opt, had little effect on yield at N-opt, and increased yield above N-opt. In the analysis of variance the effect shows as a significant interaction between late split nitrogen and level of nitrogen. Similar interactions occurred at 15 other trials. In the following discussion trials with statistically significant interactions are included with trials showing overall reductions in yield from late split nitrogen; those showing detectable yield increases at nitrogen levels above N-opt have been excluded.

Increased yield from late split nitrogen below or around N-opt must be due to a beneficial effect from applying some nitrogen late instead of applying the same amount in April. Any reduction in yield, however, suggests that late nitrogen has been relatively ineffective; the alternative explanation, that the late nitrogen has a deleterious effect, seems less likely. Thus there are 17 trials where late split nitrogen was 'effective' and 17 where it was 'ineffective'. Yield reductions occurred in only two trials on clay or deep alluvial soils, whereas yield increases were more frequent on these soil types (Figure 14). There were few yield reductions in 1979 or 1981 (years with high rainfall in early summer and dry in July) whereas yield increases occurred in all years (Figure 14). However, responses do not appear to be directly linked to monthly amounts of rain. There was no apparent difference in the effectiveness of late split nitrogen according to the N Index or the maximum yield achieved.

It is concluded that late nitrogen tends to be less effective than nitrogen applied in April. The frequency of a yield increase from late split nitrogen is less than one in five and only one in eight at levels of nitrogen below optimum. Yield

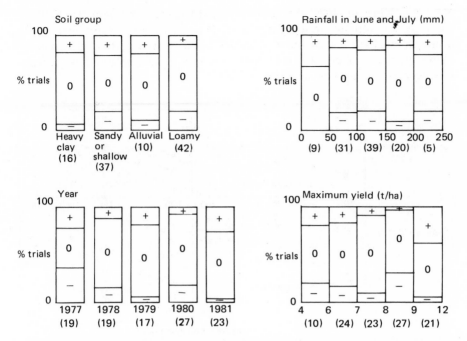

Fig. 14 Frequencies with which late split nitrogen was effective (+), had no statistically significant effect (0), or was ineffective (–), according to soil group, summer rainfall, season, and maximum yield. The number of trials in each category is shown in brackets. For definition of effectiveness see the text.

reductions were rare at levels close to optimum, but there was a high risk of yield loss when late split nitrogen was used and the total nitrogen application was less than N-opt. In view of these conclusions, and the difficulty in predicting N-opt from known characteristics of the sites (see earlier), the use of late split nitrogen in normal commercial practice would appear unwise.

Delay of late applications

Out of 46 trials in the SS.76 series from 1977 to 1979, in which a delay of the late split nitrogen from GS 37 to 39 until GS 45 to 50 was tested, 30 showed yield reductions but only four of these were statistically significant. Only one trial showed a signficant benefit (0.45 t/ha) over both other timings of nitrogen. Another trial had significantly higher yields than the late split nitrogen applied at GS 37 to 39, but this was not significantly higher than the single dressing in April.

Interactions between early and late split nitrogen

The presence of a statistically significant interaction between the two timing regimes in eight trials demonstrates differences in the effect of late split nitrogen, depending on whether early split nitrogen had been applied (Figure 15). The pattern of this interaction is not consistent and in some cases (e.g. the Llancadle site in 1981) its statistical significance probably only reflects unusually low error variance. Late split nitrogen with early split nitrogen (three way split nitrogen) generally reduced yield below N-opt but gave similar yields in the vicinity of

N-opt (e.g. Kingston, 1979). At only two trials (Llancadle and Scunthorpe in 1980), was three way split nitrogen slightly better than other timings. Most interactions occurred on shallow soils and all occurred in the west or north of the country. However, it is not possible with these few sites to discern any link between interactions and growing conditions.

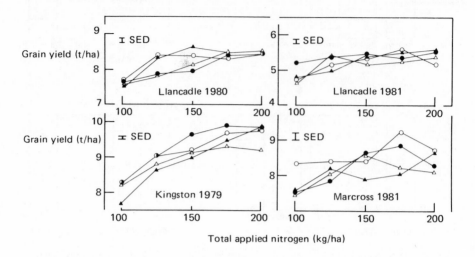

Fig. 15a Effect of nitrogen on grain yield where there was no overall effect of early split nitrogen but there were interactions with late split nitrogen. Single application (o), early split nitrogen only (△), late split nitrogen only (●), and three–way split nitrogen (▲).

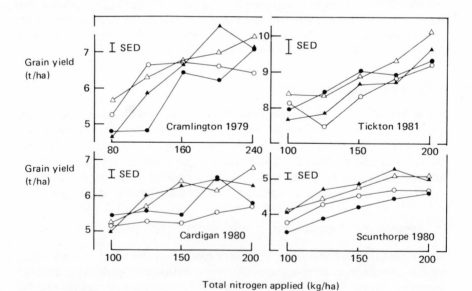

Fig. 15b Effect of nitrogen on grain yield where there was an overall effect of early split nitrogen but there were interactions with late split nitrogen. Symbols as for Figure 15a.

170

Effects of late foliar sprays of urea

Urea sprays were tested at anthesis (GS 65) and a fortnight later (GS 75) in 32 trials between 1975 and 1977 (series SS.68). The main purpose of these trials was to assess effects on grain quality but effects on yield were also recorded and are considered here. The levels of nitrogen at GS 31 were set to straddle the expected optimum level at each site. Unfortunately optima were successfully predicted in only six trials; the 12 trials in 1976 all had low optima due to the exceptionally dry and hot conditions, and optima in most other trials were underestimated.

The first urea spray (GS 65) caused some scorch of flag leaves in almost all trials, especially at the highest urea concentration (60 kg/ha in 500 litres; i.e. 27 per cent w/v), but in only one trial was there a statistically significant reduction in yield (0.24 t/ha). Flag leaf area was never reduced by more than 40 per cent and with the two lower concentrations of urea (9 per cent and 18 per cent w/v) the worst scorch was 20 per cent. The 14 sites which were scored for scorch showed a mean reduction in flag leaf area of 10 per cent from all concentrations of urea, compared with the control. All three years were dry in July and flag leaves were usually senescing when the second spray was applied. Scorch effects from the second spray were, therefore, difficult to discern. Although effects of scorch on yield were infrequent in these trials they should not be ignored. Yields were generally low; mean yields for the three years were 5.5, 4.7, and 5.7 t/ha respectively and no trial yielded more than 8 t/ha. It is likely that scorch would have a worse effect on higher yielding crops where leaves tend to remain green almost until harvest.

Statistically significant yield increases from the first urea spray were recorded in four trials. Effects ranged from 0.17 to 0.36 t/ha and were all in trials where optimum nitrogen level had been underestimated; the urea nitrogen was apparently compensating for the inadequate levels of nitrogen applied in April. In only one of these trials was there a yield benefit from the second urea spray.

Conclusions

Variation in the response of winter wheat to nitrogen, as displayed in Figure 3, is extraordinary; it is apparently greater than for either winter or spring barley (Grylls and Archer, 1984; Johnson, 1984) and is probably greater than for any other controllable factor in the husbandry of cereal crops. The single factors or pairs of factors tested in our analysis have accounted for very little of the variation: although the median optimum for trials at N Index 0 is about 200 kg/ha of nitrogen and that for trials at N Index 1 or 2 is 120 kg/ha of nitrogen, a real difference between the N Indices is unproven because optima for each Index range from zero to greater than 200 kg/ha of nitrogen.

The poor distinction between N Indices, and also soil groups (Figure 6), is disquieting since these are the principle parameters on which ADAS's nitrogen recommendations are based (Needham, 1984). Further disquiet is caused because a third of the trials had optima greater than the maximum level of nitrogen tested, and optima for about one-third of the remaining trials were subject to considerable uncertainty, having SEs greater than 20 kg/ha (Figure 2). Despite these considerable qualifications it must be recognised that there is no other body of information available which encompasses more fully the circumstances in which winter wheat is currently grown in England and Wales, or which gives any better account of the variation in nitrogen response found in these highly variable conditions. For this reason fertiliser recommendations must largely be based on these data. Also, for the present the recommendations must continue to be based on previous cropping and soil type because, from evaluation of the data so far, no other parameter has been found to account for more of the variation.

Therefore, comparing the median optima (determined from Figure 6) with current recommendations (MAFF, 1981) it appears that there is scope for an increase in the recommended amount of nitrogen of the order of 50 kg/ha for most winter wheat crops.

The economic implications of varying the timing of nitrogen applications are considerably less than of varying the total amount of nitrogen applied; yield differences due to the use of either early or late split nitrogen were usually less than 0.5 t/ha. However, there is a predominance of trials showing a benefit from early split nitrogen (Figure 8) which favours a less tentative recommendation for this policy than has been given previously (MAFF, 1981).

Decisions on the use of late split nitrogen are more complex than for early split nitrogen (Figure 12). These data have shown that the chances of late split nitrogen giving a yield increase are poor where a farmer tends to be cautious in the total amount of nitrogen he applies. Conversely, if the total nitrogen to be applied is higher than the median optimum the use of late split nitrogen is unlikely to cause a yield loss. However, in considering the merits of late split nitrogen any effect on grain protein content must not be overlooked.

Looking to the future, it may be that further analysis of data from these trials will reveal a more satisfactory explanation of the variation. There is a need to compare separate response curves for each timing treatment. There is also scope for using multiple regression techniques to check whether certain combinations of factors could explain more of the variation than has been possible by taking factors one at a time. The penalty of applying an amount of nitrogen different from the optimum is an important aspect which must also be assessed. The size of any such penalty depends on the slope of the response curve in the region of the optimum, so there is a need to identify not only the factors governing the optimum but also the factors governing the shape of the response curve.

To assist in identifying the factors influencing nitrogen response there are advantages in increasing the number of trials in the analysis. This could be done because results are available from a roughly equivalent number of nitrogen trials which were conducted concurrently with those reported here but which had different experimental designs.

Even when the above analyses are complete, it is likely that there will still remain a need for more precise information on nitrogen fertiliser use for winter wheat. The nature of further experimentation must, therefore, be considered carefully. Before launching a further programme of experiments it should be recognised that if more thorough analysis shows response to nitrogen to be affected by weather conditions after the start of stem extension, then precise advice on nitrogen fertiliser use will not be possible without accurate long-range weather forecasts: the value of further experimental work would, therefore, be limited.

172

It would seem that future experimental work must be directed at describing more fully the mechanisms controlling nitrogen requirements of winter wheat, and evolving models which improve the precision of recommendations. Similar experimentation to that described in this paper may provide improved estimates of the extent of variation in nitrogen response, but it would seem most unlikely that more of the variation could be accounted for without more comprehensive measurement of the various environmental, husbandry and crop factors thought to contribute to the variation (see other papers in this volume). Experiments need to place more emphasis on measuring characteristics of the site and season rather than the differences in crop growth caused by the different nitrogen treatments. A more co-ordinated approach to site selection should therefore be adopted to ensure that a sufficient number of sites are examined for a particular selected factor, e.g. soil type or cropping sequence. Also, to distinguish as far as possible between effects of site and season, a proportion of trials should be conducted in the same field in successive years, and these should be situated where accurate meteorological data are available. The choice of treatments in such experiments should be directed at examining effects of differing nitrogen amounts rather than timing, because uncertainties from varying the amount of nitrogen, and the economic consequences, are far larger than varying the timing. To do this and to be confident of obtaining an estimate of N-opt, levels of nitrogen exceeding 300 kg/ha should always be tested.

Essential requirements for success in any such programme of experiments, involving great spatial and temporal contrasts, are in the standardisation of measurements and recording methods, and in the co-ordinated interpretation of data. Thus, tighter strategies for the management of experiments must be developed.

Acknowledgements

We are indebted to Dr. R. A. Bailey, Rothamsted Experimental Station, who provided the section on unbiased estimation of N-opt and its variance. We are also grateful to many colleagues in ADAS and at Rothamsted for their assistance in collating the data, the Soil Survey of England and Wales for information on soils, and the Meteorological Office for rainfall data.

References

BOYD, D. A., YUEN, L. T. K. and NEEDHAM, P. 1976 Nitrogen requirements of cereals. Part I: Response curves. *Journal of Agricultural Science* **87**, 149–162.

COX, D. R. and HINCKLEY, D. V. 1974. *Theoretical Statistics,* p. 260. London: Chapman and Hall.

GEORGE, B. J. 1984. Design and interpretation of nitrogen response experiments. Ministry of Agriculture, Fisheries and Food, Reference Book 385, *The Nitrogen Requirement of Cereals,* pp. 133–148. HMSO, London.

GRYLLS, J. P. and ARCHER, J. R. 1984. The response of winter barley to nitrogen. Ministry of Agriculture, Fisheries and Food, Reference Book 385, *The Nitrogen Requirement of Cereals,* pp. 191–207. HMSO, London.

JOHNSON, P. A. 1984. The response of spring barley to nitrogen. Ministry of Agriculture, Fisheries and Food, Reference Book 385, *The Nitrogen Requirement of Cereals,* pp. 209–221. HMSO, London.

MAFF. 1981. Lime and fertiliser recommendations — Arable crops and grassland. Booklet 2191, HMSO, London.

NEEDHAM, P. 1984. The basis of current nitrogen recommendations for cereals. Ministry of Agriculture, Fisheries and Food, Reference Book 385, *The Nitrogen Requirement of Cereals,* pp. 245–254. HMSO, London.

NELDER, J. A. 1966. Inverse polynomials, a useful group of multi-factor response functions. *Biometrics* **22,** 128–141.

SPARROW, P. E. 1979. Nitrogen response curves of spring barley. *Journal of Agricultural Science* **92,** 307–317.

ZADOKS, J. C., CHANG, T. T. and KONZAK, C. F. 1974. A decimal code for the growth stages of cereals. *Weed Research* **14,** 415–421.

Discussion

Mr Webb questioned whether the nitrogen Index was a good predictor for optimum nitrogen rate, since there were large differences in median values obtained for each nitrogen Index in the data presented. Dr Sylvester-Bradley replied that the nitrogen Index was currently the best predictive method available. The majority of trials had however been carried out on N Index 0 sites rather than at higher indices and so data was more reliable for Index 0.

Dr Smith commented that all the yield response curves would have been affected to some extent by factors such as residual soil nitrogen and water stress. He queried the validity of grouping data from such sites, unless these factors had been taken into consideration, and suggested that more useful information could be obtained from observations on the same site for a number of years, in an attempt to eliminate soil and climatic variations. Dr Sylvester-Bradley agreed with these comments and noted the high seasonal variability in yield data which could not be explained. He concurred that long-term studies in a particular location had not been set up previously to study these effects further. Mr Archer agreed with Dr Smith's point on yield variability and commented that trials work in the Eastern Region was now concentrating on specific soil types for that reason.

In discussion of specific data shown earlier in the paper, *M. Viaux* thought that the effect of late nitrogen application in one particular trial could be the result of a main application of less than 15 kg/ha of N at GS30 reducing the final number of fertile tillers. Mr Hubbard clarified the point by suggesting that the split treatments modified the development of the crop structure and thereby influenced final yield.

175

Nitrogen uptake of winter wheat

H J Lidgate
ICI Jealotts Hill Research Station, Bracknell, Berks.

...., ... ugen response experiments have been performed with winter wheat on ICI's major cereal sites at Jealotts Hill and Ropsley.

Jealotts Hill farm operates a rotation of two years grass, grazed and cut, receiving 400 kg ha^{-1} year^{-1} of N, and three years of cereals. The experimental crop is the second cereal.

Ropsley operates a rotation of peas and three years of cereals. The experimental crop is the second cereal.

Figure 1 shows the yield vs. nitrogen fertiliser response curves obtained in 1980. For some of the treatments in these experiments, crop dry matter production

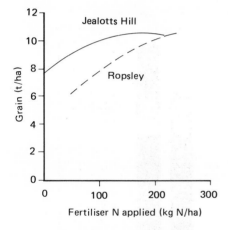

Fig. 1 Wheat nitrogen responses 1980.

and nitrogen uptake were recorded. Figure 2 shows the data for the Jealotts Hill crop receiving 200 kg fertiliser nitrogen and yielding 11.0 t/ha of grain.

Figure 3 shows the dry matter production observed in mid-June and at harvest, on crops receiving either 50 or 200 kg of fertiliser nitrogen in spring.

Figure 4 shows the nitrogen uptake and content of the crops. It is clear that the highest yielding crops took up most nitrogen. With only 50 kg/ha of fertiliser nitrogen applied at Jealotts Hill the crop yielded 10.4 t/ha of grain compared with 7.2 t/ha from the Ropsley crop. At Jealotts Hill nitrogen uptake was 198 kg/ha compared with 115 kg/ha at Ropsley. This is an indication of the higher nitrogen status of the Jealotts Hill soil resulting from the grass-livestock based rotation.

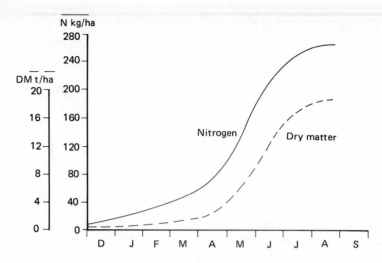

Fig. 2   Winter wheat dry matter production and nitrogen uptake.

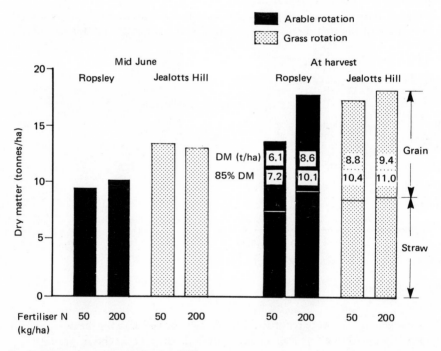

Fig. 3   Wheat dry matter production 1980.

The effect of 200 kg/ha of fertiliser nitrogen in both crops was to increase ear numbers, grains per ear, grain protein content and yield. Thousand grain weight was not affected at Ropsley and decreased at Jealotts Hill (see Table 1).

Historically seedbed nitrogen or early topdressing have had no effect on grain yield at Jealotts Hill but yield increases have been recorded at Ropsley (1978 and 1979). One of the purposes of the detailed crop recording was to observe what

178

Table 1 Components of yield of wheat crops, 1980

Fertiliser N kg/ha	Jealotts Hill		Ropsley	
	50	200	50	200
Ears/m^2	456	531	508	575
Grains/ear	39.2	41.9	31.8	39.1
TGW at 85% DM	50.0	46.5	44.7	45.2
Grain at 85% DM t/ha	10.4	11.0	7.2	10.1

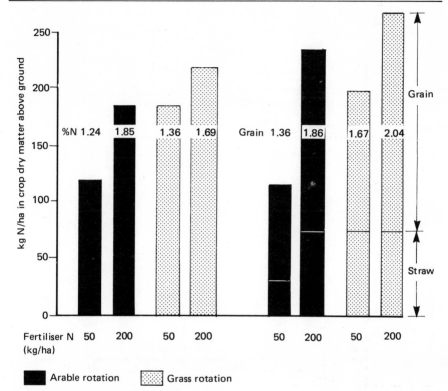

Fig. 4 Wheat nitrogen uptake at harvest 1980.

differences occurred in the crops in autumn-early spring which lead to these grain yield increases.

Figures 5 and 6 show the recorded effects of seedbed nitrogen and early spring applied nitrogen on the wheat crops at Jealotts Hill and Ropsley.

The Jealotts Hill data shows a significant increase in dry matter production, decrease in nitrogen content and increased nitrogen uptake in mid-March from 25 kg/ha seedbed nitrogen.

Seedbed nitrogen gave no signficant effect on grain yield.

Early spring topdressing gave a small increase in dry matter and a large increase in crop nitrogen content and uptake by mid-April. The early spring topdressing did not give increased grain yield. This could have been due to a delay in the main nitrogen application till mid-May. Final dry matter production and nitrogen uptake were reduced compared with main applications of nitrogen in mid-April.

179

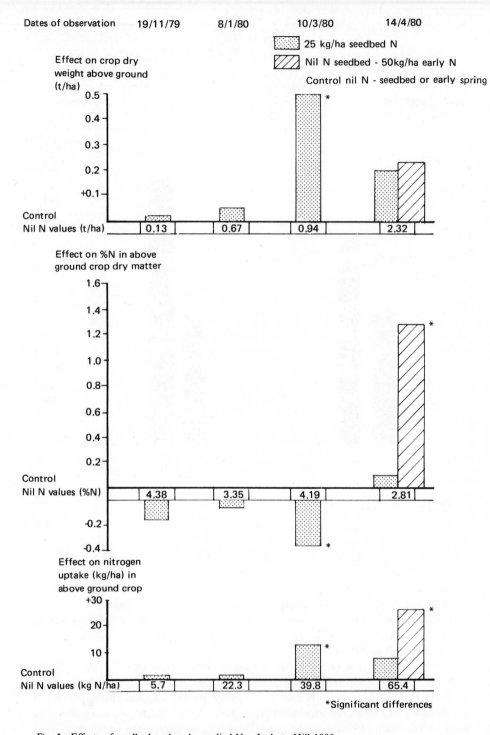

Dates of observation   19/11/79   8/1/80   10/3/80   14/4/80

25 kg/ha seedbed N

Effect on crop dry
weight above ground
(t/ha)

Nil N seedbed - 50kg/ha early N

Control nil N - seedbed or early spring

| Control Nil N values (t/ha) | 0.13 | 0.67 | 0.94 | 2.32 |

Effect on %N in above
ground crop dry matter

| Control Nil N values (%N) | 4.38 | 3.35 | 4.19 | 2.81 |

Effect on nitrogen
uptake (kg/ha) in
above ground crop

| Control Nil N values (kg N/ha) | 5.7 | 22.3 | 39.8 | 65.4 |

*Significant differences

Fig. 5 Effects of seedbed and early applied N – Jealotts Hill 1980.

180

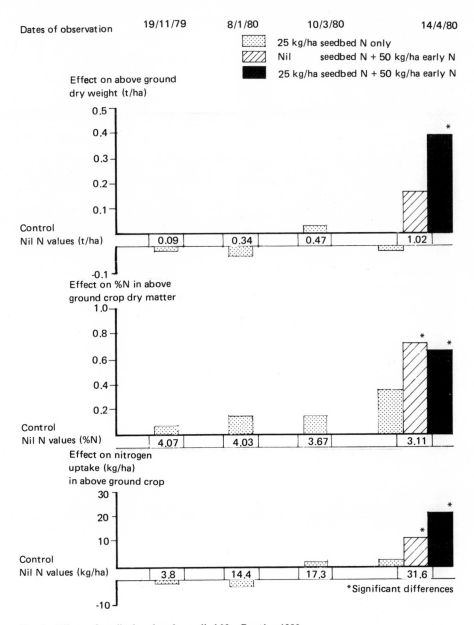

Fig. 6 Effects of seedbed and early applied N – Ropsley 1980.

At Ropsley from November to April differences between seedbed nitrogen and no nitrogen crops were very small and statistically non significant, though a grain yield increase was recorded in the main experiment (+0.4 t/ha).

Early topdressing in March increased shoot numbers, dry matter production, nitrogen content and uptake by mid-April.

By harvest the differences had reduced to very small non significant ones. This was perhaps due to the overriding effect of the total amount of nitrogen applied, the same for all treatments.

Determining the nitrogen requirements for winter wheat using an experiment of Simplex design

B J George
Rothamsted Experimental Station, Harpenden
R J Skinner
ADAS, Cardiff

Summary

A series of nine trials was conducted on shallow chalk soils in Hampshire 1979–81 using an experiment of Simplex design with large incremental steps of total nitrogen (80 kg/ha). Rates of nitrogen giving optimum and maximum yields were determined by fitting an exponential curve of the type $y = a + br_N + cN$ (where $r = 0.99$) to the data. The average optimum total nitrogen top dressing rate was found to be 200 kg/ha. Maximum yield was obtained using an average 253 kg/ha N. Splitting the nitrogen and applying some at GS 21 and the rest at GS 31 gave consistent yield increases compared with applying it all at GS 31. On average this increase was almost 0.5 t/ha. Late splits (at GS 39) gave a small additional benefit to yield only when an early split was also applied. Late nitrogen also increased grain nitrogen content.

Introduction

The experiments described in this paper were carried out in Hampshire on the chalk soils of the Andover series or close variants. These soils are silty loams overlying chalk at 25–45 cm. Despite the soils being shallow, cereals seldom suffer badly from drought as their roots can extract moderate quantities of water from the chalk below. Upward movement of water in the chalk can be appreciable under dry conditions and frequently plant roots can penetrate the chalk where it is soft and more deeply fissured. The moderately high rainfall in Hampshire also contributes to good cereal growing conditions; it is some 30 per cent higher than in the drier cereal areas of eastern England. Wheat yields in Hampshire are on average amongst the best in the UK, the county average being the highest in the UK in 1980. Cereals are commonly grown on a continuous basis or with infrequent one year break crops of herbage seeds or oil seed rape. The nitrogen Index is therefore invariably 0 as it was in the nine trials described in this paper.

The origin of this series of trials goes back to the mid 1970s, when the farming press featured several articles on continental methods for wheat growing, including several describing the great improvements in Belgian cereal yields due to the adoption of a method propounded by Professor Laloux of Gembloux University. These articles caught the imagination of many farmers and a large agricultural corn and seed merchant in Hampshire set up a series of meetings explaining and advocating the Laloux method. Members of Professor Laloux's team were brought over to help put the Belgian method into the English farming scene. Many farmers adopted the Laloux method or certain parts of it. Implicit in the method was the way in which the nitrogen top dressings were split; up to 20 kg/ha N should be applied in late February or early March depending on winter nitrogen leaching losses, 75 kg/ha N at GS 31 and 25 kg/ha N at GS 39. The ADAS advice at the time tended to minimise the value of split nitrogen dressings. One dressing at GS 31 was considered to be more or less unbeatable with the possible exception at N Index 0 when up to half the nitrogen could be applied in mid to late March, none should be applied after GS 37. Naturally, this approach was seriously questioned by farmers, many of whom had adopted the Laloux principles of early and late top dressings and claimed substantial benefits as a result.

From 1976 –78 a series of nitrogen on winter wheat trials was conducted to look at all possible combinations of nitrogen splitting at the three 'Laloux' growth stages. The design of these trials was a half replicate of a $4 \times 4 \times 4$ factorial, four levels of nitrogen being applied at each of the three times in 32 combinations. Whilst this work gave some useful information about optimum nitrogen rate and timing, in retrospect it was noted that it tested many unproductive split nitrogen combinations and missed out altogether some important possible treatments.

In 1978, therefore, a new design was sought. The new national design was considered but it did not fit the special requirements for Hampshire and could not easily be adapted to do so. The main deficiency in that design was the limited levels of early and late nitrogen split dressings being tested. Our earlier work had indicated that quite large responses could be obtained from moderately large early dressings and late nitrogen also appeared to give moderate benefits in some seasons. Several statisticians were approached over this matter and the design which met the ADAS authors' requirements most closely was one drawn up by Dr R Mead of Reading University. He seemed most able to squeeze the proverbial quart out of a pint sized pot. (One restriction was to keep the number of plots to below 50 per site as these were to be run with farmer assistance at harvest on commercial farms.) The design adopted was a bold one, the full range of total nitrogen levels 0 –320 kg/ha was tested by adopting large incremental steps of 80 kg/ha. This left plenty of room in the design to test a wide range of split nitrogen combinations. These combinations were looked upon as mixtures of early, mid and late applied nitrogen. The Simplex technique for rationalising possible mixtures was adopted (Mead and Pike, 1975). Early and late nitrogen splits were each applied at three levels 0, 40 and 80 kg/ha. This gave 34 possible mixtures to be tested. Of these the 10 least interesting were omitted leaving 24 treatments in the design; the five single dressings at GS 31 and 19 combinations of split dressings. These were replicated twice at each site giving 48 plots per site. The fact that the steps in total nitrogen were large was not considered to be a disadvantage – sophisticated curve fitting techniques could be used to define the optimum nitrogen rates with reasonable accuracy. Many designs of trials have suffered by not spanning a wide enough range of fertiliser levels.

During the years 1979 – 1981, three trials were conducted per year at the same three farms, at Upton Grey, Easton and Red Rice, Hampshire. The standard of management on each of these farms was excellent, each farmer being capable of occasionally producing 10 tonne/ha yields.

Results

Single nitrogen dressings

Considering single nitrogen dressings only, seven of the nine cases had fairly smooth curves; five of these had distinct maxima but two were still apparently increasing at the highest nitrogen level. The remaining two cases were less regular but, considering also the responses to split dressings, even these had the same general shape. The degree of similarity was sufficient to suggest fitting a family of curves, with constant shape but differing in yield level and possibly also in the nitrogen level at which the maxima were attained.

An appropriate type of curve needed to be asymmetric, and a convenient mathematical model was the modified exponential equation.

$$y = a + br^N + cN$$

From previous experience with cereal experiments, r was fixed at 0.99, and c constrained to be the same for all nine cases. Fitting different values of the constant, a, to the nine cases corresponds to allowing fixed differences in yield at all values of N. If the exponential coefficient, b, also varies this corresponds to horizontal shifts in the curves, i.e. to differing N levels at which the maximum yield is attained.

Curves of this type were fitted in stages. Initially a single curve was fitted to all the data. This was clearly inadequate. Curves differing only in the constant values, i.e. yield levels, accounted for 85.1 per cent of the total variation. As prediction equations these would all have maxima at the same level of N equal to 253 kg/ha. Curves differing in both horizontal and vertical location increased the variation explained to 88.7 per cent. The overall increase was significant but individual terms were almost all non-significant. The interpretation of this is that sites and years vary in the nitrogen required to produce maximum yield but no one combination of sites and years differs much from any other. The experiments at Red Rice were the most variable; in 1979 the response to nitrogen was low but in both 1980 and 1981 the response was high. The responses in the other six cases were similar although the yield levels varied. The data and fitted curves are shown in Figure 1.

The calculated economic maxima at a price ratio of 3:1 was found to be 200 kg/ha for a single dressing.

Split dressings

Because of the small number of points available for each type of split dressing no individual curve fittings were attempted. From the graphs drawn it was clear that split dressings generally produced higher yields than corresponding single dressings, and that the response curves were broadly similar. Since the nitrogen levels of the maxima appeared to vary only by a small amount the yields for each split were averaged over sites and years, and these averages were plotted on a further graph (Figure 2). Compared with single dressings, late dressings alone produced almost no change, early dressings increased yield, early and late dressings together produced even more increase. In each case, the gain in yield increased with the amount of nitrogen applied either early or late, and with the total nitrogen applied. The advantages of splitting were more pronounced in years when yields were higher (1980) and at the better yielding sites.

The numerical values of these increases are tabulated in Table 1. For each type of split, average gains for each level of nitrogen are given, and these are then averaged over all levels of nitrogen. The figures in parentheses are the standard errors of these overall averages, based on the variation in gains between blocks within site/year combinations. Since the gains are calculated relative to the same total single nitrogen dressing, they are potentially net gains with little cost involved. They are, however, averages and in two cases (Easton and Upton Grey in 1981) the split dressings appeared to cause a loss or no gain in yield.

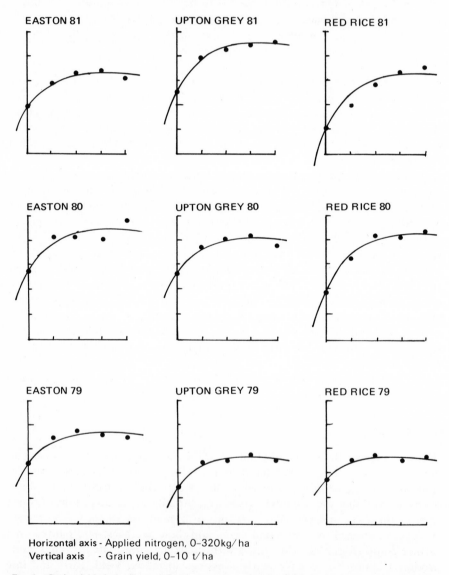

Horizontal axis - Applied nitrogen, 0–320kg/ha
Vertical axis   - Grain yield, 0–10 t/ha

Fig. 1 Grain yields in kg/ha and fitted response curves for single N dressings at each site/year.

Table 1   Yield gains in kg/ha from split dressings relative to the same amount of nitrogen as a single dressing

Late Dressing	0		40		80	
Early Dressing	Split	Gain	Split	Gain	Split	Gain
0			0–40–40	−0.110		
			0–120–40	−0.049		
			0–200–40	0.066		
			Mean	−0.031		
				(0.105)		
40	40–40–0	0.305	40–80–40	0.479	40–120–80	0.624
	40–120–0	0.328	40–160–40	0.401		
	40–200–0	0.399	40–240–40	0.571		
	Mean	0.344	Mean	0.484		
		(0.105)		(0.105)		(0.181)
80	80–0–0	0.326	80–40–40	0.389	80–0–80	0.531
	80–80–0	0.481	80–120–40	0.519	80–80–80	0.734
	80–160–0	0.407	Mean	0.454	80–160–80	0.589
	80–240–0	0.626			Mean	0.618
	Mean	0.460				
		(0.091)		(0.128)		(0.105)

Values in parenthesis are standard errors of means.

Table 2   Mean change in number of fertile tillers from split dressings relative to the same amount of nitrogen as a single dressing

Late Dressing	0	40	80
Early Dressing			
0		−15	
40	13	13	32
80	24	29	14

Fertile tillers

Inspection of the values for the nine site/year combinations shows a general increase in the number of fertile tillers with increasing level of applied nitrogen. Although this increase appears to level off in some cases, the pattern is very variable and no general function appears reasonable for all cases. In addition, the change in the number of tillers with the various split dressings is also variable.

The average number of tillers over the nine combinations is more stable. The number of fertile tillers appears to increase with increase in the amount of nitrogen applied early and to vary little with the amount applied late (Table 2).

187

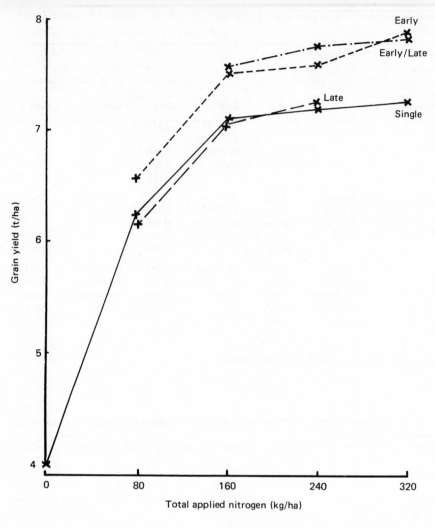

Fig. 2 Average grain yields in kg/ha over all sites/years for single and split dressings.

Table 3 Mean change in per cent N in grain from split dressings relative to the same amount of nitrogen as a single dressing

Late Dressing	0	40	80
Early Dressing			
0		0.030	
40	−0.079	−0.029	−0.063
80	−0.072	−0.103	−0.043

Per cent N in grain

Inspection of the individual values again shows a general increase with the amount of nitrogen applied, with a levelling off at the higher levels, and with a variable change in per cent N for the various split dressings. The averages over the nine site/year combinations (Table 3) show that late applications of nitrogen appear to increase the per cent N in grain slightly but early applications cause rather larger decrease in per cent N. These effects appear to be greater for the 1980 data when the per cent N in the grain was generally higher than in 1979 or 1981.

Discussion

The experimental design adopted proved satisfactory for determining the rates of nitrogen for maximum and optimum yield. The split dressing treatments used could have been improved upon with hindsight but would have needed to have included one or two extra treatments. The testing of a wide range of levels of early and late nitrogen was found to be fully justified by the findings obtained.

The average rate of nitrogen needed to obtain maximum yield was found to be 253 kg/ha. For obtaining optimum yield, assuming a price ratio of 3:1 for fertiliser and grain, 200 kg/ha of nitrogen was required if all was applied at the single (middle) application time (GS 31). Where split applications were used the optimum nitrogen rate was much the same.

The average increase in yield from using early nitrogen splits (the average of the two rates used) was almost 0.5 t/ha at the optimum total nitrogen rate. The reason for these fairly consistent large benefits from early applied nitrogen is thought to be linked to the observed fact that on these chalk soils spring plant populations are invariably low irrespective of whether a high seed rate is sown or not. Fairly generous applications of nitrogen in early March are therefore likely to encourage vigorous tillering which is needed if high yields are to be achieved. Tiller counts in these experiments confirmed that the early applied nitrogen was stimulating extra tillering. Late applied nitrogen splits (GS 39) had little effect on yield unless an early split had also been applied. Studies of tiller counts showed that the late applied nitrogen helped to maintain the higher tiller numbers established from early applied nitrogen. In the absence of a later split some of the extra tillers aborted later in the season. Late applied nitrogen is more effective in most seasons in Hampshire than in eastern counties of England, as the summer rainfall is somewhat higher. Despite this no more than 40 kg/ha would be recommended by the authors because of the risk of dry weather in June one year in four. Late nitrogen splits gave some increase in grain nitrogen content and this would be an advantage when growing quality wheats.

It appears from this work that in many respects the nitrogen requirements of cereals grown on the Hampshire chalk soils are rather different from those for cereals grown in the main cereal producing areas of eastern England.

Acknowledgements

Thanks go to Dr Roger Mead, Statistics Department, Reading University for his help in designing the experiments and to the three farmers who allowed us to conduct the trials on their farms: Mr J H Turner, Mr D Hewetson-Brown and Mr M A Barnes-Gorrel.

Reference

MEAD, R. and PIKE, D. J. 1975. A review of response surface methodology from a biometric viewpoint. *Biometrics* **31**, 803–851.

Response of winter barley to nitrogen

J P Grylls and J R Archer
ADAS, Cambridge

Summary

During the period 1977–80, a series of 76 experiments on amount and timing of nitrogen topdressing for winter barley were carried out by ADAS. Topdressings of up to 180 kg/ha N were applied at early tillering, early stem extension or equally split between these two timings.

Economic optima were derived by appropriate curve fitting for each site. These were estimated for with and without fungicide treatments. Rate of response to nitrogen and yield at the optimum were also calculated. The various soil and crop factors that might influence the optima were examined individually. There was no consistent variation due to year, variety or soil type. The previous cropping as described by the ADAS nitrogen Index system gave a marked difference in median optima between Index 0 and Index 1. Sixty-five sites in Index 0 gave a median optimum of 159 kg/ha of N, compared to 120 kg/ha of N for the 10 Index 1 sites. Yield level at the optimum did not help in explaining the variation in optima for this wide range of sites.

Where fungicide gave a yield response on 20 sites, the optimum was increased by 30 kg/ha of N compared to no fungicide usage. The other main factor influencing the optimum was lodging incidence. Half the sites did not lodge and gave a median optimum of 176 kg/ha of N; the lodged half gave a figure of 134 kg/ha of N.

Split nitrogen application was consistently better than all the topdressing applied in one dressing.

Introduction

During the 1970s the importance of winter barley has increased substantially in England and Wales. The figures in Table 1 show how the area has increased.

Throughout this period Maris Otter has been and remains the dominant malting variety. The main increase in area has been in the two feed varieties Sonja and, more recently, Igri. Most of the work reported in this paper was done on these three varieties.

A series of nitrogen topdressing response experiments were carried out by ADAS throughout England and Wales from 1977 to 1980. These seasons were generally favourable for winter barley production and high yields were common.

191

Table 1 Winter and spring barley areas (1000 ha) grown in England and Wales 1979–1981

Year	Winter barley	Spring barley	Winter barley as % total barley
1979	576	1279	31
1980	721	1108	39
1981	790	1042	43

No extremes of wetness or dryness had a major influence on yields during this four year period.

The work was initiated to meet the demands of the industry for more detailed and up-to-date information on nitrogen requirement of the crop, particularly on the heavier soils. The series was part of a major programme of experiments on all agronomic aspects of winter barley production carried out by ADAS during this period. Previous work on nitrogen requirement was very limited. It was confined to a few experiments on malting varieties at the Norfolk Agriculture Station (Anon. 1970 and 1975) and at Gleadthorpe Experimental Husbandry Farm (Anon. 1971). The two constraints of lodging susceptibility and demand for low grain nitrogen content restricted nitrogen response and usage until recently.

The change to stiffer strawed varieties grown primarily for animal feed on a wide range of soils, including more water retentive soils than those traditionally associated with winter barley growing, provided the need for new experiments and recommendations.

Because of the interest in the possible interaction of nitrogen and response of the crop to fungicides, the series of experiments reported examined nitrogen response at different levels of fungicide use. This paper concentrates on the nitrogen response data.

Most of the experiments in this series were on crops following a cereal. The largest concentration of winter barley production is in south and east England. Experimental sites were well distributed throughout England and Wales, with many in the major production areas.

Experimental sites and designs

A total of seventy-six experiments were laid down on commercial winter barley crops during the years 1977–80 to test the response of winter barley to nitrogen in the presence and absence of fungicide to control disease. Site details are given in Appendix 1 on pages 202–204. Sixty-five sites followed a cereal (N Index 0) and 10 followed a break crop (N Index 1).

Four nitrogen levels were tested, applied at three timings. In 1977 nitrogen applications of 75, 100, 125 and 150 kg/ha were made either all early (during tillering usually in March), all late (during stem extension usually in April) or split (half early plus half late). For 1978–80 rates of 90, 120, 150 and 180 kg/ha were used at similar timings. Lower levels of 0, 25 and 50 kg/ha were also tested at early and late timings in 1977. In 1978–80 lower levels (30 and 60 kg/ha) were tested at the early timing only. The nitrogen was broadcast by hand as ammonium nitrate on to plots with a minimum harvest area of 50 m^2.

The nitrogen treatments were tested under two fungicide regimes in 1977 and three in 1978–80. Blocks were used for fungicide treatments in preference to a fully randomised design because of the dangers of re-infection of fungicide treated plots where individual small plots are sprayed. A buffer zone of at least 3 m was left between and around each block. The fungicide regimes in 1977 were no fungicide and triadimefon at about the time of the first topdressing followed by a further triadimefon spray at flag leaf emergence. The 1978–80 trials additionally tested a block sprayed with triadimefon in the autumn (applied when mildew was seen in crop, or by end of the year if little disease was evident). This block also received triadimefon at about first topdressing and at flag leaf emergence. At most trial sites carbendazim to control eyespot was included with the triadimefon spray at about first topdressing date.

Yields at most sites were recorded by harvesting the plots with farm combine harvesters. Plot combine harvesters were used at a few sites. Yields were corrected to 85 per cent dry matter. At most sites mean grain weight and number of ears/m^2 were also recorded. All sites except for seven were drilled between early September and mid-October. The remaining sites were drilled in late October, except for one drilled in November. No plant growth regulators were applied.

Results and discussion

Details of the results from individual sites are given in Appendix 2. Further individual treatment yields and grain N contents are available from the authors.

Nitrogen optima

The nitrogen optima quoted in the paper are derived from curve fitting with either quadratics or straight lines as appropriate for individual sites. Separate curves were fitted and optima estimated for with and without fungicide treatment, on those sites showing significant yield difference between these treatments. All optima were estimated on a cost : value ratio of 10:3; assuming 10 kg of barley has the same value as 3 kg of N.

On several sites the optimum nitrogen level was equal to or greater than 180 kg/ha of N, the highest tested in these experiments. This is a major reason for the use of medians rather than means throughout this paper.

For each site the curves were used to estimate figures for the yield at optimum nitrogen level and the rate of response in kg grain increase per kg N fertiliser applied upto the optimum.

Factors affecting nitrogen optima

A number of single soil and crop factors that might be expected to account for some of the variation in nitrogen optima have been examined. The data has been summarised on a median optimum basis, concentrating on the main soil and crop factors which influence soil nitrogen supply and crop requirement. Where there is variation in the optimum depending on fungicide use, the with fungicide figures have been used. The number of sites for each median figure in the tables is also given.

Year

The median optima was fairly consistent, except for 1977 and are shown in Table 2.

Table 2　Effect of year on nitrogen optima

Year	Optimum N application	Number of sites
1977	124	7
1978	144	22
1979	162	20
1980	159	27

The small number of sites, the low maximum level of nitrogen tested and the high incidence of lodging probably combined to give the low optimum for 1977. Yields were high at most sites in that year.

Variety

The median optimum for each of the three major varieties in the experimental series was examined and are given in Table 3.

During the series, the percentage of sites in Maris Otter declined, and the percentage in Igri increased. The data did not show a consistent variety × year relationship. For example 11 Maris Otter sites in 1978 gave a median optimum of 165 kg/ha of N.

Table 3　Effect of variety on nitrogen optima

Variety	Optimum N application	Number of sites
Maris Otter	148	23
Sonja	163	34
Igri	164	12

Soil type

The sites were separated into four groups, primarily on soil texture and depth. The median optima for the four groups are shown in Table 4.

The sandy soils gave a lower median optimum than the other groups, which was not explained by varietal or seasonal bias.

Table 4　Effect of soil type on nitrogen optima

Soil type	Optimum N application	Number of sites
Sandy	144	19
Shallow over rock	159	13
Loamy	154	26
Clayey	153	18

Previous cropping

Previous cropping using the ADAS N Index system is currently one of the main factors determining ADAS nitrogen recommendations for a particular crop. While this series was heavily biased to previous cereal situations, 10 sites followed another crop, mainly grass or peas. Sixty-five sites following at least one cereal (N Index O) showed a median optimum of 159 kg/ha of N. The 10 sites following grass or peas (N Index 1) gave a median optimum of 120 kg/ha N. The N Index 1 sites were distributed over the four years of the series. The separation shown is consistent with work on other cereals.

Location

It is sometimes argued that sites in the west have lower optima than those in the east, due perhaps to rainfall distribution or soil organic matter differences. This data does not support that separation. Twenty-five sites in south-west England and Wales and 51 sites in the rest of England showed median optima of respectively 154 and 151 kg/ha of N.

Similarly there was a very poor correlation between optimum and soil organic matter content.

Yield level

As nitrogen uptake and yield level are broadly related, it might reasonably be anticipated that some of the variation in optima would correlate with this factor. Table 5 shows for these experiments the median optima are the same regardless of yield level. This poor relationship was not explained due to confounding with previous crop or soil type.

Table 5   Effect of yield level on nitrogen optima

Yield at optimum	Optimum N application	Number of sites
Less than 6 t/ha	152	26
6–7.5 t/ha	153	40
Greater than 7.5 t/ha	150	9

Fungicide use

Of the 76 sites, 20 mainly in 1977 and 1978 showed different optimum N rates, between with and without fungicide treatment. Of these sites, half were Maris Otter; 13 of the 20 showed an increased optimum where fungicides were supplied.

For sites where fungicide influenced the optima, the median optima was with no fungicide 120 kg/ha of N and with fungicide 150 kg/ha of N. Lodging occurred on most of the sites which gave a lower optimum in the presence of fungicide.

195

Lodging is common in winter barley and the risk is increased at higher nitrogen levels. In this series of experiments, all but one site lodged in ˙977 and around half the sites in each year 1978–80 showed some lodging at least at the highest level of nitrogen tested. The median optima showed a clear separation of lodged and unlodged sites. Thirty-eight unlodged sites showed a median optima of 176 kg/ha of N compared with 134 kg/ha of N for thirty-eight lodged sites.

Examination of the site data showed no overall increase in lodging due to yield level, variety, soil type or ear number. Crop dry matter was not measured in these experiments. Even N Index was equally distributed between lodged and non-lodged sites.

The inference is that lodging is due mainly to weather factors, particularly wind and rainfall intensity. Lodging has a considerable impact on optimum nitrogen level. On 18 sites, timing of nitrogen influenced susceptibility to lodging. For these sites all N applied early increased lodging compared to the other timings on five sites, while all N applied late increased lodging on 13 sites. There was no difference due to timing on the other 20 lodged sites.

Yield depressions

While lodging may make harvesting more difficult, it does not necessarily reduce yield. Early lodging is most likely to reduce yield. In most cases the optimum is reduced as shown in the previous section, but yield is maintained.

Only eight sites out of 76 showed a yield depression at 150 kg/ha of N plus fungicide, compared to lower nitrogen levels. All except one showed lodging. Three of these eight were in N Index 1. Three of the others were relatively high soil organic matter soils in south-west England or Wales.

Yield depression was closely related to factors affecting soil N supply. Lodging occurred over a wider range of situations, only some of which gave yield depressions.

Effect of timing of nitrogen

Nitrogen was applied at two different times in three regimes as described earlier. Table 6 shows the effect of 'early' or 'late' treatments relative to the split application.

The mean values in Table 6 show yield differences due to timing were small. However, considering individual sites where the coefficient of variation was below 10 per cent, 18 sites showed positive or negative yield difference of greater than 0.5 t/ha from using a single nitrogen application compared to a split (see Table 9). At 11 of these sites all late nitrogen decreased yield and at three it increased yield. At the other four sites early nitrogen decreased yield.

Rate of response to nitrogen

The rate of response to nitrogen used in the paper is the increase in yield (kg) achieved by applying 1 kg of N over the range 0 to the optimum in 1977 and 30 kg/ha of N to the optimum in 1978–80. With fungicide most sites were in the range 15 to 20 kg/kg of N. The overall range was 8 to 28 kg/kg of N with a mean of 17 kg/kg of N.

Table 6 Mean yield difference in t/ha caused by all early or all late nitrogen application compared with split nitrogen

Effect of soil type	Early		Late	Effect of year	Early		Late
Sandy	−0.05		−0.16	1977	0.00		−0.26
		(19)				(7)	
Shallow over rock	−0.10		−0.01	1978	0.00		−0.02
		(13)				(22)	
Loamy	−0.02		−0.02	1979	−0.02		−0.14
		(25)				(20)	
Clayey	−0.15		−0.02	1980	−0.16		−0.08
		(19)				(27)	

Figures in parenthesis are numbers of sites.

There was a marked influence on efficiency due to fungicide. For those 20 sites which showed differences in optimum and for which different curves were fitted, the mean with fungicide rate of response was 17 compared to a without fungicide mean of 12. This pattern was consistent for all varieties and years for the sites showing variation in optima due to fungicide treatment.

Other factors showed very little effect on the mean rate of response. In particular soil type, year and N Index showed no differences. For varieties, Sonja with a mean rate of response of 15 (31 sites) tended to be lower than Maris Otter with a mean of 20 (19 sites).

Maris Otter grain nitrogen content

Maris Otter grown specifically for malting generally needs a relatively low grain nitrogen content to attract a financial premium. If malting is the desired market, nitrogen application may need to be reduced, resulting in both lower grain nitrogen and lower yield in most circumstances. Due to site factors, low grain nitrogen contents are only likely to be reliably achieved on sandy and shallow chalk soils with low organic nitrogen residues from previous crops. Even in these circumstances, rainfall distribution in a particular season may cause late nitrogen uptake, resulting in too high a grain nitrogen content. For malting the aim is usually 1.6–1.8 per cent nitrogen (dry matter basis) depending on the particular market.

Mean grain nitrogen contents for 16 Maris Otter sites 1978–80 were as shown in Table 7. As the data shows, the increase in grain N tends to be linear above about 100 kg/ha of N applied.

For the 13 sites where early N was applied by mid-March, the grain N contents were 1.74, 1.83 and 1.75 per cent respectively for all early, all late and half early plus half late nitrogen application.

These figures confirm the advantage of applying at least part of the total nitrogen early to keep grain nitrogen low.

For these 13 sites the rate of response to nitrogen over the range 90–150 kg/ha of N was 9 kg of grain per kg of nitrogen. Therefore reducing the nitrogen application from 150 to 100 kg/ha of N in the hope of producing premium quality would reduce yield by an average of 0.45 t/ha.

197

Table 7   Mean effect of nitrogen rate on grain N content for 16 Maris Otter sites 1978–80

kg/ha N	Per cent N in grain
30	1.53
60	1.57
90	1.65
120	1.75
150	1.86
180	1.96

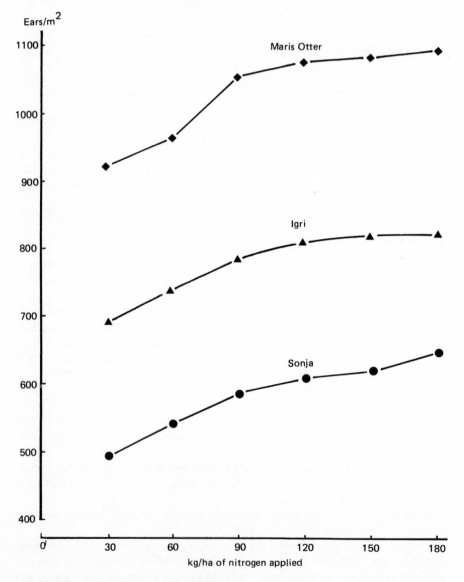

Fig. 1   Effect of nitrogen treatment on ear number.

198

Components of yield

Ear size varies considerably in winter barley varieties. This is reflected in the very different ear numbers needed for high yields of the different varieties. Figure 1 shows the mean effects of nitrogen level on the ears/m² for Maris Otter, Igri and Sonja. Ear number tended to increase up to 180 kg/ha of N, the highest level tested. For each variety the rate of increase reduced above 120 kg/ha of N.

To demonstrate the relative importance of nitrogen level on ear number and final yield, two Sonja sites have been chosen. Figure 2 shows the increase in each of the components of yield compared to 100 per cent at 30 kg/ha of N applied. On this chalky boulder clay soil in East Anglia, the optimum yield response was greater than 180 kg/ha and all yield components increased up to that level. Ear number showed the biggest per cent increase. The relatively low ear number of 540 ears per m² achieved at 180 kg/ha of N is typical of results on clay soils. This ear number is below optimum for this variety and likely to be a limitation to yield in most situations. At 180 kg/ha of N yield on this site was 6.50 t/ha, with 22.5 grains per ear and mean grain weight of 60.2 g.

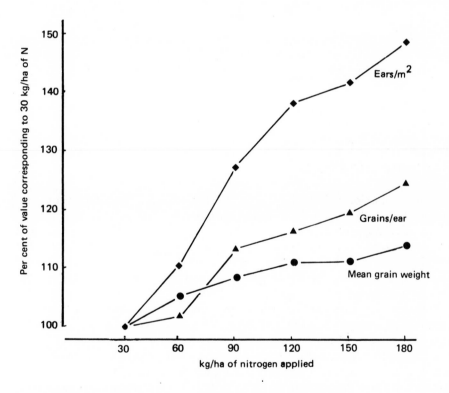

Fig. 2 Effect of nitrogen treatment on components of yield (Site No. 43).

By contrast Figure 3 shows comparable data for a deep, fine sandy loam where ear number increased only slightly above 120 kg/ha of N and optimum response was achieved at 137 kg/ha of N. Grain weight showed little change, but grains per ear number increased only slightly above 120 kg/ha of N and optimum response was 7.8 t/ha, with 950 ears per m², 23 grains per ear and mean grain weight of 47 g.

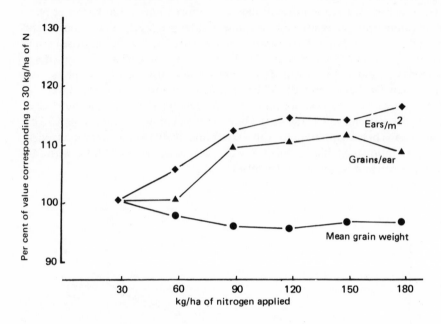

Fig. 3 Effect of nitrogen treatment on components of yield (Site No. 67).

Recommendations

For this discussion it is assumed that the requirement is maximum economic yield and that fungicides will be used as appropriate. Data on which to decide an appropriate nitrogen application for Maris Otter for malting is given in the results section.

The results of this series of experiments lead ADAS to recommend applications of 160 kg/ha of N at N Index 0 and 120 kg/ha of N at N Index 1 for current varieties on all soils.

Diseases can now be controlled by fungicides in winter barley with considerable success. The main problem is risk of lodging. As shown, in the absence of lodging larger amounts of nitrogen are justified. Unless lodging control can be achieved using growth regulators, the use of larger amounts of nitrogen on winter barley awaits the introduction of stiffer strawed or shorter varieties. On sites known to be prone to lodging, a lower level of nitrogen should be used.

A split application of nitrogen has given the most consistent result in this series, and is recommended. Part should be applied during tillering but not before the last week of February and the remainder at early stem extension. For potentially malting varieties, all the nitrogen should be applied by mid-March.

200

Acknowledgements

This series of experiments was carried out by ADAS Soil Science Departments at Starcross, Bristol, Reading, Cardiff, Trawsgoed, Bangor, Newcastle, Wolverhampton, Shardlow and Cambridge. Sites were also carried out by ADAS staff at High Mowthorpe, Bridgets and Boxworth EHFs. Analysis of data was done by the Statistics Department, Rothamsted.

References

ANON. 1971. *Gleadthorpe Experimental Husbandry Farm Report and Guide 1971.* p. 42.

ANON. 1970. *Intensive winter barley. Norfolk Agricultural Station Sixty-Second Annual Report 1969–1970.* pp. 10–11.

ANON. 1975. *Winter barley – effect of level and time of application of nitrogen. Norfolk Agricultural Station Sixty-Seventh Annual Report 1974–1975.* pp. 10–11.

Appendix 1 Site details

Year and site	Variety	N Index	Organic matter per cent	Surface soil texture	Grand mean		Ears/m²	Lodged
					Yield (t/ha)	Mean grain weight mg		
1977								
1 Cornwall	Astrix	0	4.6	Silty loam	4.47	37.6	482	Yes
2 Cornwall	Astrix	0–1	5.7	Very fine sandy loam	4.52	37.2	435	Yes
3 Warwickshire	Maris Otter	0	*	Sandy clay loam	5.59	31.1	*	Yes
4 Hampshire	Sonja	0	4.7	Silty loam (gravelly)	4.57	*	*	No
5 Bedfordshire	Maris Otter	0	2.9	Silty clay loam	4.85	35.1	971	Yes
6 Cambridgeshire	Maris Otter	1	2.4	Calcareous silty loam	5.84	34.7	879	Yes
7 Cambridgeshire	Maris Otter	0	3.3	Silty clay loam	5.81	36.7	*	Yes
1978								
8 Cornwall	Sonja	0	5.9	Very fine sandy loam	4.79	48.3	749	Yes
9 Devon	Sonja	0	4.9	Silty loam	6.66	49.3	697	Yes
10 Dorset	Sonja	0	6.8	Silty clay loam	5.01	44.6	*	Yes
11 Wiltshire	Astrix	0	3.2	Silty clay loam	7.27	41.7	*	Yes
12 Gwent	Sonja	0	4.0	Silty loam	5.61	48.2	448	No
13 Dyfed	Sonja	1	2.7	Loamy sand	5.89	34.4	732	Yes
14 Clwyd	Maris Otter	0	2.7	Loamy sand	5.31	35.5	1111	No
15 Gwynedd	Maris Otter	0	5.7	Fine sandy loam	6.44	30.3	960	No
16 West Midlands	Maris Otter	0	*	Loam	6.43	41.2	1095	Yes
17 Staffordshire	Maris Otter	0	*	Sandy loam (stony)	6.74	41.7	1294	Yes
18 Hampshire	Maris Otter	0	5.4	Calcareous silty loam	5.95	*	*	Yes
19 Hampshire	Sonja	0	3.1	Very fine sandy loam (gravelly)	7.43	46.7	*	Yes
20 Bedfordshire	Maris Otter	0	2.5	Sandy silty clay loam	5.23	38.7	*	No
21 Cambridgeshire	Maris Otter	0	3.0	Sandy clay loam	5.86	42.4	1034	Yes
22 Cambridgeshire	Sonja	0	*	Clay loam	5.93	*	523	Yes

Year and site	Variety	N Index	Organic matter per cent	Surface soil texture	Grand mean Yield (t/ha)	Mean grain weight mg	Ears/m²	Lodged
23 Cambridgeshire	Maris Otter	0	3.4	Calcareous sandy loam	4.38	34.2	777	Yes
24 Cambridgeshire	Maris Otter	1	3.8	Calcareous sandy loam	4.86	34.1	1116	Yes
25 Lincolnshire	Maris Otter	1	2.7	Sandy loam	5.79	*	*	No
26 Nottinghamshire	Sonja	1	1.6	Sandy loam	5.30	*	*	No
27 North Yorkshire	Sonja	0	*	Calcareous silty clay loam	5.90	*	566	No
28 North Yorkshire	Maris Otter	0	2.8	Very fine sandy loam	5.78	37.0	*	No
29 Northumberland	Malta	0	2.5	Sandy clay loam	5.48	46.6	558	No
1979								
30 Cornwall	Sonja	0	5.7	Silty loam	4.76	42.6	694	Yes
31 Devon	Sonja	0	6.2	Silty loam	4.74	51.8	496	Yes
32 Dorset	Sonja	0	5.4	Silty clay loam	6.33	52.0	489	No
33 Gloucestershire	Sonja	0	6.2	Silty clay loam	6.04	46.0	537	No
34 Dyfed	Igri	1	3.4	Very fine sandy loam	7.07	42.5	842	Yes
35 Powys	Sonja	0	7.7	Silty loam	5.85	45.8	813	No
36 Clwyd	Maris Otter	0	*	Loamy sand	5.40	32.0	*	Yes
37 Gwynedd	Sonja	0	*	Very fine sandy loam	7.02	42.6	*	Yes
38 Warwickshire	Sonja	0	3.3	Loamy sand	4.43	52.9	643	No
39 Staffordshire	Maris Otter	0	*	Sandy loam	5.08	36.3	977	Yes
40 Hampshire	Sonja	0	2.8	Silty loam (gravelly)	6.44	52.2	769	Yes
41 Hampshire	Igri	0	2.2	Silty loam	5.36	43.9	819	No
42 Bedfordshire	Maris Otter	0	4.3	Silty clay loam	6.51	43.0	729	No
43 Bedfordshire	Sonja	0	3.0	Clay loam	5.87	59.0	506	No
44 Cambridgeshire	Maris Otter	0	4.6	Calcareous sandy loam	6.22	40.0	961	Yes
45 Cambridgeshire	Igri	0	*	Clay loam	6.84	*	569	No
46 Lincolnshire	Maris Otter	0	2.5	Fine sandy loam	4.42	*	*	No
47 Nottinghamshire	Sonja	0	1.9	Sandy loam	3.09	39.2	*	No
48 North Yorkshire	Sonja	0	*	Calcareous silty clay loam	5.09	*	*	Yes

Year and site	Variety	N Index	Organic matter per cent	Surface soil texture	Grand mean Yield (t/ha)	Mean grain weight mg	Ears/m²	Lodged
49 Cleveland	Sonja	0	3.6	Clay loam	5.09	44.6	502	No
1980								
50 Devon	Igri	0	3.9	Very fine sandy loam	6.08	45.3	806	No
51 Devon	Sonja/Athene	0	2.2	Sandy loam	5.24	45.5	587	Yes
52 Somerset	Igri	0	3.9	Very fine sandy loam	8.67	42.0	719	Yes
53 Gloucestershire	Igri	0	6.3	Silt loam	8.32	41.4	956	No
54 South Glamorgan	Sonja	0	6.8	Silty clay loam	4.61	51.0	521	No
55 Gwent	Athene	1	3.5	Silty loam	7.48	43.3	367	No
56 Dyfed	Sonja	0	7.6	Very fine sandy loam	5.85	43.2	756	No
57 Dyfed	Sonja	0	5.6	Fine sandy loam	6.99	39.3	910	No
58 Powys	Igri	0	7.1	Silty loam	7.34	42.3	803	No
59 Powys	Igri	0	5.3	Silty loam	8.60	44.2	831	Yes
60 Clwyd	Sonja	0	6.3	Fine sandy loam	5.67	48.4	592	No
61 Gwynedd	Sonja	0	5.2	Fine sandy loam	5.73	47.8	570	Yes
62 Staffordshire	Maris Otter	0	1.8	Sandy loam	6.19	39.5	1467	No
63 Shropshire	Sonja	0	*	Sandy loam	4.23	50.3	461	No
64 Hampshire	Igri	1	2.4	Silty loam	6.98	48.1	946	No
65 Buckinghamshire	Maris Otter	0	4.6	Calcareous silty loam	6.66	41.8	1112	Yes
66 Suffolk	Athene	1	1.0	Loamy fine sand	5.62	35.4	529	No
67 Suffolk	Sonja	0	2.1	Sandy loam	7.69	46.5	937	No
68 Bedfordshire	Sonja	0	2.0	Fine sandy loam	6.30	55.5	591	No
69 Northamptonshire	Igri	0	2.8	Sandy clay loam	7.07	41.8	*	Yes
70 Northamptonshire	Igri	0	3.2	Clay loam	6.25	45.5	*	No
71 Lincolnshire	Maris Otter	0	2.5	Sandy clay loam	6.21	30.8	*	Yes
72 Lincolnshire	Sonja	1	2.4	Sandy loam	6.32	44.3	*	Yes
73 North Yorkshire	Sonja	0	*	Sandy loam	6.26	47.6	*	Yes
74 North Yorkshire	Sonja	0	*	Calcareous silty clay loam	4.85	*	607	No
75 Cleveland	Igri	0	2.9	Silt loam	5.39	42.3	*	Yes
76 Northumberland	Sonja	0	4.4	Silty clay loam	4.70	42.5	*	No

*Data not available.

Appendix 2 Results

Site No.	Optimum N (kg/ha) Without fungicide	†	Optimum N (kg/ha) With fungicide	Yield at optimum (t/ha) Without fungicide	Yield at optimum (t/ha) With fungicide	Rate of response (kg grain/kg N) Without fungicide	Rate of response (kg grain/kg N) With fungicide	Response to split compared with: All early (t/ha)	All late (t/ha)	c of v %
1	67		124	4.24	6.30	8	23	+0.06	−0.78	14.2
2		150		5.77		18		+0.22	−0.15	4.1
3	150		134	6.49	7.25	16	25	−0.02	−0.39	4.0
4	149		117	5.35	5.53	12	19	−0.12	−0.20	4.2
5		125		5.57		14		−0.37	−0.23	13.6
6	92		84	5.66	7.11	9	14	+0.43	−0.15	6.7
7	101		104	6.09	6.78	11	19	−0.18	+0.07	5.2
8	103		180	4.55	5.43	8	11	+0.25	−0.06	7.4
9	157		140	6.46	6.99	10	18	+0.14	−0.01	3.2
10		30		5.96		*	*	−0.24	+1.67	17.2
11		105		7.38		26		+0.12	−0.19	7.5
12	135		180	5.30	6.36	9	11	+0.09	−0.11	4.9
13	0		64	5.93	6.26	*	9	+0.19	+0.53	5.7
14	149		180	4.63	6.43	15	18	+0.19	+0.08	9.9
15		119		6.74		25		−0.29	+0.27	9.7
16		125		6.40		18		−0.11	+0.21	5.2
17	172		165	6.46	7.43	15	22	−0.26	+0.28	3.9
18		116		6.30		28		+0.03	−0.29	10.5
19		104		7.78		19		+0.22	−0.96	11.6
20		180		5.99		17		+0.01	−0.55	16.2
21	98		133	5.54	6.22	10	15	−0.33	−0.12	10.2
22		129		5.99		15		−0.01	+0.15	2.2
23	180		180	3.65	5.37	16	19	−0.11	−0.02	6.5
24	115		148	4.02	5.70	13	15	+0.21	−0.31	8.9
25	154		180	5.47	6.51	16	22	−0.48	−0.01	7.8
26		114		5.39		21		+0.02	−0.01	5.3
27		180		6.13		11		+0.16	−0.20	*

Site No.	Optimum N (kg/ha)			Yield at optimum (t/ha)		Rate of response (kg grain/kg N)		Response to split compared with:		c of v %
	Without fungicide	†	With fungicide	Without fungicide	With fungicide	Without fungicide	With fungicide	All early (t/ha)	All late (t/ha)	
28		180		6.23		16		+0.22	−0.13	6.0
29		180		5.99		16		−0.04	−0.66	4.8
30		154		4.98		15		+0.20	+0.10	9.8
31		176		5.11		17		−0.44	+0.28	3.4
32		180		7.16		22		−0.09	+0.15	4.5
33		154		6.21		13		−0.02	+0.11	6.0
34	82		101	6.46	7.64	15	19	+0.07	−0.46	2.6
35		120		6.42		15		+0.01	+0.18	3.8
36		144		5.58		17		−0.16	−0.47	5.7
37		97		7.07		8		−0.04	−0.10	4.9
38		180		4.87		10		−0.04	−0.01	14.2
39		128		5.14		11		+0.09	+0.03	7.3
40		121		6.51		20		+0.07	−0.24	5.7
41		180		5.86		21		−0.03	−0.67	5.0
42	152		169	6.27	7.22	21	25	−0.15	+0.07	2.5
43		180		6.50		26		−0.57	+0.08	3.3
44		149		6.50		24		−0.14	+0.06	6.0
45		178		7.08		16		−0.06	−0.54	5.5
46		137		4.57		20		+0.10	−0.06	*
47		171		3.41		15		+0.30	−0.20	14.8
48		178		7.08		16		−0.06	−0.02	4.8
49	180		180	5.12	6.09	12	17	−0.35	−1.11	4.6
50		175		6.54		20		−0.39	−0.52	6.0
51		158		5.51		18		−0.03	−0.27	3.4
52		150		8.89		16		−0.16	+0.16	8.0
53		160		8.59		19		−0.95	+0.34	3.1
54		117		4.71		13		−0.10	+0.03	4.9
55		150		7.71		21		−0.38	+0.50	6.2

| Site No. | Optimum N (kg/ha) | | | Yield at optimum (t/ha) | | Rate of response (kg grain/kg N) | | Response to split compared with: | | c of v |
	Without fungicide	†	With fungicide	Without fungicide	With fungicide	Without fungicide	With fungicide	All early (t/ha)	All late (t/ha)	%
56	180			6.37		12		+0.16	+0.48	12.8
57	180			7.85		19		−0.81	+0.01	7.3
58	167			7.60		13		−0.06	−0.03	5.6
59	148			8.76		13		+0.11	−0.37	5.1
60	172			5.96		14		+0.05	−0.31	5.9
61	180			6.50		17		−0.12	−0.14	7.4
62	180			6.75		20		+0.14	−0.81	5.6
63	150			4.40		11		−0.02	−0.67	5.7
64	147			7.15		16		+0.01	−0.33	4.2
65	159			6.98		22		−0.36	+0.59	3.3
66	125			5.79		17		+0.34	−0.13	11.8
67	120		151	7.29	8.08	12	10	−0.59	−0.03	2.2
68	177			6.71		16		−0.36	−1.34	4.5
69	122			7.17		13		−0.07	−0.08	3.9
70	161		180	6.38	6.80	18	18	−0.50	−0.33	3.2
71	153			6.41		17		−0.25	+0.07	6.7
72	90			*		*		−0.61	+0.06	7.5
73	142			6.44		20		+0.21	+0.03	12.7
74	180			4.98		*		−0.36	+0.18	3.0
75	180			6.33		20		−0.09	+0.51	6.6
76	180			5.24		17		−0.08	−0.49	6.4

†No difference in Optimum N with or without fungicide.

Discussion

Dr Jenkyn commented that the use of fungicide had increased grain size and consequently diluted the grain nitrogen content in trials at Rothamsted and wondered whether the ADAS work had provided any information on the influence of fungicide on grain nitrogen levels. Mr Archer stated that although the relevant data was available, it had not been analysed in great detail.

Mr Needham said that the data from ADAS trials on Maris Otter had indicated an increase in grain nitrogen content of 0.1 per cent, as well as increased grain size, as a result of fungicide treatment.

Mr Lidgate asked whether the data could be used to assess the nitrogen supplying power of the soil and crop efficiency in utilising the nitrogen, as a means of classifying soil instead of categorising the data according to the nitrogen Index. Mr Archer however queried the value of using N_0 yields as a suitable indicator. Dr Sylvester-Bradley agreed with the suggestions raised and considered that they could be usefully investigated in the future. Mr Lidgate also asked how consistent was the nitrogen supplying power of the soil between years and what influence was there from the nitrogen fertiliser applied to the preceeding crop. Mr Archer replied that no account had been taken in the data presented of the nitrogen fertiliser applications made to the crop immediately preceeding the winter barley crop at each trial site.

Dr Tinker referred to Dr Boyd's earlier paper in which he had calculated yield losses in sugar beet due to sub-optimal nitrogen application and asked what would be the overall yield losses if the nitrogen recommendations for winter barley were applied to all the sites instead of individual optima. Mr Archer suggested that the calculation of the $N_{optimum}$ rate was not the most satisfactory method, as the economics of nitrogen application over the whole response curve should be considered. Consequently recommendations based on $N_{optimum}$ could be an under-estimation.

Dr Little asked if the relationship between soil organic matter and optimum nitrogen level had been investigated. Mr Archer said that no relationship had been found between soil organic matter content and optimum nitrogen rates. Dr Little suggested that very low mineralisable nitrogen levels in the soil after harvest may be desirable in the future for environmental reasons.

Dr Holmes stated that most of the experiments had been carried out in intensive cereal growing areas where take-all was also prevalent. As high nitrogen applications were known to reduce take-all infection, he wondered whether the high nitrogen optima could be related to overcoming take-all. Mr Archer thought that take-all was unlikely to be a serious problem in winter barley. Dr Sylvester-Bradley commented that detailed assessments of take-all had not been made on most of the winter wheat trial sites included in his joint paper, but that the $N_{optimum}$ was reduced at a small number of sites where take-all occurred in 1977 and 1978. Mr Archer considered however that $N_{optimum}$ was most likely to be higher where take-all occurred and Mr Yarham suggested that winter barley could be more susceptible to take-all than previously assumed.

Mr Wadsworth considered that a more detailed assessment of the variable and unexpected yield results often obtained at high rates of nitrogen application could provide a better understanding of the N Index. Dr Sylvester-Bradley agreed with this suggestion.

The response of spring barley to nitrogen

P A Johnson
ADAS, Shardlow

Summary

The rapid increase in the area of winter barley grown in the UK has occurred at the expense of spring barley, and this has been reflected in the lower input of resources for research and development associated with the latter crop. Varieties of spring barley grown have changed completely since the early 1970s when the trials, on which the present recommendations for nitrogen are based, were carried out. Although at any one particular time there may be little if any difference in response to nitrogen between varieties, the complete change in varieties plus improved pest and disease control could mean that changes in nitrogen requirement have occurred. Recent trial work on nitrogen responses suggests that this is the case but further work is required to confirm this on a wider range of soils and climatic situations. The effect of timing, particularly for early sown crops and on chalk soils, also requires further investigation. As an interim measure it is suggested that the nitrogen recommendation for mineral soils at N Index 0 should be raised to 125 kg/ha.

Introduction

Spring barley has in the last few years become a 'Cinderella' crop. Greater emphasis in trial work has been placed on winter wheat and of course on the expanding acreage of winter barley, which has itself been one of the major reasons for the reduction in spring barley acreage. Although the area sown to the crop has fallen by nearly 20 per cent in the period 1979–81 (Table 1) there were still over one million hectares sown in 1981, some 200 000 hectares more than sown to winter barley.

Table 1 The area sown to spring and winter barley in England and Wales. Data from annual census, MAFF.

	Winter barley hectares	Spring barley hectares
1981	789 926	1 041 758
1980	721 225	1 107 923
1979	575 852	1 278 814

Oats and spring wheat have also received little attention, but the area sown to these crops is significantly lower than the three major cereals. Thus, over the last few years, few trials have been carried out on the nitrogen requirement of the spring barley crop by ADAS, although other organisations have been carrying out some trials over the last two or three years using modern varieties. Trials in the early 1970s carried out by ADAS, such as the 'SA52' series, have never been reported in detail, although the form of the response curves in this particular set of trials has been thoroughly investigated by Sparrow (1979). It is possibly inappropriate to use trials from this period in a discussion of the present day nitrogen requirements as not only have the varieties grown completely changed (Table 2), but also fungicide use has improved and the switch to winter barley has meant that spring barley has been grown less and less on those soils where seedbeds are difficult to produce in spring.

Table 2   Varieties of spring barley recommended by the National Institute of Agricultural Botany for 1976 and 1982 (NIAB, 1976; 1982)

	1976	1982
Recommended	Mazurka	Triumph
	Lofa Abed	Atem
	Abacus	Goldmarker
	Wing	
	Hansen	
	Julia	
	Maris Mink	
	Armelle	
	Proctor	
Provisionally	Ark Royal*	Kym
recommended	Aramir	Patty
	Georgie*	Carnival
	Sundance*	Koru
	Varunda	Egmont
	Tyra	

*On 'becoming outclassed' list, 1982.

The question of change in variety can also be levelled against the series of trials (coded SA57) reported by Johnson et al. (1977) and Johnson and Zemroch (1980), though in the former paper the question of soil type and increasing acreage of winter barley may be less in question as a very large area of spring barley is still grown on the chalk soils of southern England. It was only in 1981 that a new series of trials was initiated by ADAS Soil Scientists (coded SB06) with eight sites scattered through the western and northern parts of the country; the results are therefore biased towards the wetter counties. Of the fertiliser companies, ICI have had trials at their Jealotts Hill, Ropsley and West Isley sites and Fisons have carried out 28 trials in Scotland, Devon, Norfolk and Lincolnshire over the last three years. The results of all series of trials are discussed later.

Nitrogen rates in practice

Traditionally, large areas of spring barley were sown with 3 cwt/acre of a 20–10–10 compound (75 kg N, 37.5 kg/ha P_2O_5 and K_2O) combine drilled. It would appear from the annual survey of fertiliser practice (Tables 3 and 4) that nitrogen use has increased well beyond this figure for most crops.

The average use of nitrogen in 1981 was very close to the standard recommendation for most mineral soils at N Index 0 of 100 kg/ha N (MAFF, 1979). The dramatic jump in nitrogen use between 1980 and 1981 is partially due to farmers compensating for likely loss of nitrogen by leaching, following very heavy rain in parts of the country; much of this nitrogen was applied as a topdressing.

Results of trials

Before interpreting trials results within a particular treatment series it is necessary to establish the form of the response curve. In the past the 'diminishing returns' curve has been extensively used, particularly on trials where only a few levels of treatment have been used. However, for response curves to be plotted accurately, sufficient treatments must be employed – a minimum of five is suggested for trials on nitrogen response.

The forms of response to nitrogen are discussed in general elsewhere in this volume (George, 1984, pages 133–148) and the response curves to spring barley, based on 83 experiments carried out by ADAS in the early 1970s, have been

Table 3 Percentage of spring barley crop area receiving differing amounts of nitrogen in 1981 (MAFF, 1982)

N kg/ha	% of crop area
0	2
0 – 25	1
25 – 50	4
50 – 75	15
75 – 100	27
100 – 125	27
125 – 150	16
>150	8

Table 4 Average use of nitrogen on spring barley (MAFF, 1982)

Year	kg/ha of N
1981	98
1980	87
1979	88
1978	83
1977	82
1976	78
1975	76
1974	73

extensively discussed by Sparrow (1979). He found that the inverse quadratic, Greenwood's modification of the inverse linear and two intersecting straight lines represented the yield-fertiliser relationship well, although no one model fitted best at every site. Optimal yields varied little between models but slightly smaller optimal dressings were predicted from two straight lines. Earlier, Boyd *et al.* (1976) had also suggested that two intersecting straight lines gave the lowest residual mean square of a number of models. A few results from one group of 17 experiments were best represented by smooth curves; these were from crops much affected by leaf diseases. It should be borne in mind that the symptoms caused by leaf pathogens are usually increased by fertiliser nitrogen (Jenkyn, 1976) and that the pathogen may, directly or indirectly, affect root growth, transpiration and photosynthesis capacity, and thus the ability of the plant to absorb, translocate and metabolise nitrogenous compounds. How far these factors will affect the plants response to nitrogen is uncertain, but the increasing effectiveness and use of fungicides makes this more of an academic question. Can we, however, expect more straight line type responses as leaf diseases are better controlled, or will other limiting factors such as low moisture availability lead to curvilinear responses also?

Results from sites where the highest yields are obtained from the highest levels of nitrogen are difficult or impossible to interpret, as are those where there are few levels of nitrogen tested. This problem seems particularly common with spring barley. Several of the trials mentioned elsewhere in this paper had maximum yields at the top level of nitrogen applied. What happens beyond here? Even the latest ADAS Soil Science trials failed to find the turning point in several trials in 1981 with application rates of up to 180 kg/ha (almost twice the present standard recommendation for non-sandy mineral soils). A similar situation is found with many of the current winter barley and wheat trials: that the optimum apparently exceeds the highest level of nitrogen used. This contrasts with the situation reported by Johnson *et al.* (1977) and Johnson and Zemroch (1980) where only three out of 22 trials in the SS 57 series, carried out on mineral soils at N Index 0, failed to show an optimum.

In the discussion below only results from trials carried out in the 1970s and 1980s will be considered, but it must be borne in mind that varieties have changed considerably and may affect results even though, and any one time, there appears to be little difference in nitrogen response of the varieties currently on the recommended list.

Rate of nitrogen

Trials in the ADAS South Western Region in the early 1970s (Eagle *et al.*, 1976) on thin chalk and limestone soils showed that at that time optimum nitrogen rates for spring barley grown in a cereal rotation were between 90 and 100 kg/ha. A response rate of 23 kg grain/kg N was recorded in three years, but less in one year when growing conditions were poorer. Yields were, however, all less than 5 t/ha. The optimum nitrogen application was very close to the 90 kg/ha used on farms as reported for spring barley on chalk and limestone soils by Church (quoted in Eagle *et al.*, 1976). Trials mentioned in the same paper on other soils at various sites through central England had optimum nitrogen requirements of 120–135 kg/ha. These trials showed lower rates of response particularly where levels of nitrogen were greater than 40–50 kg/ha. Yields were higher, in the range 5.0–5.7 t/ha, than on the chalk and limestone soils and the extra nitrogen required on these sites could be in part, to supply the larger quantities of nitrogen being removed in the grain from these soils. A yield of 5 t/ha of grain at 1.8 per cent N in the dry matter will remove 76.5 kg/ha of nitrogen. This figure is, of course, below the optima quoted above, but some further nitrogen will be removed or lost when the straw is burned or baled and removed from the field.

Later trials restricted to chalk soils (Johnson *et al.,* 1977) confirmed the nitrogen optimum of 90–100 kg/ha where other nutrients were not limiting on mineral chalk soils but also suggested that 20–25 kg/ha less was required on organic soils of the Icknield series. It was also apparent that nitrogen was used less effectively on the Icknield series (9 kg grain/kg N as compared to 27 kg grain/kg N on other soils) a factor which is possibly related to the greater reserves of soil nitrogen in this soil type. In further trials similar to those mentioned above, Johnson and Zemroch (1980) report results from non-chalk soils. In this series some of the results appear to have been affected by a year × N Index interaction as the majority of the N Index 2 sites were in the excessively dry summer of 1976. Yield responses were significantly lower:

(1) for N Index 2 than N Index 0 ($P < 0.05$)
(2) for 1976 than the other three years ($P < 0.05$) and
(3) Northern Region and Wales than the South West ($P < 0.05$).

The third of these factors is almost certainly linked to the fact that seven out of eight sites in the South West were at N Index 0. However, despite all the problems of interactions the mean optimum nitrogen rates of 92, 64 and 27 kg/ha at N Index 0, 1 and 2 respectively were tolerably close to the standard recommendations for mineral soils at that time of 100, 60 and 30 kg/ha N (MAFF, 1979).

Turning to the late 1970s ICI report trials at several of their centres (ICI, 1979; 1980). In 1978 the optimum nitrogen application rate was not reached (top rate 140 kg/ha) at Jealotts Hill, West Isley (200 kg/ha) or Ropsley (150 kg/ha). At West Isley in 1979 with a late drilled (early April) crop responses to 175 kg/ha occurred in two trials and at Ropsley the response was to 180 kg/ha N where a growth regulator was applied (165 kg/ha without the growth regulator). Strangely at Jealotts Hill in 1980 there was no response to nitrogen, averaged over 10 varieties, in a similar position in the rotation to 1978. At West Isley in 1980 the economic response was to 140 kg/ha N (ICI unpublished), but in 1981 the maximum rate of nitrogen (220 kg/ha) produced the highest yield at West Isley with a calculated optimum of over 280 kg/ha. The Ropsley site on a Beccles series soil showed a nitrogen rate for maximum yield of 189 kg/ha and an economic rate of 177 kg/ha N.

In 1981 a new series of trials was initiated by ADAS Soil Scientists on the response of spring barley to nitrogen. Responses on non sandy, mineral soils ranged, at N Index 0 from 100 kg/ha N to greater than 180 kg/ha N (the highest rate tested), and on the two sandy sites, where a response was obtained, to a mean of 130 kg/ha (split 30 kg/ha in the seedbed and the remainder at GS 21) (Table 5).

As a result of their experiments Fisons have issued a revised recommendation of 115 kg/ha N at N Index 0 (Anon, 1982). Seven of the sites showed some advantage of split dressings, but in general splitting the nitrogen application with 40 kg in the seedbed and the remainder either at the 3 leaf stage, or four weeks later, had no affect on yield.

Table 5 Optimum nitrogen treatment in trials on spring barley in 1981 (ADAS series SB06)

Region	Site	Optimum N* kg/ha
Light soils		
Northern		30 + 115
West Midlands		30 + 90
Other soils		
Northern	1	90 + 0
	2	180 + 0
Wales	1	105 + 0
	2	0 + 120
South West	1	180 + 0
	2	150 + 0

*The best combination of applications made to the seedbed and during tillering (GS 21).

The conclusions which can be drawn from these trials is that the nitrogen recommendations for the spring barley crop could be raised above those given in Bulletin GF1, *Fertiliser recommendations* (MAFF, 1979) but it is difficult to specify to what level. The reported ICI work is at three sites only and of the 28 Fisons trials 13 were on Lincolnshire Limestone soils and seven (including three at N Index 1) responded to at least 140 kg/ha N. It would appear that in recent years there has been a large variation in the optimum nitrogen rate for spring barley but how far this has been connected with different sowing dates and variable soil conditions is uncertain.

On very light soils (loamy sands) the present recommendation of 125 kg/ha appears to be correct, as optima from the recent trials by ADAS and Fisons on these soils are close to it. More trials are obviously required on shallow chalk soils to confirm the response found at West Isley. These should use early drilled crops with the bulk of the nitrogen being applied after tillering. In view of the large acreage of spring barley grown on these soils this work is urgently required. A separation for the Icknield series would still need to be made.

The work by Fisons on soils over Lincolnshire limestone appears to indicate an optimum of 130–140 kg/ha; this figure is close to that found in an ADAS trial near Lincoln in 1981 comparing nitrogen from pig slurry with inorganic nitrogen. Sufficient trials have probably now been carried out on this soil type. However, there remain many areas and soil types on which no recent experimentation has taken place. There is a particular need for experimentation on farms where spring barley is grown in rotations with short and long-term leys, for example where barley is grown on the dairy farm.

Timing of nitrogen

Sand land

With very early sowing of spring barley on sand lands, often in January or February, there is a considerable risk of nitrogen applied to the seedbed being leached below the rooting zone of the crop. Studies with lysimeters at Gleadthorpe EHF (Selman and Dampney, 1978 and unpublished) over 11 years have shown very large losses of nitrogen in wet periods following early applications. In this experiment nitrogen at 113 kg/ha was applied to separate lysimeters on 1 February, 1 March and 1 April. All were sown to spring barley and the leachate collected and analysed for nitrogen (Table 6).

Table 6 Effect of time of application of 113 kg/ha N to spring barley on amount of nitrogen leached from a sandy soil

	1970–71	71–72	72–73	73–74	74–75	75–76	76–77	77–78	78–79	79–80
Mean volume of leachate, mm										
	72	*	149	221	212	63	445	252	483	398
Total nitrogen leached, kg/ha										
Nil N	14	*	13	71	43	29	96	68	71	66
February 1	13	*	9	91	74	37	216	90	222	130
March 1	10	*	13	94	74	36	143	74	200	75
April 1	19	*	10	104	63	49	128	62	ND	ND

*contamination of plots by livestock – results discarded.
ND = not determined.

It can be seen that in those years with high volume of leachate nitrogen loss in excess of that from controls was considerable. Average losses have been 40 per cent, 25 per cent and 9 per cent of February, March and April applications respectively. In wet springs almost all the February applied nitrogen was lost by the beginning of April and the crop was forced to rely on nitrogen released from the soil.

Concurrent with these lysimeter experiments at Gleadthorpe EHF there were six experiments on the timing of nitrogen applications to the early sown crop. Only three rates of nitrogen were compared (75, 113 and 150 kg/ha) and thus the mean optimum rate of 113 kg/ha (over the four years of completed trials) must be treated with caution. The timing treatments along with the mean yields are given in Table 7.

Table 7 Effect of applying 113 kg/ha N at different times on yield of grain from drillings in January or February. Mean (t/ha) of 4 years (1971, 1973, 1974, 1976) at Gleadthorpe

Time of application	Grain yield t/ha	Difference from all on seedbed t/ha
All on seedbed	3.80	–
All on braird	4.17	+0.37
Half on seedbed, half on braird	3.95	+0.15
Half on seedbed, half at tillering	3.69	–0.11
Half on braird, half at tillering	4.15	+0.35

In these trials with barley sown in early February, a single dressing on the braird (i.e. at emergence) was on average as good as or better than split dressings. However, in two years a split dressing with half the total dressing on the braird and half at tillering was better than applying all the nitrogen on the braird. Leaving the application of half the dressing until tillering is risky because wet weather could delay the application further, or the onset of very dry weather may delay its uptake.

With later drillings there may be no advantage in applying the fertiliser on the braird (as occurred at Gleadthorpe in 1972). In 1981 on two trials on sand land in Herefordshire and Cumbria an application of 30 kg/ha N at sowing followed by 115 or 85 kg/ha at growth stage 21 (GS 21, Zadoks *et al.*, 1974) respectively gave better yields than applying all nitrogen at GS 21.

Shallow chalk soils

At Bridgets EHF in Hampshire trials have indicated that there is no advantage to splitting the nitrogen application where the fertiliser is broadcast at or about sowing. However, if combine drilling is required, application of the optimum nitrogen level which would have been 150 kg/ha in their trials during the early 1970s (MAFF, 1980) would slow down drilling, and there are, therefore, organisational reasons for splitting the application.

Work by ICI at their West Isley site (unpublished, 1982) has shown different timing requirements for different drilling dates.

Table 8   Effect of nitrogen on yield of spring barley drilled in February or April 1981 at West Isley

Seedbed	N level		Grain yield t/ha at 85% DM
	GS10–21 kg/ha	GS15–30	
Drilled 6 February			
20	160	0	6.13
20	0	160	6.56
20	80	80	6.53
60	120	0	5.72
60	0	120	6.38
60	60	60	6.48
Drilled 6 April			
60	120	0	5.52
60	0	120	5.37
60	60	60	5.51
120	60	0	5.56
120	0	60	5.68
120	0	0	5.27

The 1981 trials quoted in Table 8 are not available with standard errors, but they appear to show that for early drilling (6 February) small amounts of nitrogen in the seedbed are required, followed by the remainder of the nitrogen at GS 10–21 and GS 15–30 or all at GS 15–30. This may reflect the very high rainfall during early spring of 1981 which is likely to have leached the nitrogen into the underlying chalk. The differences between nitrogen timings were smaller for the early April sowing. The higher level of nitrogen in the seedbed was superior if combined with a later top dressing.

Other soils

At Ropsley in Lincolnshire in 1979 and 1980 ICI found no significant interaction between amount and timing of nitrogen. It was concluded that the nitrogen dressing could have been applied either all in the seedbed or split with part in the seedbed and part as a top dressing at GS 10 to 30, with no difference in yield.

On a wide range of sites covering England and Scotland at nitrogen Indices 0 and 1 Fisons have reached similar conclusions.

Advice for early drilled crops would be to apply a small dressing, say 20 kg/ha, in the seedbed followed by a top dressing to supply the remainder of the nitrogen required at GS 15–30.

Variety × nitrogen interaction

There is often discussion as to whether particular cereal varieties respond differently to nitrogen. ADAS advice has consistently stated that there is no evidence, over a run of years, that one variety consistently differs from another.

Individual trials may show differences between varieties, as occurred at a site near Wye, Kent in 1971 (unpublished) where the varieties Vada and Zephyr responded to higher levels of nitrogen than Proctor, Sultan or Deba Abed. However, the differences could not be fully confirmed because the response curves were based on insufficient levels of nitrogen. It is interesting to note that only one of the varieties used in that particular trial was on the Recommended List by 1976.

More recently trials have been carried out in Scotland by the North of Scotland Agricultural College which showed no differences in nitrogen requirement between varieties (unpublished, 1981). Similar trials testing a wide range of varieties have also been carried out by ICI (1980). In one trial at West Isley the results suggested that varieties may differ in the form of their response curve giving linear or curvilinear responses. However, subsequent results from the same site in 1981 showed no significant difference between varieties in terms of their response to nitrogen.

Although there may be some sites and years in which different nitrogen responses occur with different varieties it would take a very large experimental programme to obtain an accurate assessment. Also, changes in variety would make such results out of date very rapidly.

Interactions with other nutrients

In a field situation the response of spring barley to nitrogen is severely restricted if the soil pH is below a critical level of 5.8 (MAFF, 1979).

Turning to the major nutrients other than nitrogen, in a series of trials on shallow chalk soils in the early and mid 1970s (Johnson *et al.*, 1977) interactions between the level of applied potash and the response to nitrogen were found on soils low in available potassium. Five trials on shallow chalk soils (Andover and Upton series) with K Indices of 0 or 1 showed a response of only 14 kg of grain per kg of nitrogen with low levels of applied potash (less than 64 kg/ha K_2O), and 100 to 125 kg of nitrogen per hectare was needed for maximum yield (Figure 1).

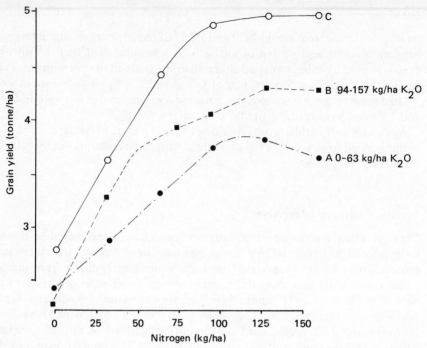

Fig. 1 Effect of soil potash status on form of yield response to nitrogen in spring barley. A and B, means of five trials on sites with K Index of 0 or 1 (A, mean of 0, 31, and 63 kg/ha K_2O; B, mean of 94, 126, and 157 kg/ha K_2O). C, mean of five trials on sites with K Index of 2 or 3 (after Johnson *et al.*, 1977).

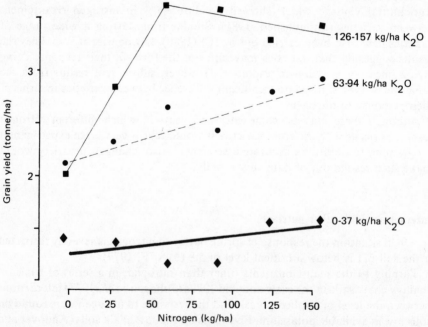

Fig. 2 Effect of soil potash status on form of yield response to nitrogen in spring barley. Means of two trials on sites with K Index of 0 or 1 (◆, mean of 0 and 37 kg/ha K_2O; ●, mean of 63 and 94 kg/ha K_2O; ■, mean of 126 and 157 kg/ha K_2O (Johnson *et al.*, 1977).

218

Larger applications of potash (94–157 kg/ha K_2O) much increased the response to nitrogen (Figure 1, line B) but as the potash was broadcast it was possibly not used efficiently. On similar soils with greater potash reserves (line C) nitrogen was used much more effectively, resulting in an almost linear response to nitrogen at a rate of about 27 kg of grain per kg of nitrogen, up to 100 kg/ha nitrogen.

At two further sites (Figure 2) the effect of applying large rates of potash was to raise the effectiveness of nitrogen remarkably at levels below 60 kg/ha. Mean slopes were 27 kg of grain per kg of nitrogen as compared to 2 kg grain per kg of nitrogen with little or no potash. Also, with large potash applications an optimum nitrogen application could be defined, whereas at lower potash applications no optimum point was reached. At a site of N Index 2 and K Index 0 at Alnwick in 1976 there was little or no response to nitrogen when low rates of potash were applied (Johnson and Zemroch, 1980); again these were broadcast rather than combined drilled and thus would not have been used effectively. However, where larger quantities of potash were applied a response to nitrogen was apparent (Figure 3), with an optimum of around 94 kg per hectare.

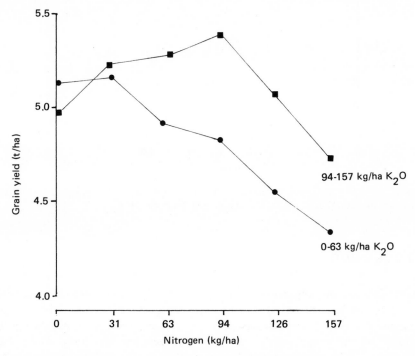

Fig. 3 Effect of K dressing on N response at Alnick, 1976. Means of 0,31, and 63 kg/ha K_2O (●) and 94, 126 and 157 kg/ha K_2O (■) (Johnson and Zemroch, 1980).

In the same series of trials, a crop at phosphate Index 0 gave a higher maximum yield and responded to higher levels of nitrogen when adequate phosphate was applied as a broadcast dressing (Figure 4).

These results clearly illustrate that, if an economic return from nitrogen is to be obtained, dressings of phosphate and potash are needed where these are deficient in the soil, and show the need to base fertiliser use on soil analyses.

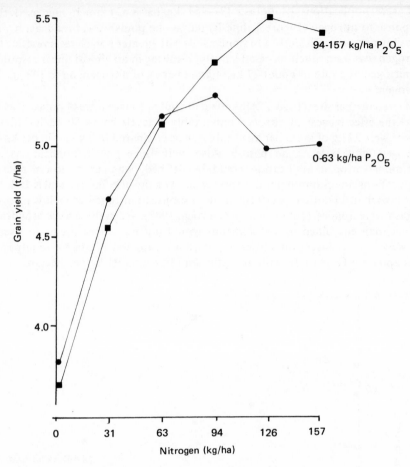

Fig. 4 Effect of P dressing on N response at Plympton, 1974. Means of 0, 31, and 63 kg/ha K_2O (●) and 94, 126, and 157 kg/ha K_2O (■) (Johnson and Zemroch, 1980).

Discussion

It will have become apparent that, in terms of number of nitrogen response trials, the spring barley crop has been sadly neglected over recent years. Varieties have changed completely and disease control has improved remarkably during this period, so the recommended rates of nitrogen are uncertain. These have remained static and on some soils are less than those suggested nine years ago (MAFF, 1973), whilst nitrogen rates recommended for winter wheat and barley have been steadily increasing during this period (Needham, 1984). With modern spring varieties, in many instances capable of yielding as well as autumn sown ones and at less cost, more emphasis should be placed on this crop by experimenters and by the farming industry. This is particularly so as several of the spring varieties have malting potential and exports could be increased.

From the existing trial data it seems that nitrogen rates need not be increased for crops grown on very light soils but, particularly for those sown early, the nitrogen should be delayed to prevent loss by leaching in wet springs. Leaching losses not only give rise to a need for compensatory nitrogen applications, but the leached nitrate could also pollute ground water. More work is required on shallow chalk soils because results from ICI at West Isley on both rates and timing of nitrogen differ in some years from those reported by Johnson *et al.* (1977), and are much higher than those reported from Bridgets EHF (MAFF, 1980). Apart from a few trials by Fisons and the small number by ADAS in 1981 little evidence is available for other soils, However, this information indicates an optimum nitrogen rate for non organic soils at N Index 0 of 125 kg/ha N. In view of the very high levels of response on some sites in arable areas there is a need for further trials to take place in eastern and southern England. If the high requirements are confirmed then trials refining the timing of the applications will be justified.

References

ANON. 1981. West of Scotland Agricultural College Report, 1980. Auchincruive, Ayr.

ANON. 1982. *Barley in the 1982 cost structure.* Fisons Ltd., Levington, Suffolk.

BOYD, D. A., YUEN, L. T. K., LOWRING, T. K. and NEEDHAM, P. 1976. Nitrogen requirements of cereals. Part I: Response curves. *Journal of Agricultural Science* **87**, 149–162.

EAGLE, D. T., RUSSELL, R. D., BOYD, D. A. and DRAYCOTT, A. P. 1976. Using response curves to estimate the effect on crop yield on profitability of possible changes in fertiliser recommendations. In: *Agriculture and water quality,* MAFF Technical Bulletin 32, pp. 355–370, London, HMSO.

GEORGE, B. J. 1984. Design and interpretation of nitrogen response experiments. Ministry of Agriculture, Fisheries and Food, Reference Book 385, *The Nitrogen Requirement of Cereals,* pp. 133–148. HMSO, London.

ICI. 1979. Annual report on field experiments, 1978. ICI Agricultural Division, Jeallotts Hill Research Station, Bracknell, Berkshire.

ICI. 1980. Annual report on field experiments, 1979. ICI Agricultural Division, Jeallotts Hill Research Station, Bracknell, Berkshire.

JENKYN, T. F. 1976. Nitrogen and leaf diseases in spring barley. In: *Proceedings of the 12th Colloquium of the International Potash Institute,* pp. 119–128. Berne: International Potash Institute.

JOHNSON, P. A., BOYD, D. A. and SPARROW, P. E. 1977. Manurial experiments with spring barley on chalk soils in southern England. *Experimental Husbandry* **32**, 8–18.

JOHNSON, P. A. and ZEMROCH, P. T. 1980. Manurial experiments with spring barley on non-chalk soils. *Experimental Husbandry* **36**, 34–43.

MAFF. 1973. *Fertiliser recommendations.* Bulletin 209. London: HMSO.

MAFF. 1979. *Fertiliser recommendations.* Booklet GF1 London: HMSO.

MAFF. 1980. *Growing barley at Bridgets.* Bridgets EHF, Martyr Worthy, Hampshire.

MAFF. 1982. *Survey of fertiliser practice. Fertiliser use on farm crops in England and Wales, 1974–1981.*

NEEDHAM, P. 1984. The basis of current nitrogen recommendations for cereals. Ministry of Agriculture, Fisheries and Food, Reference Book 385, *The Nitrogen Requirement of Cereals,* pp. 245–254. HMSO, London.

NIAB. 1976. *Recommended varieties of cereals,* Farmers Leaflet No. 8. Cambridge: NIAB.

NIAB. 1982. *Recommended varieties of cereals,* Farmers Leaflet No. 8. Cambridge: NIAB.

SELMAN, M. and DAMPNEY, P. M. R. 1978. The application of nitrogen to spring barley. In: *Gleadthorpe Annual Review* 1977, pp. 25–29. Gleadthorpe EHF, Mansfield, Nottinghamshire.

SPARROW, P. E. 1979. Nitrogen response curves of spring barley. *Journal of Agricultural Science* **92**, 307–317.

ZADOKS, J. C., CHANG, T. T. and KONZAK, C. F. 1974. A decimal code for the growth stages of cereals. *Weed Research* **14**, 415–421.

Discussion

Dr Smith commented that if the efficiency of nitrogen recovery in the crop remained static in the future, greater use of nitrogen on the crop could produce a pollution hazard as a result of increased nitrate levels in ground water supplies owing to leaching losses. He suggested that an improvement in the efficiency of nitrogen fertiliser use was needed before higher rates of application were advocated. Mr Johnson sympathised with the view expressed and thought that the question of inputs should be considered carefully. Mr Unwin stated that some Water Authorities were concerned in case higher nitrogen inputs, to give further yield increases, also resulted in greater pollution. Mr Lidgate commented that data from ICI trials at West Isley had shown only a small loss of nitrogen fertiliser when applied at high rates for spring barley and that some loss was inevitable.

Dr Holmes asked why the optimum nitrogen level had increased in recent years and particularly in 1982 when, according to the limited ADAS trials data currently available, the optimum rate seemed to be at least 180 kg/ha of N. Mr Johnson replied that he did not at that stage have sufficient information on the 1982 trials to explain the trend in optimum levels.

Mr Archer asked whether the variety and its resistance to lodging could be a key factor in the nitrogen response of spring barley. Mr Whitear stated that variety was only a small factor. In his work Triumph had so far shown the greatest response to nitrogen and this had not been simply related to the degree of lodging.

Nitrogen for spring barley

J D Whitear and M R J Holmes
Norsk Hydro Fertilizers Limited, Levington Research Station, Ipswich

Information on two aspects of nitrogen use on spring barley are provided by recent experiments carried out by Levington Research Station.

Optimum nitrogen level

Twenty-eight field experiments sited on commercial farms in the arable areas of the UK from Scotland to Devon were done in the period 1978–1980. Each experiment compared levels of nitrogen from nil to 140 kg/ha applied in the seedbed and also four split programmes. Details can be seen in Figure 1 below

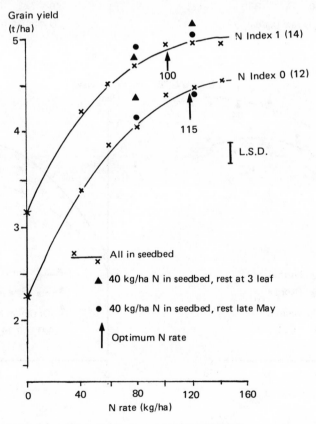

Fig. 1 Grain yield response, 26 spring barley experiments, 1978–80.

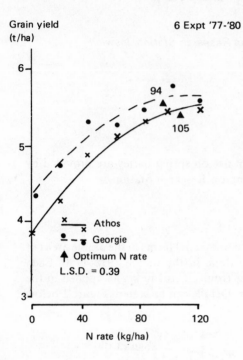

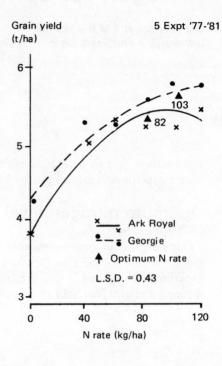

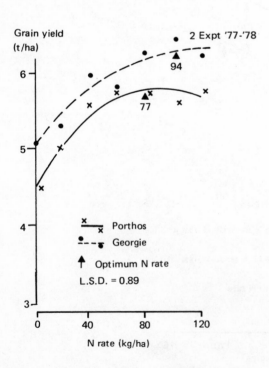

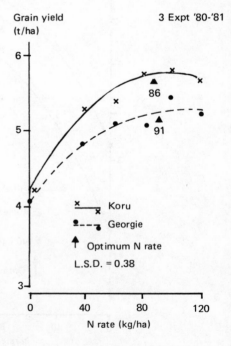

Fig. 2 Grain yield response to N; selected varieties.

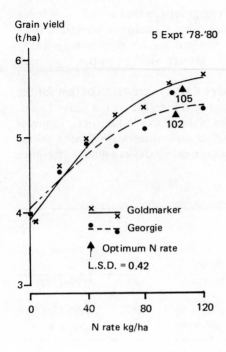

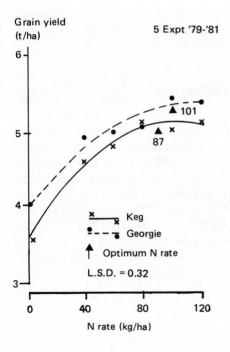

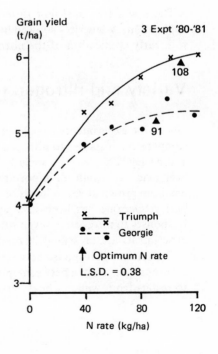

which shows the yield results from 26 of these experiments. The other two were on sites with an N Index of 2.

The experiments have been divided into two groups on the basis of site N Index (ADAS scale). Responses have been fitted using a quadratic equation. Both groups show a mean optimum level of nitrogen greater than now generally accepted by farmers, probably related to greater yield potential from new varieties and improved husbandry.

The optimum nitrogen level for the Index 0 sites is greater than that for the Index 1, and the yield without fertiliser nitrogen is higher on the Index 1 sites. However, this general relationship between N index and soil nitrogen supply is subject to considerable variation on individual sites, as shown in Table 1 below, confirming the well recognised lack of precision in N Index as a guide to fertiliser nitrogen requirement.

Table 1

N Index	0		1	
No. of sites	12		14	
	Mean	Range	Mean	Range
Grain yield at nil N (t/ha)	2.42	(1.60–4.01)	3.21	(1.27–4.53)
Response to N at optimum N level (t/ha)	2.15	(1.43–4.29)	1.70	(0.97–3.25)
Optimum N level (kg/ha)	115	(92–>140)	100	(58–>140)

There was no consistent difference between seedbed and split methods of application. A few sites showed higher yield from split, in most cases associated with early application of the nitrogen in a wet spring.

Variety and nitrogen requirement

Since 1966 experiments have been carried out by Levington Research Station to compare the response to nitrogen of the main recommended varieties of wheat and barley. The varieties included have changed with time but an attempt has been made to include all important varieties for at least three years. Each variety has been grown at seven levels of nitrogen in a split plot design and, for spring barley, Georgie has been used as a common control variety in recent years. Responses to nitrogen in seven spring barley varieties taken from the 1977–1981 experiments are presented in Figure 2, using a quadratic fit for the response.

Differences in response between varieties is not always clear cut but a general relationship is shown between optimum level of nitrogen and yield level, similar to results from winter wheat variety experiments.

Plant growth and composition as predictors of nitrogen requirements

T Batey
University of Aberdeen

Investigations into the use of plant growth and composition as predictors of the nitrogen requirement for cereals were conducted in south-east England 1966–1969 with winter wheat. Plant samples were taken on several occasions in spring; dry matter (DM) yield and nitrogen concentration (per cent N) were determined. Full details of the experiments and the effects of nitrogen on grain yield, grain size and composition and the use of leaf analysis to predict nitrogen

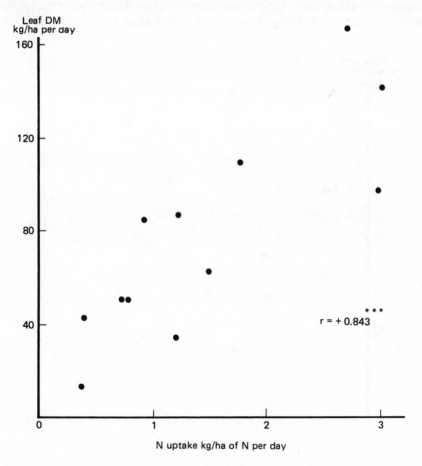

Fig. 1 Rate of increase in leaf DM (kg/ha per day) v. rate of increase in N uptake (kg/ha of N per day) (winter wheat 1966–67).

fertiliser requirements have been published (Batey, 1976, 1977a and 1977b; Batey and Reynish, 1976). Some of the conclusions were:

1. Dry matter growth was related to nitrogen as shown by the significant relationship between rate of increase in DM and rate of increase in nitrogen uptake (both expressed as kg/ha per day, Figure 1).

2. Early plant growth was related to the optimum rate of nitrogen fertiliser, e.g. for rate of DM increase, and for rate of increase in nitrogen uptake (Figure 2).

3. Optimum levels of nitrogen fertiliser varied between 0 and 195 kg/ha yet only 9 per cent of the total variation in these levels could be removed by regression against the corresponding levels recommended by the ADAS N Index System (Greenwood, 1982).

Further work has been done in north-east Scotland, using spring barley. (O'Neill, 1980; O'Neill, Batey and Cresser, 1983a and 1983b).

In these investigations one site was used each year and samples of plants were taken weekly during vegetative growth for DM yield, N concentration and plant pigment determinations.

Early season parameters were compared with grain yield, final DM yield, final nitrogen uptake and other end-of-season parameters. A selection of the results is shown in Figures 3–6. These show that, as early as three to five weeks after plant

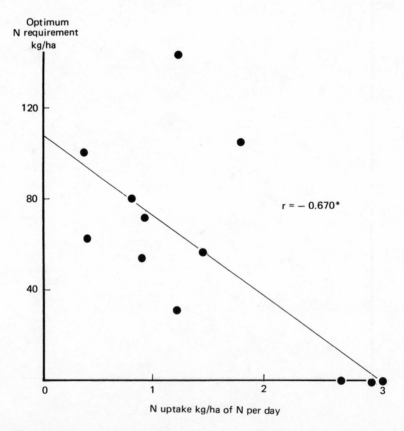

Fig. 2 N requirement (kg/ha) v. rate of increase in N uptake (kg/ha of N per day) (winter wheat 1966–67).

emergence, the crop was already reflecting the nitrogen status of the soil in which it was growing. Grain yield was predicted from plant nitrogen concentration, chlorophyll a concentration, and from an estimate of nitrogen stress based on DM growth rate. Further work with this approach appears fully justified.

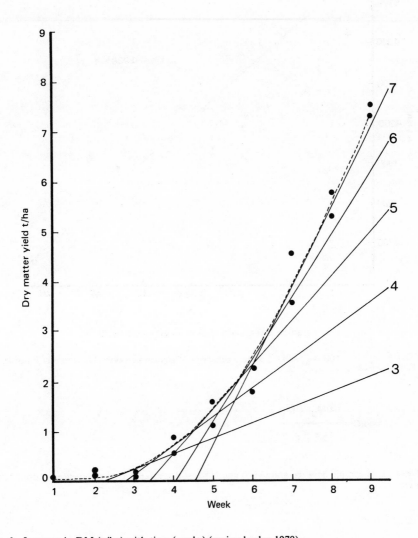

Fig. 3 Increase in DM (t/ha) with time (weeks) (spring barley 1979).

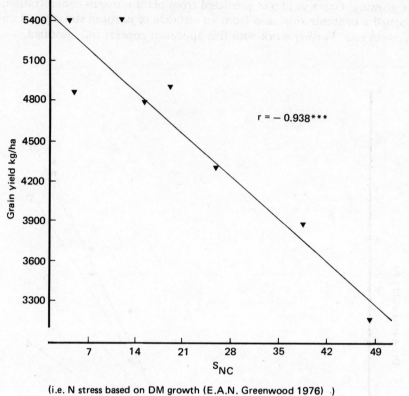

(i.e. N stress based on DM growth (E.A.N. Greenwood 1976))

$$S_{NC} = \frac{100\ (C_M - C)}{C_M}$$

Where subscript M signifies growth rate where N is not limiting

$$\text{and } C = \frac{DM_2 - DM_1}{T_2 - T_1} \quad g\ m^{-2}\ day^{-1}$$

Fig. 4 Relationship between grain yield and N stress three weeks after emergence of spring barley 1979.

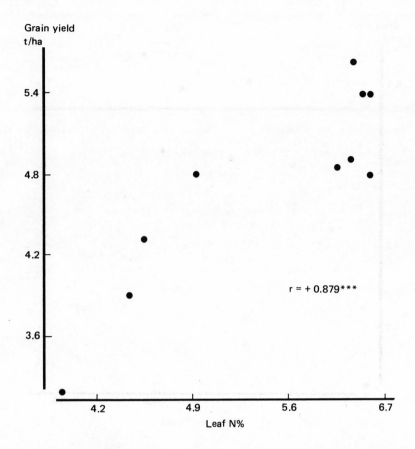

Fig. 5 Grain yield (t/ha) v. leaf N (%) four weeks after emergence (spring barley 1979).

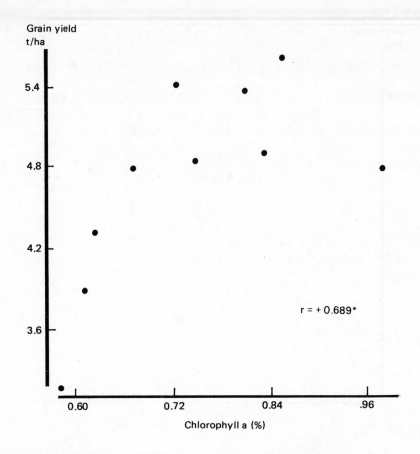

Fig. 6 Grain yield (t/ha) v. plant pigment concentration five weeks after emergence (spring barley 1979).

References

BATEY, T. 1976. Some effects of nitrogen fertiliser on winter wheat. *Journal of Science Food and Agriculture* **27**, 287–297.

BATEY, T. 1977a. Prediction by leaf analysis of nitrogen fertiliser required for winter wheat. *Journal of Science Food and Agriculture* **28**, 275–278.

BATEY, T. 1977b. Assessment of the nitrogen requirement of winter wheat. *Journal of Science Food and Agriculture* **28**, 874.

BATEY, T. and REYNISH, D. J. 1976. The influence of nitrogen fertiliser on grain quality in winter wheat. *Journal of Science Food and Agriculture* **27**, 983–990.

GREENWOOD, D. J. 1982. Modelling of crop response to nitrogen fertiliser. *Philosophical Transactions of the Royal Society of London, series B* **296**, 351–360.

GREENWOOD, E. A. F. 1976. Nitrogen stress in plants. *Advances in Agronomy* **28**, 1–35.

O'NEILL, E. J. 1980. *Assessment of nitrogen status of soils with respect to the growth of cereal crops.* Ph.D. Thesis, University of Aberdeen.

O'NEILL, E. J., BATEY, T. and CRESSER, M. S. 1983a. I Effects of nitrogen fertiliser on growth, composition and yield of spring barley. *Journal of Science Food and Agriculture* **34**, 541–548.

O'NEILL. E. J. BATEY, T. and CRESSER, M. S. 1983b. II Use of plant and soil analysis to diagnose nitrogen status of spring barley. *Journal of Science Food and Agriculture* **34**, 549–558.

An assessment of nitrate reductase activity as a predictor of nitrogen requirement of winter cereals

R Sylvester-Bradley, P A J Barnard and P F W Hart
ADAS, Wolverhampton

Summary

Nitrate reductase activity (NRA) was measured in leaf discs from 57 cereal trials during March and April 1980. The optimum level of nitrogen was determined in 35 of these trials but neither this nor yield nor rate of response to nitrogen was related to NRA. In other experiments differences in NRA were found between varieties and between growth stages. These accounted for some of the variation in NRA between sites. Time of day and air temperature at sampling may also have affected NRA. These difficulties are discussed and it is concluded that NRA is too labile to be used as a predictor of soil nitrogen status or cereal nitrogen requirement.

Introduction

Nitrate reductase has been claimed to catalyse the rate limiting step in the nitrogen assimilation pathway of plants (Schrader *et al.,* 1968). This conclusion has given rise to a number of attempts, principally by Hageman and co-workers, to correlate nitrate reductase activity (NRA) with total nitrogen uptake and yield of several cereals. Interest has centred on predicting varietal differences in yield from NRA during early growth. Eilrich and Hageman (1973) found that an integral of NRA through the season was closely correlated with total uptake of nitrogen and yield of nitrogen in wheat grain within a particular variety, but was not so closely correlated with yield of dry matter. Croy and Hageman (1970) related grain yield of wheat to NRA within a variety but there was no correlation amongst different varieties.

Bar-Akiva *et al.* (1970) have suggested that if NRA was measured both with and without added nitrate the degree to which the enzyme was restricted by lack of substrate might provide an index of requirement for fertiliser nitrogen. More recently Johnson *et al.* (1976) have claimed, on limited evidence, a general association in spring barley between NRA at the 3–4 leaf stage and final grain yield. Such correlations may be misleading because they only link NRA with yield differences caused by nitrogen applied at one site in one season, whereas a successful predictor must correlate with nitrogen requirement over a range of sites and seasons.

It has been shown for most winter cereal crops in the UK that nitrogen dressings are most efficiently used when they are applied at or before the beginning of stem extension. Thus, an index of nitrogen requirement can only be of value if it is known at an early date. Availability of soil nitrogen changes throughout the life of the crop depending on many factors. However, it is possible that such changes may be sufficiently small for these to be an association between soil-derived nitrogen taken up by the crop before fertiliser application (assessed by NRA), and that available later (which will determine nitrogen requirement).

This paper therefore considers a range of experiments on winter wheat and winter barley in which NRA was measured shortly before stem extension and nitrogen requirement determined by measuring grain yield at a range of fertiliser nitrogen levels.

Methods

The experiments

Samples were all taken during the spring of 1980 from experiments in which six or more levels of fertiliser nitrogen were being tested. Most trials were components of national series of experiments (coded SA 80 for winter barley and SA 92 for winter wheat) covering a range of varieties and husbandry practices. The experiments are described in more detail elsewhere in this publication (Grylls and Archer, 1984, pages 191–207; Sylvester-Bradley et al., 1984, pages 151–174).

In a subsidiary exercise differences in NRA between the different varieties used in the above experiments were assessed on two blocks of variety trials conducted by the National Institute of Agricultural Botany (NIAB) at Rosemaund Experimental Husbandry Farm and Harper Adams Agricultural College. The effect of stage of sampling was investigated, at one site only, by taking 10 samples between March and June from an experiment on winter wheat.

The nitrogen requirement in each experiment was determined from a curve fitted by eye to the graph of the yields of grain corrected to 85 per cent dry matter. Where agronomic factors other than nitrogen were being investigated in the trial, the mean yields over all levels were taken. Where nitrogen was applied at different times, yields were only taken from the single dressing made at the beginning of stem extension. The nitrogen requirement was defined as the lowest level of applied nitrogen (to the nearest 25 kg/ha) at which a further 25 kg/ha did not increase yield by more than 0.1 t/ha grain. At several sites nitrogen requirement was apparently greater than the largest level tested; only yield and rate of response to nitrogen were examined on these trials.

Sampling and analyses

Shortly before the beginning of stem extension (4 –12 March for winter barley and 8 –17 April for winter wheat) a plot with no applied nitrogen from each block of each experiment was sampled by taking the youngest fully extended leaf blade from 100 plants. Samples were taken during the morning and were stored in moist, cool, dark conditions for up to 4 h. Records were made of air temperature at the time of sampling and temperatures during storage. Records of recent rain at the nearest rain gauge were obtained from the Meteorological Office.

For each assay 108 discs 2.5 mm in diameter were punched from nine leaf blades giving a total fresh weight of approximately 110 mg. These were incubated in 10 ml phosphate buffer pH 7.4 in the dark at 30 °C. After incubation nitrite was determined by mixing 2 ml of the solution with 9 ml of 0.11 per cent sulphanilic acid in 0.22M hydrochloric acid and, after 1 min, 1 ml of N 1-Napthylethylenediaminedihydrochloride (NEDD) was added. Optical density at 535 nm was read after 30 min.

All samples were assayed both with (NRA+) and without (NRA−) 0.05M nitrate in the incubation buffer, and each assay was conducted twice. Under these conditions nitrate reduction in the NRA+ treatment continued at a constant rate for more than 2 h and NRA− declined to zero as endogenous nitrate in the discs became exhausted. Incubation time for all assays was set at 1 h.

Determinations of fresh disc weight, dry matter content, nitrate, and total nitrogen were made on each leaf sample (MAFF, 1981) in addition to NRA− and NRA+. NRA has normally been expressed on a fresh weight basis. However, the samples of winter barley were taken during a spell of wet weather and moisture content varied according to the quantity of recent rain. Results are, therefore, expressed on a dry matter basis. The samples of winter wheat which were taken during dry warm weather were not affected in this way, but it was necessary to reject some wheat samples which experienced temperatures of over 30 °C before analysis.

Results and discussion

Austin, Rossi and Blackwell (1978) have investigated varietal differences in NRA of young winter wheat plants and found that these could largely be explained by the level of nitrate supply and plant size; smaller plants tended to develop higher levels of nitrate in their leaf tissue, which induced higher levels of NRA. Inherent differences in NRA of the winter wheat and winter barley varieties were assessed on two NIAB variety trials. There were consistent differences in NRA but these were generally small compared to the differences found between sites in the ADAS nitrogen trials (Table 1) and they did not account for a significant proportion of variation in either crop (winter barley, $r = +0.40$, 22 df; winter wheat, $r = +0.02$, 26 df).

Measurements of NRA made by this Unit over a number of seasons (D R Wade, unpublished) have shown marked fluctuations in NRA from week to week, and a tendency for NRA to decline fairly sharply during stem extension. Fluctuations during 1980 at Rosemaund (Figure 1) were less pronounced than previously but again there was a drop in NRA during stem extension (April). This was associated with a spell of dry weather and was only counteracted where nitrogen was applied and when rainfall recommenced at the beginning of 'booting' (late May).

No measurements were made of soil nitrate levels or plant size but the reduction in April appears to be due to rapid dry matter production during stem extension which depleted soil and tissue nitrate levels, and consequently NRA.

Assays on the 25 ADAS winter barley trials took place over a period of nine days during early March. Most crops were still tillering and their NRA levels had

Table 1 NRA of different varieties of winter barley and winter wheat grown together (NIAB trials) and at different sites (ADAS trials) in 1980

Variety	NIAB trials	ADAS trials		
	Mean of two trials	Mean	Range	No. trials
	NRA+ (μmol NO$_2$ h^{-1} g^{-1} DM)			
Water barley				
Maris Otter	13.4	18.6	12.2–24.9	2
Sonja	10.3	13.8	9.7–22.4	10
Athene	9.1	14.5	7.2–22.8	3
Igri	9.0	10.1	5.1–16.3	8
SED (10 df)	1.08			
Winter wheat				
Flanders	14.5	6.0	–	1
Aquila	14.3	10.7	–	1
Hobbit	14.3	5.3	2.7–12.1	7
Maris Huntsman	14.2	5.4	3.8–9.3	9
Bounty	13.6	5.3	4.8–5.7	2
Armada	13.2	3.0	–	1
Hustler	12.7	8.2	4.9–11.8	3
Mardler	12.4	4.4	4.1–4.6	3
SED (22 df)	1.63			

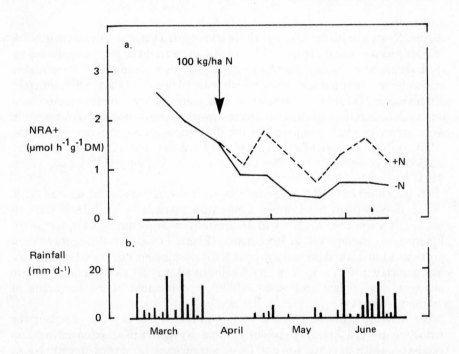

Fig. 1a Effect of 100 kg/ha N on NRA+ in winter wheat cv Hustler.
  b Rainfall at Rosemaund EHF during 1980.

236

a significant inverse correlation with their average number of tillers (recorded as growth stage, Zadoks et al., 1974, and thus a very crude estimate, r = 0.42*, 20 df) despite the range of varieties and widely differing environmental conditions.

There was also a similar relationship with growth stage of the 27 winter wheat crops, the least tillered crops having the highest NRA levels. It is, therefore, clear that plant size is an important determinant of NRA level in both crops, and this introduces a difficulty when making inter-site comparisons.

In addition, it must be noted that the time of day when the samples were taken varied unavoidably between 0820 and 1300 hours and it is possible that some high values in the wheat samples taken around midday were due to the diurnal maximum in NRA that is expected at that time (Bowerman and Goodman, 1971; NRA+ vs. time of day, r = +0.34, 26 df). Also, air temperatures at sampling ranged from 1 °C to 21 °C and it is possible that some of the high values in the barley samples were caused by temperatures below 3 °C (NRA+ vs. air temperature, r = +0.40, 22 df).

The nitrogen requirements of these crops ranged from 100 kg/ha to over 200 kg/ha in winter barley and from 75 kg/ha to over 320 kg/ha in winter wheat. The various difficulties in determining nitrogen requirements reliably and precisely are described elsewhere. In the 1980 trials a definite conclusion on optimum nitrogen level was possible on only 12 of the winter barley trials and 18 of the winter wheat trials. Components of the nitrogen requirement have, therefore, been calculated so that all sites could be examined. These include the residual fertility of the site (Y-30, expressed as grain yield at 30 kg/ha N), the maximum yield at the site (Y-max), and the rate of response to nitrogen up to the optimum or the maximum level tested (kg grain per kg nitrogen applied).

The factors suggested as predictors of the nitrogen requirement are in vivo NRA (NRA+, Johnson et al., 1976) and nitrate assimilation capacity (NAC = NRA+/NRA-, Bar-Akiva et al., 1970). Correlation coefficients between these and the site parameters are given in Table 2. None approaches statistical significance. Additional factors thought to have possible predictive value were unsaturated NRA (NRA+ − NRA-), NRA+ corrected for variety, total nitrogen content of the leaf, and nitrate content of the leaf. However, there was also no significant correlation with any of these.

Table 2   Coefficients of correlation between nitrate reductase activity (NRA+), nitrate assimilation capacity (NAC), and nitrogen requirement and its components (for definitions see text). No coefficient is significant at the 0.05 level.

	N requirement kg/ha	Y-30 t/ha	Y-opt t/ha	Rate of response kg/kg
Winter barley				
degrees of freedom:	11	22	22	22
NRA+	−0.13	−0.16	−0.14	+0.04
NAC	−0.15	−0.10	−0.05	+0.21
Winter wheat				
degrees of freedom:	17	25	26	25
NRA+	−0.27	+0.15	+0.18	−0.27
NAC	−0.11	+0.15	+0.24	+0.20

Predictors of the nitrogen requirement such as previous crop and soil type have been discussed elsewhere and difficulties in the use of predictors need not be repeated here. However, it is clear that predictors such as NRA which are based on plant analysis are subject to marked short-term fluctuations, influenced by factors such as recent rainfall, the extent of early tillering, the time of day and the temperature at sampling. None of these has any bearing on later growth of the crop. What is required is the most stable integral of available soil nitrogen over the period prior to fertiliser application. It seems reasonable to expect that the total nitrogen content of the plant would be more stable than the activity of a single enzyme. However, due to the effect of plant size discussed earlier some careful correction of this measurement would be necessary before it could be sensibly assessed as a predictor of nitrogen requirement.

Acknowledgement

We are most grateful to many ADAS colleagues for providing samples, laboratory facilities and yield data, to NIAB for allowing access to their experiments, to the Meteorological Office for rainfall data, and to Mrs J C Smallshire for technical assistance.

References

AUSTIN, R. B., ROSSI, L. and BLACKWELL, R. D. 1978. Relationships between nitrate reductase activity, plant weight and nitrogen content in seedlings of *Triticum, Aegilops* and *Triticale. Annals of Botany* **42**, 429–438.

BAR-AKIVA, A., SAGIV, S. and LESHEM, J. 1970. Nitrate reductase activity as an indicator for assessing the nitrogen requirement of grass crops. *Journal of the Science of Food and Agriculture* **21**, 405–407.

BOWERMAN, A. and GOODMAN, P. J. 1971. Variation in nitrate reductase activity in *Lolium. Annals of Botany* **35**, 353–366.

CROY, L. I. and HAGEMAN, R. H. 1970. Relationship of nitrate reductase activity to grain protein production in wheat. *Crop Science* **10**, 280–285.

EILRICH, G. L. and HAGEMAN, R. H. 1973. Nitrate reductase activity and its relationship to accumulation of vegetative and grain nitrogen in wheat. *Crop Science* **13**, 59–65.

GRYLLS, J. P., and ARCHER, J. R. 1984. Response of winter barley to nitrogen. Ministry of Agriculture Fisheries and Food, Reference Book 385, *The Nitrogen Requirement of Cereals,* pp. 191–207. HMSO, London.

JOHNSON, C. B., WHITTINGTON, W. J. and BLACKWOOD, G. C. 1976. Nitrate reductase as a possible predictive test of crop yield. *Nature* **262**, 133–134.

MAFF 1981. Reference Book 427, *The analysis of agricultural materials,* 2nd edn. HMSO, London.

SCHRADER, L. E., RITENOUR, G. L., EILRICH, G. L. and HAGEMAN, R. H. 1968. Some characteristics of nitrate reductase from higher plants. *Plant Physiology* **43**, 930–940.

SYLVESTER-BRADLEY, R., DAMPNEY, P. M. R. and MURRAY, A. W. A. 1984. The response of winter wheat to nitrogen. Ministry of Agriculture, Fisheries and Food, Reference Book 385, *The Nitrogen Requirement of Cereals,* pp. 151–174. HMSO, London.

ZADOKS, J. C., CHANG, T. T. and KONZAK, C. F. 1974. A decimal code for the growth stage of cereals. *Weed Research* **14**, 415–421.

Nitrate reductase activity and the assessment of nitrogen status

L M J Verstraeten and K Vlassak
Katholieke Universiteit Leuven, Leuven, Belgium

Summary

In an experiment on winter wheat during 1981, it was shown, using a combination of soil nitrogen and plant growth parameters, that nitrate reductase activity (NRA) is a useful assay for assessment of nitrogen status of plants. The nitrate assimilation capacity (NAC), or ratio of 'induced' to 'endogeneous' activity, was used for the identification of nitrogen stress. NAC values between 1 and 10 corresponded to optimum nutrient conditions, whereas poor nitrogen status was indicated when values gradually increased to 100 and more.

Introduction

Nitrate reductase, being the first and limiting step in the metabolism of nitrate by plants before assimilation to protein (Hewitt, 1980; Klepper *et al.,* 1971), has been suggested as an indicator of nitrogen requirement on several occasions (Bar-Akiva *et al.,* 1970; Dalling *et al.,* 1975; Johnson *et al.,* 1976). Recently, evidence has been obtained by Sylvester-Bradley *et al.* (1984) that nitrate reductase activity (NRA) may be too labile in this respect. However, during the past two years, NRA has been thoroughly examined for its possible use as an index of nitrogen stress (Verstraeten and Vlassak, 1981) or as a simple tool for the assessment of nitrogen status (Vlassak *et al.,* 1982). The experiment reported here considers a number of soil and plant analyses during growth in order to prove the reliability of NRA as a predictor of the time and the amount of nitrogen that should be applied.

Methods

The experiment

In 1980–81 two varieties of winter wheat, Celesta and a breeding line 01104–76, were grown at Heverlee, Belgium with five treatments testing different amounts of nitrogen, including a nil-N treatment. The soil was loamy with 1.43 per cent organic matter. There was a large amount of mineral nitrogen remaining in the profile, half in the ammonium form, following the previous crop of peas (Table 1).

Sampling and analysis

Sampling started shortly before the first nitrogen application (31 March) and extended throughout the season on a fortnightly basis. During critical periods, such as at the beginning of May, this schedule was increased to a weekly sampling. The samples were taken in the morning, at about ten o'clock, and were assayed within an hour for their NRA (Sylvester-Bradley, 1979). The analytical procedure was the same as outlined by Sylvester-Bradley et al. (1984). Additional determinations included nitrate analysis of plant 'stems' and mineral nitrogen analysis of soil samples taken at various depths. Larger plant samples were also taken (0.25 m²) and their dry matter yield and total nitrogen concentration were transformed into plant growth parameters such as rate of increase in dry matter (kg ha⁻¹ d⁻¹) and rate of nitrogen uptake (kg ha⁻¹ d⁻¹) (Batey, 1970; Batey, 1984, this volume (pages 227–232); Vlassak et al., 1982).

Results and discussion

In order to improve advice on nitrogen as given on the Continent, with successive applications at growth stages 20–22, 30 and 39 (Zadoks et al., 1974), a correct assessment of nitrogen status during this period is of vital importance. Verstraeten and Vlassak (1981) showed earlier that nitrogen supply, from either fertiliser applications or soil mineralisation, is almost the only variable governing nitrate reductase activity. Smaller effects are due to variety and growth stage, the latter reflecting a general ontogenetic trend (e.g. Blahova and Segeta, 1980). One similar approach to the use of NRA has been the use of colour tests on stem sap by German workers (Wollring and Wehrmann, 1981) and by Scaife (1979) in the UK.

Realising the high amounts of mineral nitrogen in the soil profile of the crop described here (Table 1), as well as the potential effect of the previous crop on the release of further soil nitrogen, the assumption was made that nitrogen supply by the soil would be quite adequate for crop growth. This was more or less

Table 1 Mineral nitrogen in the profile during the growing season

	Soil depth cm	NH_4^+-N kg/ha	NO_3^--N	Total mineral N kg/ha
24th November 1980	0–30	39.8	40.1	79.9
	30–60	0.5	49.5	50.0
	60–90	0.6	18.2	18.8
Total	0–90	40.9	107.8	148.7
4th march 1981	0–30	0.1	9.9	10.0
	30–60	1.0	45.4	46.4
	60–90	16.2	27.3	43.5
Total	0–90	17.3	82.6	99.9
15th August 1981	0–30	1.7	6.1	7.8
	30–60	1.9	2.7	4.6
	60–90	1.9	1.1	3.0
Total	0–90	5.5	9.9	15.4

confirmed by the NAC values obtained, at least until the end of April or beginning of May (Table 2). Therefore only two nitrogen applications were tested, both at rather low levels.

Table 2   NAC values during growth of two cultivars of winter wheat during 1981

N level kg/ha	Date 16/3	22/4	13/5	20/5	1/6
Celesta					
0 + 0	1.7	11.5	170	28.5	32.5
26 + 0		9.3	47	–	–
26 + 13			50	51	–
26 + 26			42	–	–
26 + 36			2.6	40.0	22.0
01104 –76					
0 + 0	2.7	14.0	19.6	20.5	79.0
26 + 0		14.2	30.0	–	–
26 + 13			28.2	75.0	–
26 + 26			23.0	–	–
26 + 39			7.1	32.5	67.0

Half way through May nitrogen stress became obvious, except at the highest N level (Table 2). In order to make sure that the nitrogen status was deficient at that stage and to obtain additional proof that NRA reflects nitrogen status, the nitrate concentration of the stem sap was determined (Table 3).

Table 3   Nitrate concentration in leaves on 13 May for different nitrogen applications

	Total N level kg/ha	NO_3^- ppm
Celesta	0	868
	26	1244
	52	1054
	65	3450
01104 –76	0	1310
	26	1054
	52	1178
	65	2360

As can be seen, the 'critical' level of 1000 ppm nitrate was only just reached in treatments other than at the highest nitrogen level. At the same time, nitrogen offtake figures for the nil-N plots made it clear that between 70 and 100 kg/ha of N, depending on the cultivar involved, had already been taken from the profile. So the conclusion was reached that the profile was already 'empty' and this was confirmed by soil analysis (Table 4): only 13 kg/ha of N remained in the soil. However, half of this soil nitrogen was in the ammonium form, indicating that nitrogen was still being mineralised from residues of the previous pea crop.

Only an additional 8 kg/ha of N remained from the 65 kg/ha of N application, indicating impending nitrogen stress in this treatment as well. Verification was provided by the NAC values of 20 May and 1 June (Table 2). On the other hand

Table 4 Mineral nitrogen in the soil profile on nil-N plots and at the highest nitrogen level

Soil depth cm	NH$_4^+$-N	NO$_3^-$-N	Total mineral-N kg/ha
	kg/ha		
Nil-N plot			
0–30	2.39	2.88	
30–60	2.03	2.39	
60–90	1.53	1.76	
Total 0–90	5.95	7.03	12.98
65 kg/ha			
0–30	3.42	4.14	
30–60	3.02	3.65	
60–90	3.29	3.92	
Total 0–90	9.73	11.71	21.44

the rates of nitrogen uptake for the second half of May were 2.1 and 2.8 kg ha^{-1}d^{-1} respectively for Celesta and cultivar 01104–76. This means that the mineralisation rate must have been quite high to cope with the demands of nitrogen assimilation by the crop.

Summarising, it is quite clear that a combination of several plant and soil tests enable assessment of nitrogen status. In other words these tests can best describe the dynamic relationships that exist between nitrogen supply and nitrogen uptake, assimilation and translocation, and they can identify any resulting nitrogen shortage, or depletion of nitrogen in the profile. The importance in this of plant tests must be stressed, and especially nitrate reductase activity as this gives a more fundamental insight into the results of sap tests for nitrate (Alcaraz *et al.,* 1979; Gasic *et al.,* 1981). Nitrogen requirement is established over several different stages of growth and so improved nitrogen fertilisation in terms of quantity and timing is most likely to be achieved by regular tests. These should eventually lead to a more economic approach to the use of nitrogen.

Acknowledgement

The authors are most grateful to several colleagues from the MAFF, especially Mr P Needham, Dr R Sylvester-Bradley and Mr R J Skinner and to Dr T Batey (University of Aberdeen) for useful discussions. Thanks are also due to Ir J Niclaes, Director of the Breeding Station at Heverlee, for collaborating in conducting the experiment. The IWONL is gratefully acknowledged for financial support.

References

ALCARAZ. C. F., BANET. E., HELLIN. E. and LIORENTE. S., 1979. Nitrogen and nitrate reductase activity in Verna Lemon tree leaves. *Journal of Plant Nutrition* 1, 347–354.

BAR-AKIVA, A., SAGIV, S. and LESHEM, J. 1970. Nitrate reductase activity as an indicator for assessing the nitrogen requirement of grass crops. *Journal of the Science of Food and Agriculture* 21, 405–407.

BATEY, T. 1976. Some effects of nitrogen fertiliser on winter wheat. *Journal of the Science of Food and Agriculture* 27, 287–297.

BATEY, T. 1984. Plant growth and composition as predictors of nitrogen requirements. Ministry of Agriculture, Fisheries and Food, Reference Book 385, *The Nitrogen Requirement of Cereals,* pp. 227–232. HMSO, London

BLAHOVA, M. and SEGETA, V. 1980. Nitrate reductase activity in the course of cucumber leaf ontogenesis. *Biologia Plantarum* **22**, 176–182.

DALLING, M. J., HALLORAN, G. M. and WILSON, J. H. 1975. The relation between nitrate reductase activity and grain nitrogen productivity in wheat. *Australian Journal of Agricultural Research* **26**, 1–10.

GASIC, O., KRALJEVIC-BALALIC, M., POPOVIC, M. and POPOVIC, J. 1981. Nitrate reductase activity and soluble leaf protein content in wheat crosses. *Zeitschift fur Pflanzenzuchtung* **87**, 25–32.

HEWITT, E. J. 1980. *Crop physiology.* Wageningen: Pudoc Press.

JOHNSON, C. B., WHITTINGTON, W. J. and BLACKWOOD, G. C. 1976. Nitrate reductase as a possible predictive test of crop yield. *Nature* **262**, 133–134.

KLEPPER, L., FLESHER, D. and HAGEMAN, R. H. 1971. Generation of reduced nicotinamide adenine dinucleotide for nitrate reduction in green leaves. *Plant Physiology* **48**, 580–590.

SCAIFE, A. 1979. The snappy sap test. *Big Farm Management* (November), 17/20.

SYLVESTER-BRADLEY, R. 1979. *Measurement of nitrate reductase activity in crops.* MAFF: Plant Physiology Unit (Wolverhampton) (Internal report).

SYLVESTER-BRADLEY, R., BARNARD, P. A. J. and HART, P. F. W. 1984. An assessment of nitrate reductase activity as a predictor of nitrogen requirement of winter cereals. Ministry of Agriculture, Fisheries and Food, Reference Book 385, *The Nitrogen Requirement of Cereals,* pp. 233–238. HMSO, London.

VERSTRAETEN, L. M. J. and VLASSAK, K., 1981. Nitrogen stress and plant growth in relation to the nitrogen status of plant and soil. *Pedologie* **31**, 379–392.

VLASSAK, K., VERSTRAETEN, L. M. J. and BATEY, T. 1982. Dry matter production and N offtake as parameters in the assessment of N status for winter wheat. *Proceedings of the Ninth International Plant Nutrition Coloquium* (Warwick), Vol. **2**, 695.

WOLLRING, J. and WEHRMANN, J. 1981. Der Nitrat-Schnelltest Entscheidungshilfe fur die N-Spatdungung. *DLG Mitteilungen* **8**, 448–450.

ZADOKS, J. C., CHANG, T. T. and KONZAK, C. F. 1974. A decimal code for growth stages of cereals. *Weed Research* **14**, 415–421.

The basis of current nitrogen recommendations for cereals

P Needham
ADAS, London

Summary

The development of the current ADAS system of nitrogen recommendations for cereals is reviewed. It is only during the last 15 years that attention has been focussed on the accurate estimation of optimal nitrogen requirements, in an attempt to improve the reliability of recommendations.

Many different site and crop factors have been suggested as possibly influencing nitrogen requirements. Experimental evidence has shown the effects of most of these to be either small or inconsistent.

Soil analysis for mineral or mineralisable nitrogen and measurement of plant nitrogen status, have also so far failed to demonstrate any value as predictors of nitrogen requirements.

Apart from soil type, the factor which most consistently influences nitrogen requirement is previous cropping. The soil nitrogen Index has been developed to give a simple but reasonably reliable assessment of the influence of previous cropping on nitrogen supply, in the absence of a reliable analytical method.

The next step in the improvement in the precision of nitrogen recommendation is likely to be the introduction of calculation or model-based methods, but current information may well be inadequate to give these methods the reliability and general applicability which is needed.

Introduction

Although the value of fertilisers for cereals has been established for more than a century, early publications on fertiliser use placed relatively little emphasis on quantities. For example, Hall (1911) recommended the application of farmyard manure (FYM) to a ley before ploughing, with no other fertiliser for the following wheat crop, and 1 cwt per acre of ammonium sulphate (25 kg/ha of N) for a barley crop following the wheat.

In the first MAFF bulletin on fertiliser use (MAFF, 1931) the recommendation was for 1 cwt per acre of ammonium sulphate for both winter and spring sown cereals. The recommended timing was at the end of tillering for winter cereals, and at sowing for spring sown crops.

Most cereal crops at this time were grown in short rotations with grassland, and FYM was often applied, so responses to fertiliser nitrogen were sometimes small. Response was also limited by the weakness of the straw of varieties grown at that time.

More numerous experiments during the 1950s and early 1960s provided more information on the nitrogen requirements of cereals, although these experiments frequently included other factors such as forms of nitrogen, timing of nitrogen and interactions with other nutrients. The small number of nitrogen levels in these experiments prevented any accurate location of optima, but nevertheless identified some of the factors influencing response to nitrogen. These were incorporated in the first attempt at comprehensive fertiliser recommendations for all crops, first published in 1967 (MAFF, 1967).

The form of the response curve

For early experiments with only three or at the most four levels of nitrogen interpretation consisted either of tests of significance (which are not appropriate for nitrogen response experiments), the response to a fixed increment of nitrogen, or the fitting of a standard curve, often a quadratic. Doubts over the precision of optima derived from curve fitting with very few data points, and over the consistency of the form of the curve, led to the introduction in the mid 1960s of multi-level nitrogen experiments. It has since become accepted practice to include at least five amounts of nitrogen in nitrogen response experiments, and up to nine levels have been used in various series. Such multi-level tests permit the fitting of a range of response functions, and usually a more precise estimate of the response parameters, including the optimum. The advantages of multi-level experiments have sometimes been offset by reduced replication and greater variability of individual data points, especially at high nitrogen levels (George, 1984). In recent years, optima have tended to increase due to higher yields, and changes in cropping resulting in a reduced supply of nitrogen from the soil. Even experiments with a wide range of nitrogen levels have sometimes failed to span the optimum (Sylvester-Bradley et al., 1984).

Factors influencing response to nitrogen

A major difficulty in the prediction of nitrogen requirements is their variability between sites and years, and the difficulty in identifying factors which consistently influence response.

During the last 10 years, much of the ADAS work has been concentrated in national series, where the same experiment is carried out over a range of soil types and climates. These experiments were designed to test and improve existing recommendations, and in some cases showed that factors taken into account in the recommendations could not be supported.

Table 1 shows the various factors taken into account in the recommendations during their development up to the present day. The two most important factors in the recommendations are soil type and soil N Index, which is based on previous cropping. The soil type categories are based on texture and depth. Surface texture alone is insufficient, as the texture/depth relationship is

Table 1 Factors taken into account in NAAS/ADAS nitrogen recommendations for cereals

Publication	Date	Soil N	Soil type	Winter rainfall	Other factors
NAAS Advisory Paper No. 4	1967	5 class system	Textural groups	± 25 kg/ha after exceptionally wet or dry winters	Lower recommended amounts for areas of high average summer rainfall
Advisory Paper No. 4, 2nd Edn	1971	5 class system	Textural groups: soil series for organic soils	As above	(1) Summer rainfall (as above) (2) Soil depth (3) Variety (spring barley only) (4) Limitations due to droughtiness or take-all
MAFF Bulletin 209	1973				
MAFF Booklet GF 21	1978	3 class system	Soil groups based on texture and depth Soil series as examples	−25 kg/ha after very dry winters in east England at N Index 1 or 2	(1) +25 kg/ha in seedbed for direct drilled winter cereals (2) +25 kg/ha in poor soil conditions (e.g. after sugar beet) for winter wheat on silt and clay soils
MAFF Bulletin GF 1 (RB 209)	1979				(3) Additional N as foliar sprays or very late top dressing to increase grain N content
MAFF Booklet 2191 MAFF Booklet 2191	1979 Revised 1981	3 class system	As above	As above	As above
MAFF Booklet 2191	Revised 1983	3 class system	As above, revised groupings	As above	As above: (2) limited to silty soils (4) +50 kg/ha on long term arable soils with yield potential 8 t/ha, for N Indices 0 and 1, except silty soils

247

important in the retention of residual nitrogen. The soil categories also separate organic and peaty soils which have much smaller requirements for applied nitrogen.

The soil nitrogen Index

Experiments and experience over many years demonstrate the effects on nitrogen requirements of residual nitrogen in the soil from previous crops and applications of bulky organic manure. Investigation of these effects was one of the objectives of the 'ley fertility' series of experiments.

The need to take account of residual nitrogen from previous crops, including the long-term effects following grassland, led to the development of the soil nitrogen Index. This was first introduced in 1967 (MAFF, 1967) as a five class system with Indices from 0 to 4. This method of classifying residual nitrogen was used to parallel the introduction of Indices for the classification of soil analytical results for the other major nutrients.

The system was based on the crop preceding that for which the recommendation was being made. To take account of longer-term effects, the Index was presented as a series of tables for arable or ley/arable systems, or ploughed-out permanent grassland.

Although there was an extensive experimental background for the system, its empirical nature made it inevitable that further testing would reveal limitations and inconsistencies. In particular, it was found that the differences in residual effects between some of the crops separated in Indices 0 and 1 were small, and also the differences between crops with very large residual effects (Indices 3 and 4) could not be consistently separated.

Following further evaluation and discussion of the system in 1976, a simplified system with three classes was introduced from 1977 (MAFF, 1978; 1979). The simplification consisted essentially of the amalgamation of the earlier Indices 0 and 1 into the new Index 0, and of the old Indices 3 and 4 into the new Index 2. This system, with minor modifications in presentation, is still in use today.

Although the system is rather simple, and still suffers the limitations of its empirical base, it provides a convenient method for estimating the residual effects of previous cropping, covering the wide range of possible cropping sequences in a way which can be relatively easily explained to farmers.

The system has also been accepted by commercial organisations involved in fertiliser recommendations. Although no detailed tests of farmer acceptance have been carried out, some survey data suggests that farmers are still taking rather little account of the influence of previous cropping on nitrogen requirements.

In correlation exercises to compare nitrogen requirements measured in field experiments with possible predictors of nitrogen response, the soil nitrogen Index system has been more successful than any of the other soil or plant parameters which have been tested as predictors so far.

The Index system attempts only to assess the amount of residual nitrogen in different cropping sequences. The differing capacity of soils to retain residual nitrogen is covered by the inclusion of soil type as an additional factor in the

248

recommendations, as well as some modifications for variations in winter rainfall. In the 15 years since its introduction, the Index system has demonstrated its value as a simple method of assessing residual nitrogen levels, and it's likely to continue in this capacity until sufficient information is available for it to be replaced by a more precise system.

The Index system is capable of further refinement. For example, experiments on wheat after various break crops have indicated that residual nitrogen after oilseed rape is more easily lost over-winter on coarse textured soils than residual nitrogen from some other crops which are included in the same Index, such as peas and beans. This might be because much of the nitrogen in oilseed rape is in the leaves, which are shed early and therefore subject to more rapid mineralisation in the autumn than residues from later-maturing crops. Another example is the residual effect of sugar beet, which tends to be very variable. This could be due to variations in denitrification losses, since incorporated sugar beet leaves readily form anaerobic layers. Such effects are difficult to allow for in any predictive system.

Soil and plant analyses as response predictors

Considerable effort has been directed towards the use of soil or plant analysis to predict nitrogen requirements. Numerous methods have been proposed to measure the potentially mineralisable nitrogen in soils, usually based on incubation or hydrolysis. These methods have generally had little success in the prediction of nitrogen requirements (Robinson, 1975), and this is the experience in the UK, where no correlation has been found between mineralisable nitrogen measured by a variety of methods, and response to nitrogen in field experiments.

In recent years there has been considerable interest in the measurement of soil mineral nitrogen in the later winter (usually at the end of February). Such measurements have been found useful in parts of Northern Europe, particularly on deep loess soils. This method has been tested in this country over the last 10 years. In particular, measurements were made on national series of experimental sites in the years 1978 to 1980. Again no correlation was found between these measurements and a variety of response predictors, including optimal nitrogen treatment, and rate of response to applied nitrogen. The reasons for this poor relationship are not clear, but may be associated with the wide range of soils and climates in which cereals are grown in this country. The greater variability of weather in spring in the UK compared with mainland Europe may also be a contributory factor.

Early stage plant analysis for either total nitrogen or nitrate-N content has also been suggested as a response predictor. Since nitrogen concentrations in plant dry matter decrease with growth, various ways of expressing plant nitrogen analysis have been suggested, including nitrogen uptake on a unit area basis, and nitrogen concentration in relation to mean plant dry weight (Møller-Nielsen and Friis-Nielsen, 1976). The series of experiments from 1978 to 1980 showed no relationship between these plant nitrogen parameters and response to nitrogen although all possibilities for transforming the plant nitrogen data have not yet been tried.

It is perhaps optimistic to expect any measurement of plant nitrogen status in the early spring, which will have been influenced by conditions up to the point of sampling, to be related to the subsequent response of the crop in grain yields.

Activity of the enzyme nitrogenase in cereal plants in the early spring has been tested as a measure of adequacy of nitrogen supply to the crop (Sylvester-Bradley *et al.*, 1983) but has shown no promise as a predictor of response to applied nitrogen.

Uptake of nitrogen by ryegrass grown in pots in a glasshouse has also been used as a measure of nitrogen potentially available from the soil. This has shown slightly more promise than the other analytical methods, but is still far too poor to justify its development as a predictive measure.

The use of any laboratory-based analytical method for the prediction of nitrogen requirement on an individual field basis would pose enormous logistical problems of sampling, sample preparation, and analysis. This would only be acceptable if the method improved the accuracy of prediction substantially, and none of the methods tested so far has shown the potential to achieve this.

Other factors which may influence response to nitrogen

Many other environmental and agronomic factors have been suggested as influencing or interacting with nitrogen response. These include, *inter alia*, cultivar, disease control, water supply, and the use of growth regulators. These interactions have all been tested to varying extents, but have been found in most cases to be either small or inconsistent.

Cultivar

There are rather few experiments where the nitrogen response of different cultivars has been measured adequately at the same site. Comparisons of different cultivars on different sites are of limited value because of confounding effects. Although there have been examples of appreciable differences in nitrogen requirements between cultivars at particular sites, these have been inconsistent between the sites. An added practical difficulty is that consistent differences between cultivars would take some time to establish, while the rate of change of cultivars in general use is now rapid.

Disease control

Several of the important foliar pathogens of cereals are strongly influenced by the nitrogen content of the plant. It has, therefore, been suggested that the use of fungicides to control such pathogens would result in an increased response to nitrogen. While experiments have shown such interactions to occur, they have with a few exceptions been relatively small. The mean increase in optimum where fungicides were used has been of the order of 10 kg/ha of nitrogen. An important aspect of the interaction is that the use of fungicides frequently increases the rate of response up to the optimum, thereby giving a more efficient use of the applied nitrogen. The largest interactions have occurred where severe attacks of foliar

250

disease have limited yields and reduced response to nitrogen in the absence of fungicide treatment.

Water supply

Because of very limited commercial use of irrigation for cereal crops in this country, interactions between water supply and nitrogen response have been little investigated on a field scale. Information from other crops would suggest that adequate available water during the growing season would improve efficiency of utilisation of applied nitrogen, rather than altering the optimum. Crops subjected to severe water stress tend to show a low rate of response to nitrogen with a poorly defined optimum.

Growth regulators

A large number of experiments has failed to show any interaction between nitrogen and chlormequat applied to reduce straw length in winter wheat. Fewer experiments have been done on nitrogen and straw shorteners for winter barley, and no consistent effects have yet emerged. There is currently interest in the use of growth regulators for altering the crop structure of winter cereals, and the effect of these treatments (if successful) on nitrogen response will need to be investigated.

Alternative nitrogen prediction systems

Other organisations involved in fertiliser advice have in recent years developed alternative systems for generating nitrogen recommendations. These are mainly based on simple models, or on 'balance sheet' methods. Presentation ranges from simple charts and calculators for use by farmers to more sophisticated computer-based systems. These may need the input of a large number of site and crop parameters, some of which are only assessed subjectively. The experimental basis for some of the variations in recommendation made for these site and crop factors is open to question. The major limitations to this approach at present are the necessity for predicting the yield potential of the site, and the supply of nitrogen from the soil, neither of which can be done with accuracy. Although it is likely that the development of nitrogen recommendation systems in the future will be based on modelling and calculation methods, it is obvious that these cannot give greater precision than the data on which they are based.

Recommendations for timing of nitrogen

The timing of nitrogen for cereals has become the subject of contentious debate, although most experiments show the effects of timing on yields to be comparatively small compared with effects of total amount of nitrogen applied.

Results of timing of nitrogen applications for spring sown cereals have been fairly straightforward, with little difference between timing treatments up to the

251

3 leaf stage. Current recommendations are concerned mainly with the avoidance of potential hazards, such as leaching loss from very early applied nitrogen, and damage to germination when large amounts of nitrogen are combined drilled.

Seedbed nitrogen for winter wheat has been very extensively tested over many years, often in association with other factors such as form of nitrogen, time of sowing, and cultivation system. Most of the experiments have shown little or no benefit from seedbed nitrogen when sufficient nitrogen is applied in the spring. The present trend towards earlier sowing of winter cereals leads to much greater dry matter production and nitrogen uptake during the autumn. It has been suggested that this would result in responses to seedbed nitrogen but experimental evidence for this is lacking at present.

Mineralisation of soil nitrogen is slower under direct drilled than under cultivated conditions, and responses to seedbed nitrogen have been found with some direct drilled crops. However, even these responses have been inconsistent, and the 25 kg/ha of nitrogen recommended in the seedbed for direct drilled crops can be regarded as an insurance measure.

There is less information available on response of winter barley to seedbed nitrogen. Responses have been rather more common than in winter wheat, but have still been limited to a few sites.

The small amount of work done with ^{15}N labelled fertiliser applied in the autumn has shown that only a small proportion of such treatment is taken up by the crop.

Interest in the timing of spring nitrogen has been very much influenced by the possible effects of timing on crop structure. Although application of nitrogen during the tillering phase almost invariably results in an increased emergence of tillers as well as an increase in vegetative growth of existing tillers, this does not always result in an increase in the final ear number, or in grain yield. Efforts have been made to explain differences in the effect of timing between sites by assessments of crop structure, but there have not so far been sufficient detailed measurements on enough sites to permit reliable predictions of the effects which will occur. Present evidence indicates that responses to nitrogen during the tillering phase are likely on direct drilled crops, on crops on sandy or shallow chalk soils, and crops with a low post-winter plant population. Responses to nitrogen at this stage are less likely on well structured clay and silty soils, especially at N Index 1 or 2. Responses to early nitrogen have occurred more frequently on clay soils at N Index 0 in recent years. Where nitrogen is applied during the tillering phase, only 40 kg/ha is recommended. Applying a large amount of nitrogen at this stage increases the risk of leaching loss, and also of lodging in weak-strawed crops.

The most important stage for nitrogen application, when the main dressing is recommended, is at the early stem extension stage, to coincide with the rapid increase in rate of uptake of nitrogen. There is often no yield loss in delaying application to the first node or even second node stage, but there is no advantage in delaying beyond the stem extension stage. Very rapid growth in the spring means that a short delay could result in the second node stage being passed, and there is an increased risk of reduced efficiency of nitrogen due to dry soil conditions in the later spring.

An interesting aspect of experiments on timing of nitrogen is the relative insensitivity of many crops. In about half the experiments, there has been no measurable difference in effect of nitrogen applied between the mid-tillering and second node stages.

A straightforward practical method recommended for organising nitrogen top dressing on a farm is to apply 40 kg of nitrogen during the tillering stage (usually early March) to those crops most likely to respond, as specified above. The full nitrogen requirement is then applied at the beginning of stem extension (early to mid-April) to those crops which did not receive any early nitrogen, followed by the remainder of the dressing for the crops which received early nitrogen. In the event of adverse weather, no crop will reach an advanced stage without having received some top dressing.

Although timings are specified primarily by growth stage, there are overall constraints of calendar dates. The constraints are designed to avoid both the unnecessary application of nitrogen during the autumn or winter to very advanced crops, and undue delay in applying the main treatment to very backward crops, which may not reach the stem extension stage until mid-May in some areas.

Application of small amounts of nitrogen during the winter (November to early February) has frequently been advocated as a means of influencing crop development, growth and thereby yields. Experimental evidence to substantiate worthwhile effects from treatments during this period is lacking.

Very late top dressing, at or about flag leaf emergence, is a common practice in some northern European countries. Experiments in this country have seldom shown yield responses from such treatment which could not be obtained with nitrogen applied at the early stem extension stage. In many cases, responses to late nitrogen have been small, probably due to dry surface soil conditions at and after application. Since there is no justification for delaying part of the main top dressing, recommendations for the use of very late top dressing are confined to an assessment of the circumstances in which a yield benefit from extra nitrogen at this stage is most likely, i.e. crops of high yield potential, where soil water reserves are adequate at the time of application.

Grain nitrogen content

Grain nitrogen content is increased by increasing application of fertiliser nitrogen. The effect is usually near-linear, irrespective of yield responses to nitrogen. This increase occurs with any nitrogen treatment from early stem extension onwards, including foliar sprays as urea applied post anthesis. Since grain nitrogen content is influenced by uncontrollable site and environmental factors, and the present premium structure for protein content is a step-wise one, there can be no guarantee that the use of additional nitrogen to increase grain protein content will result in an increased price for the crop, and economic assessments of the worthwhileness of these treatments, therefore, cannot be made.

References

GEORGE, B. J. 1984. Design and interpretation of nitrogen response experiments. Ministry of Agriculture, Fisheries and Food. Reference Book 385, *The Nitrogen Requirement of Cereals*, pp. 133–148. HMSO, London.

HALL, A. D. (1911) The feeding of crops and stock. Part II: Soils and Fertilisers. John Murray, London.

MAFF 1931. Artificial fertilisers. Ministry of Agriculture, Fisheries and Food, Bulletin No. 28, HMSO, London.

MAFF 1967. Fertiliser recommendations for agricultural and horticultural crops. NAAS Advisory Paper No. 4. Ministry of Agriculture, Fisheries and Food, London.

MAFF 1973. Fertiliser recommendations. Ministry of Agriculture, Fisheries and Food. Bulletin 209. HMSO, London.

MAFF 1978. Lime and fertiliser recommendations. Arable Crops and Grassland GF 21. Ministry of Agriculture, Fisheries and Food, London.

MAFF 1979a. Fertiliser recommendations. Ministry of Agriculture, Fisheries and Food. GF1. HMSO, London.

MAFF 1979b. Lime and fertiliser recommendations. Arable crops and grassland. Booklet 2191. Ministry of Agriculture Fisheries and Food, London.

MAFF 1983. Lime and fertiliser recommendations No. 1 – Arable crops 1983–84. Booklet 2191 (83/84). Ministry of Agriculture, Fisheries and Food, London.

MØLLER NIELSEN, J. and FRIIS-NIELSEN, B. 1976. Evaluation and control of the nutritional status of cereals. I. Dry matter weight level. *Plant and Soil* **45**, 317–338.

ROBINSON, J. B. D. 1975. The soil nitrogen Index and its calibration with crop performance to improve fertiliser efficiency on arable soils. Commonwealth Bureau of Soils, Special Publication No. 1 53 pp.

SCHARPF, H. C. and WEHRMANN, J. 1976. Die Bedentung des mineralstick-stoffrorrates des bodens zu vegetationsbeginn für die bemessung der N-Düngung zu winterweizen. Landwirtschaftliche Forschung Sonderheft **32**, 1, 100–114.

SYLVESTER-BRADLEY, R., DAMPNEY, P. M. R. and MURRAY, A. W. A. 1984. The response of winter wheat to nitrogen. Ministry of Agriculture, Fisheries and Food. Reference Book 385, *The Nitrogen Requirement of Cereals*, pp. 151–174. HMSO, London.

Discussion

Mr Webb asked how much work had been carried out to investigate the rates of recovery of fertiliser nitrogen on a variety of soil types during a particular season.

Mr Needham said that information was limited because only ^{15}N can distinguish between fertiliser derived nitrogen and nitrogen supplied by the soil. In reply to a further question from Mr Webb upon the possible use of regression equations for obtaining more information on fertiliser nitrogen recovery on different soil types, Mr Needham stated that their application was limited.

Nitrogenous fertilisation of winter wheat in France: How is the balance method to be improved?

Ph. Viaux

Institut Techniques des Céréals et des Fourrages (ITCF), Paris, France

Summary

In an earlier publication, we summarised all the results obtained with the balance method between 1975 and 1979, and showed that some progress must be made if the intention is to extend the use of such a method generally throughout France on the one hand, and improve its reliability on the other.

The earlier results have led us to modify the model initially proposed by the INRA Centre in Laon, by introducing an efficiency factor for the nitrogen made available to the plant. Recent studies with nitrogen-15 have enabled us to propose nitrogen efficiency values on the basis of a number of criteria. Other studies are aimed at improving the way the choice of a target yield is taken into account. A third aspect is the acquisition of a fuller knowledge of the nitrogen provided by the soil.

We report results achieved in France in these areas since 1979.

The modification of the model and its consequences

The new model for forecasting the nitrogenous fertilisation of wheat differs from the previous one through the presence of the term 'C: the efficiency of the nitrogen'.

The equation therefore becomes:

$$bR = (Rsh + Ms + Mr + Mo + E) \, C$$

Nitrogen requirements
$$\begin{cases} R &= \text{hoped-for yield in quintals} \\[6pt] b &= \text{total quantity of nitrogen per quintal of grain produced} \end{cases}$$

Contribution from the soil
$$\begin{cases} Rsh &= \text{residue of mineral nitrogen measured at the end of winter} \\ Ms &= \text{mineralisation of stable organic matter} \\ Mr &= \text{mineralisation of the harvest residues from the previous crop} \\ Mo &= \text{mineralisation of organic manures} \\ E &= \text{nitrogen fertiliser to be applied} \end{cases}$$

Efficiency $\quad C = $ efficiency of the nitrogen

It will be noted that the term corresponding to the nitrogen not used by the plant does not appear. In fact, this term (hitherto regarded as a constant characteristic of the soil) becomes a variable value depending on the value of C.

$$\text{Unused nitrogen} = (1 - C)(\text{Rsh} + \text{Ms} + \text{Mr} + \text{Mo} + \text{E})$$

Thus, the lower the efficiency, the higher the quantity of nitrogen unused by the plant will be.

In order to appreciate the importance of this factor fully, reference needs to be made to Figure 1.

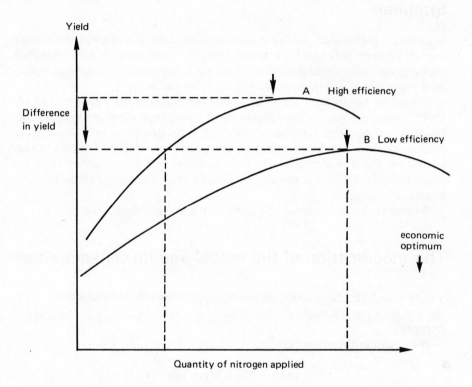

Fig. 1 Theoretical curve showing the response of nitrogen with two types of efficiency.

Curve A corresponds to *high efficiency* of nitrogen use, while Curve B corresponds to *low efficiency*. In order to achieve an identical yield, applications of nitrogen which are far higher in the case of B than A are needed. It is quite obvious that, bearing in mind the cost of nitrogen fertilisers, the best possible efficiency should be sought.

On the other hand, when the efficiency decreases, the nitrogen not used by the plant increases and accordingly there is liable to be a greater risk of pollution of underground water by nitrate. We may point out that the nitrate contents of many French waters are very close to the maximum values regarded as acceptable for human consumption.

258

The factors causing nitrogen efficiency to vary

The studies in question have enabled us to identify or confirm the effects of a number of factors which cause the efficiency of nitrogen to vary. In some cases, it has been shown that certain factors had no effect.

In particular, the level of nitrogen fertilisation does not seem to affect nitrogen efficiency greatly. In trials conducted with several levels of labelled nitrogen, we showed that within a relatively wide band of nitrogen application, the utilisation coefficient did not vary with the amount applied (see Table 1). We also found that even in the case of low efficiency levels (e.g. in the case of crops affected by frost) efficiency is not influenced by the amount of nitrogen applied.

Table 1 Real utilisation coefficient of the 2nd application of nitrogen (the roots are counted at a standard rate of 30 per cent of the aerial parts). INRA/ITCF, 1979 and 1980.

Level of nitrogen (constant tillering dose)	Place			Average
	Aisne (2 trials)	Champagne Berrichonne (2 trials)	Beauce (1 trial)	
1	73.5	77.8	61.8	71.0
2	77.3	82.9	64.1	74.8
3	83.9	75.3	57.5	72.3
4	88.1	74.3	61.8	74.7

The second factor which seems to affect nitrogen efficiency to a great extent is soil structure.

In this case, it is the functioning of the root systems of the plant which is deficient, either because the rooting density is insufficient or because it is not functional (e.g. in the case of anoxia).

It has thus been possible, in south-western France, to relate an arbitrary structure mark to efficiency of nitrogen use (Figure 2). The problem may be approached by bringing into play the concept of 'root interception'. The volume of soil explored is a function of root length and of the effective radius of the root. A simple calculation results in the concept of 'critical length' beyond which the soil is no longer entirely explored (Table 2). Root activity may be assessed using a tracer. This is located in the profile by means of a system of injection to different depth, the quantity of the tracer being measured in the aerial part (Table 3). It is important to note that in the event of a poor soil structure ($C = 0.7$), there may well be reason to double the nitrogen fertiliser to be applied. The financial effect on the farmer is such that technical choices (harvesting equipment, sowing equipment, rotations, date of sowing, etc.) deserve to be reconsidered at farm level with a view to improving both the state of the soil and rooting.

In a number of trials conducted with nitrogen-15, we showed that the date of nitrogen application modified the fertiliser utilisation coefficient (see Figure 3). The highest efficiency is achieved with nitrogen applications made from the beginning of flag leaf emergence to the 'boot' stage; the utilisation coefficient is in this case of the order of 80 per cent (including the roots); on the other hand, from sowing until the end of tillering, efficiency increases in a virtually linear way.

Since the trials were carried out on deep soils, the leaching of the nitrogen is not sufficient to account for this lack of effectiveness of the early applications. It is probable that transformations of the nitrogen are responsible for this phenomenon; the longer the nitrogen remains in the soil without being absorbed, the greater the risk of the mineral nitrogen being immobilised by micro-organisms.

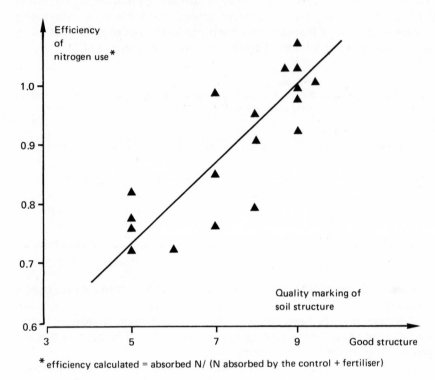

*efficiency calculated = absorbed N/ (N absorbed by the control + fertiliser)

Fig. 2 Effects of soil structure quality on nitrogen efficiency (ITCF – 16 trials – 1981).

Table 2 Critical root length (INRA–Laon)

Effective radius of root (cm)	Section (cm²)	Critical root length (cm/cm³)
1.00	3.1400	0.32
0.30	0.2800	3.60
0.10	0.0310	32.00
0.03	0.0028	357.00

Finally, the destruction of part of the conducting vessels at the base of the stem by fungi also limits the efficiency of the nitrogen by limiting the transfer of mineral elements to the aerial parts.

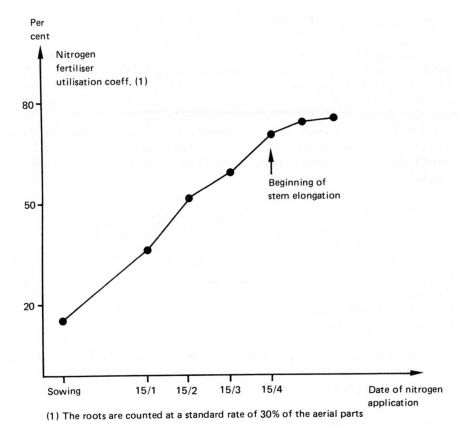

(1) The roots are counted at a standard rate of 30% of the aerial parts

Fig. 3 Coefficient for the utilisation of nitrogen fertiliser as a function of the date of application (average of two ITCF/INRA trials – 1981).

Table 3 Example of root activity profile obtained at Boigneville in 1981 – Feekes growth stage 5 (INRA/ITCF)

Depth cm	Copper ppm	%*	^{15}N excess %	%*
0–20	31.1	(34)	0.026	(53)
20–40	28.6	(30)	0.014	(29)
40–60	24.9	(23)	0.007	(14)
60–80	19.2	(13)	0.0002	(4)
Control	12.2	–	0.000	–

*Per cent of the total

Selecting the yield target correctly

The nitrogen requirements of wheat are proportional to the yield. One of the difficulties in using the balance method lies in a reasonable choice of yield target. No reliable method currently allows one to forecast accurately what the yield will be in a clearly-defined soil and climate situation. Studies on this subject are currently in progress, and they have enabled us to propose a restricted multiplicative model based only on data relating to the soil and the vegetative state of the plant:

$$R = Rp \times f1 \times f2 \times f3 \times f4$$

Rp is the potential yield of the variety in the most frequently-occurring climatic conditions in the absence of any limiting factors either at plant level or soil level. The coefficients f1, f2, f3, f4 are all less than or equal to 1. They are the expression of yield-limiting factors – useful reserve, soil structure, date of sowing and vegetative density at the end of winter, respectively.

An attempt has been made, in the case of each of these factors, to determine the law of yield decrease. Thus, for example, it has been possible to calculate, on the basis of numerous sowing density trials, the law which links the yield to the plant population at the end of winter.

$$F4 = 0.773 + 0.404\,\frac{P}{P_O} - 0.1746\left[\frac{P}{P_O}\right]^2$$

F4 = correction factor for the yield target depending on the population at the end of winter
P = population on the plot at the end of winter
P_O = optimum population for the site

Naturally, this law is only valid if the population is uniform. It is possible to prepare such models in respect of all the factors referred to above. We have not taken any existing interactions into account.

The nitrogen supplied by the soil

In this sphere, the only real progress achieved recently relates to measurement of the mineral nitrogen residue and its being taken into account in the balance method.

Estimation of spring residues by means of an investigation shows that the most important variable factors are the previous crop and the year.

Furthermore, in the case of so-called 'rich' preceding crops, such as potatoes and sugar beet, a gradual decrease in the quantities found has been recorded. This fact is to be aligned with a more rigorous adjustment of fertiliser for the starter crop (Table 4). This may be seen in the table of values obtained in Picardy by the INRA's centre at Laon.

Table 4 Nitrate residues measured in February in deep loam soil in Picardy (kg/ha in 1 m) INRA – Laon

	1976	1977	1978	1979	1980	1981	1982	Average
Sugar beet	71	97	58	51	60	58	47	63
Potatoes	104	138	76	91	85	68	59	89
Maize	83	124	62	61	63	70	51	73
Peas/beans	93	120	115	105	95	104	69	100
Averages	88	120	78	77	76	75	57	–

Since systematic measurement of the residual nitrogen at the end of winter is extremely expensive, an attempt has been made to obtain models, by regression, whereby the residue may be forecast. Thus, a model based on the cropping history of the plot and winter rainfall has been obtained in Lorraine (eastern France). The model may be written as follows:

$$Rsh = 10 + 0.189 \, B + 0.375 \, RU - 0.498 \, S - 0.054 \, P$$

Rsh = residue of mineral nitrogen at the end of winter
B = nitrogen balance from the previous crop
RU = useful reserve
S = proportion of sand
P = rain from 1 October to the '1 cm ear' stage.

Conclusion

In a way it could be said that the balance method is both ultra-simplistic and extremely ambitious. It is simplistic on account of the whole set of laws which govern the dynamics of nitrogen in the soil not being taken into account (denitrification, for example), and it is ambitious because, despite the simplifications of the plant/soil system, it is extremely difficult to give numerical values to each of the parameters.

Nevertheless, we feel that drawing up such a model is extremely profitable for all concerned. Firstly, for the researchers, who thus realise the absence of scientific data in important areas and secondly for the technician or the farmer for whom models combining the maximum data may be proposed. Thus, all the studies we have just reported will be taken into account in an informative model for the forecasting of the nitrogen fertilisation of winter cereals.

This experimental software will doubtless be operational during the 1983/84 season.

Discussion

Dr Little asked M. Viaux what he meant by a 'cultivation profile' in his model. M. Viaux replied that the term referred to the degree of compaction caused to the soil structure.

Dr Smith thought that the data presented in the paper suggested a very low addition of ^{15}N to the soil and asked whether that was correct. M. Viaux said that nitrogen fertiliser with an enrichment of 1 to 1.5 per cent ^{15}N had been used and the data referred to by Dr Smith related to plant uptake of nitrogen.

Dr Addiscott thought that some of the factors used in the basic equation within the model could be interrelated. If this was correct then only the smaller values of related factors should be used in the equation instead of multiplying all the factors together. M. Viaux agreed that the suggestion could be correct and stated the model was still at an early stage and therefore likely to be modified.

Dr Powlson noted that the model assumed the same efficiency of soil and fertiliser nitrogen and questioned this assumption. M. Viaux replied that there may be small differences but they were unlikely to be sufficiently important to warrant separate efficiency values.

Modelling of the nitrogen requirement of cereals

P B Tinker and T M Addiscott
Rothamsted Experimental Station, Harpenden

Introduction

The nitrogen requirement of cereals is affected by a wide range of processes: the soil nitrogen cycle, crop growth and the efficiency of nitrogen uptake. All these subjects or processes have been modelled in various ways (Greenwood, 1982; Frissell and van Veen, 1982), and the aim of this paper is to set the various models in context, to assess the current success and likely prospects of these methods, and their possible practical importance. The success of a model in scientific terms is determined by its accuracy in describing the real process over a range of conditions. When models are being developed for the practical purpose of predicting the amount of nitrogen fertiliser required by cereals on individual fields, their success must also be assessed by their practicability and dependability.

This practical use of modelling methods is of particular interest because of the notorious difficulty of predicting nitrogen fertiliser need by other means (Greenwood *et al.,* 1974; Batey, 1976). This difficulty is at least in part a consequence of the complexity of the processes involved in the nitrogen cycle in soil. Modelling methods are pre-eminently suited to dealing with interlocking processes of this sort. Soil analysis has been tried over many years (see Jenkinson, this volume, pages 79–92), but has always failed, except in extreme cases. Plant analysis has been successful in many crops, but almost all these are perennials. The need for rapid and accurate sampling and analysis, the changing value of the critical concentration in the plant with time, and the early stage at which such information is needed for it to be of value, are all barriers to the successful application of such methods to cereal growing, except perhaps as a warning of serious deficiency.

Much effort has also gone into investigations of the general relationships between soil, climatic and agronomic variables, and nitrogen need. There is a clear relationship with previous cropping, which forms the core of the present ADAS N Index system, but it is still felt that better methods would be desirable (Cooke, 1979).

Types of models

In agricultural science the term 'model' has been used to describe anything from a single regression equation to an elaborate computer program with thousands of lines. In the present context we take it to mean a representation of physical and biological systems in the soil and crop that is broadly mathematical in nature. Many such representations depend on the use of a computer. An individual model is defined by its purpose, level of complexity and the way it functions. Level of complexity is used to mean the number of processes modelled and the degree of detail which is attempted, particularly in respect of the number of factors considered to affect the system. The main distinction in defining the way models function is between 'correlative' and 'conceptual' models.

Correlative models for nitrogen requirement are based on statistical analysis of past results and are developed from relationships between yield or nitrogen requirement and factors such as previous cropping and nitrogen nutrition, soil type and weather. The level of complexity in such models depends mainly on the number of factors included. The forerunners of this approach are to be found in Fisher's (1924) classic paper on the effects of rainfall on wheat yields in the Broadbalk Experiment at Rothamsted and the work by Boyd *et al.* (1957) on the fertiliser requirements of sugar beet. More recent and more complex models for predicting fertiliser need are given by Heapy *et al.* (1976) and Colwell (1978). The system described by Sylvester-Bradley *et al.* (1984) in this volume also contains correlative elements. The ICI 'N-counter' scheme (Hollies, personal communication), now in commercial use, is in principle a correlative model.

Conceptual models do not initially depend on statistical analysis. A model of this type is based on a prior concept of the process being modelled, which is translated into equations or a computer program. It is thus in effect a hypothesis and needs to be validated against measured data. Correlative models may of course stimulate the development of conceptual models, and the latter may contain correlative sub-models or relationships, so the boundary is not necessarily sharp. Conceptual models are described as 'mechanistic' when they postulate specific basic mechanisms for processes, often defined by differential equations. Models working at a simpler mathematical level are not usually described as 'mechanistic', even though they may contain a simplified mechanism. The distinction is seen below in discussions of models used for simulating three processes important in nitrogen behaviour, solute and water transport, microbial transformations, and uptake by crop roots and the effect of crop demand.

Solute and water transport

Fully mechanistic models of transport in soils (e.g. Tanji *et al.*, 1981; Wagenet, 1981) usually calculate *fluxes of water* from differential equations incorporating the hydraulic conductivity (K) (equation (1)) and *fluxes of solute* from an equation (2) which allows for diffusion and convection (Figure 1).

$$C(\Theta) \frac{\partial H}{\partial t} = \frac{\partial}{\partial z} \left[K(\Theta) \frac{\partial H}{\partial z} + K(\Theta) \right] + S \quad \ldots \ldots (1)$$

$$\frac{\partial(\Theta c)}{\partial t} = \frac{\partial}{\partial z} \left[\Theta D(\Theta, q) \frac{\partial c}{\partial z} \right] - \frac{\partial(qc)}{\partial z} \quad \ldots \ldots (2)$$

where C = differential soil-water capacity $\partial\Theta/\partial H(cm^{-1})$; H = soil-water pressure head (cm); t = time (hour); z = depth (cm); Θ = volumetric water content (dimensionless); s = sink term for root extraction; c = solute concentration (mg litre); $D(\Theta, q)$ = apparent diffusion coefficient; q = water flux (cm h⁻¹)

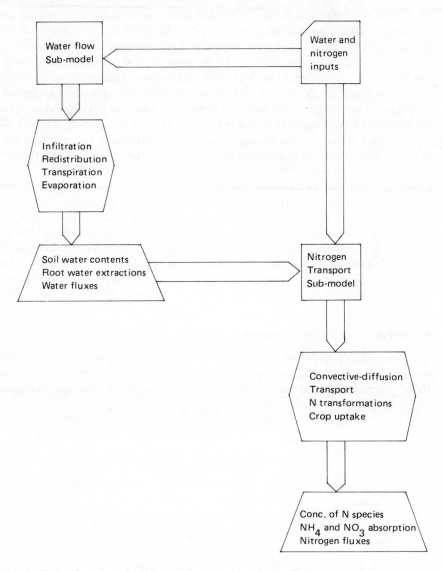

Fig. 1 Outline flow-chart for water and nitrogen (after Tanji, 1981).

Such equations represent the most sophisticated approach to transport modelling, but have the following disadvantages. (a) The mathematical solutions are often difficult and may be possible only when simplifying assumptions are made. This is especially so when the geometry or boundary conditions are complex. (b) The hydraulic conductivity (K) and the diffusion coefficient (D) both vary considerably with the moisture content of the soil and are not easily measured. (c) Even in a sandy soil near field capacity K and D vary sharply over short distances, but in a soil with aggregates, cracks or large macropores they may vary by 1–2 orders of magnitude.

Simple (non-mechanistic) conceptual transport models (e.g. Burns, 1974; Addiscott, 1977; Rao *et al.*, 1981) usually calculate the **quantities** of solute moved but do not relate these to time so they cannot calculate fluxes. Such models are sometimes called 'capacity' models. The extent to which solute is moved in the profile is calculated by relating the amount of water supplied to the soil surface as rain or removed by evaporation to the proportion of the soil volume through which water is conducted. Models of this kind are usually mathematically simple and, more importantly, their inputs are simple and relatively easily measured. Solute movement is governed by a water capacity factor, largely dependent upon the volumetric field capacity which is far less variable, by a factor of about 30, than K, and which is approximately normally distributed whereas K is log-normally distributed. One practical consequence of this is that very many more replicates measurements are needed to obtain a reliable value of K than to obtain a reliable value for the capacity factor.

The choice between the two kinds of model depends on the purpose for which the model is needed. If it is intended to improve and extend the scientific understanding of solute and water transport, the fully mechanistic model is most likely to be relevant, although a simple conceptual model may be helpful. If, however, the model is needed to assist with management decisions relating to the use of nitrogen fertiliser, the simple conceptual model with its easily obtained inputs will probably be of most practical use. (See also Addiscott *et al.*, 1981)

Microbial nitrogen transformations in the soil

The microbial population is responsible for mineralisation, immobilisation, nitrification and denitrification in the soil, so any fully comprehensive model for these processes should ideally be a complete model of the soil microbial

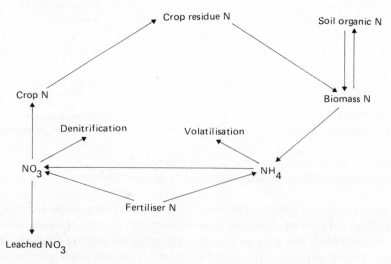

Fig. 2 Outline diagram of N-cycle.

population and its substrates. Such a model would be very speculative at present, but modern methods of studying the biomass may make it possible. The inter-relationship between these processes in shown in Figure 2.

Nitrogen transformations, like water and solute transport, have been modelled at several levels of complexity, but the distinction between mechanistic and simple conceptural models is not really applicable here, because far fewer exact mathematical statements of processes are available. Clearer distinctions may be made in terms of the following questions. Does the model use Monod kinetics, which allow for fluctuations in the microbial population (Equation 3a) as well as its substrates (Equation 3b), or does it use simple chemical kinetics? Does it allow for the inter-relationship between the nitrogen cycle and the carbon cycle in the soil? Does the model partition the organic carbon and nitrogen into appropriate 'pools'? How does it allow for physical and chemical changes in the soil environment (see also Bosatta et al., 1981)?

$$\frac{dA}{dt} = \frac{\mu_{max} NA}{K_n + N} - K_A A \quad \ldots \ldots (3a)$$

$$\frac{dN}{dt} = \frac{\mu_{max}}{Y} \frac{NA}{K_n + N} \quad \ldots \ldots (3b)$$

where A = no. of organisms per unit volume; μ_{max} = maximum specific growth rate (d^{-1}); N = N-substrate concentration; K_n = saturation constant; K_A = decay rate constant; Y = yield (cells mg^{-1} N metabolised).

Mineralisation/immobilisation

A few comprehensive models (e.g. van Veen and Frissel, 1981) (Figure 3) have been developed which use Monod kinetics to describe C and N transfers between clearly-defined pools and in so doing simulate mineralisation and immobilisation. Several other models (Paul and van Veen, 1978; Juma and Paul, 1981) perform broadly similar simulations, but with first-order chemical kinetics in place of Monod kinetics. The models with Monod kinetics suffer from the disadvantage that the constants needed (the maximum specific growth rate and the half-saturation constant) are not independently known for soils. Those using first-order kinetics do not have the overall limitation on transfer rates given by the Monod kinetics, hence may become unrealistic. However, both types have proved capable of giving impressive simulations of these transformations and have contributed usefully to the understanding of them.

These comprehensive models should probably be regarded mainly as research tools or as models to assist with long-term organic matter management. In less detailed work, net mineralisation (i.e. mineralisation less immobilisation) measured in incubation experiments has usually been found to be simply related to time of incubation, sometimes directly (Tabatabai and Al-Khafaji, 1980), sometimes in a $\sqrt{\text{time}}$ or first-order kinetic relationship (Stanford and Smith, 1972).

269

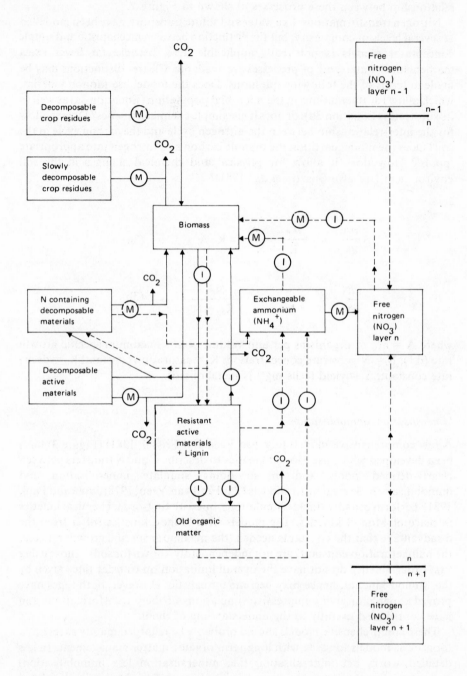

Fig. 3 Flow-chart for the model of van Veen and Frissel (1981): ——Carbon flow,- - - - - N flow; M = Michaelis-Menten kinetics, I = first-order kinetics.

$$N = N_i + k_1 t \ldots (4)$$

$$N = N_i + k_r \sqrt{t} \ldots (5)$$

$$N = N_0 (1-e^{-k_i t}) \ldots (6)$$

where N_0 = potentially mineralisable N; N_i = initial mineral N; t = time; and the k's are constants. The distinction between the empirical linear and square-root relationship with time is probably not important and may well depend on the details of the experimental approach. The first-order kinetic approach yields a first-order rate constant and a quantity usually known as N_0, the 'potentially mineralisable N' (Stanford and Smith, 1972). N_0 should be interpreted with caution, since it is probably not a 'pool' of N in the sense used in the comprehensive models, and its size will almost certainly be strongly affected by temperature.

When models dealing with simultaneous or parallel processes are to be linked, the level of complexity and comprehensiveness should be about the same in each case. The 'comprehensive' microbiological models discussed above would, therefore, be appropriate for linkage with the mechanistic water and solute transport models and the simple net mineralisation relationships with the simple conceptual transport models.

Nitrification

Only a very few microbial species are involved in nitrification and these have been clearly identified. This makes the modelling of nitrification simpler than that of mineralisation/immobilisation, in which an indefinite number of species are involved. Both comprehensive models using Monod kinetics and simpler models using zero- or first-order chemical kinetics have been used successfully to simulate nitrification. However nitrification is a very much more rapid process than mineralisation, so that the latter is usually the rate-determining step, and when mineralisation and nitrification are modelled simultaneously it is the mineralisation model that will have most influence on the success of the simulation.

Denitrification

Denitrification is probably the most difficult of the processes discussed to model, because of the diversity of the anaerobic micro-organisms involved and the problems of simulating the development of anoxic zones and the availability of carbon substrates. The problem is intensified by the likelihood that denitrification occurs at specific anaerobic micro-sites. Smith (1981) developed an interesting diffusion model for the development of anoxic zones in soil aggregates (Figure 4), but at the time of its publication it had not been validated. Both Monod and chemical kinetic approaches have been used to simulate the microbial process but each has its problems: doubts about the values of the constants for the Monod approach, and the failure to take account of biological restraints in the chemical kinetic approach.

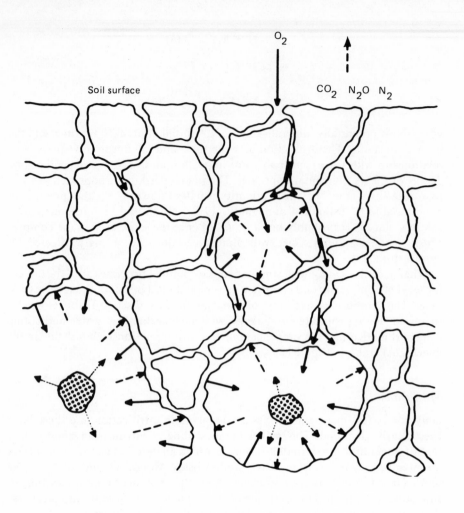

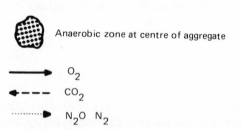

Fig. 4 Gas diffusion pathways in an aggregated soil, showing anaerobic zones within larger aggregates. (Smith, 1981)

Plant growth and nitrogen demand

These factors are crucial elements in the whole nitrogen system, because crop biomass in different fields varies greatly, for reasons unconnected with nitrogen supply. Models of crop growth and nitrogen content therefore form an important part of this topic because they can determine nitrogen demand. One of the earliest nitrogen response models (Greenwood *et al.,* 1974) started from the rate of growth of a crop not limited by nitrogen supply, which avoids this difficulty.

Demand can be expressed as a dynamic, varying value of kg N taken up per day, or as the final maximum N content of the crop, usually at or shortly before harvest. In both cases, the initial step is to model the dry matter accumulation (Biscoe and Willington, this volume, pages 53–65). The conversion efficiency of intercepted light into dry matter is fairly constant between crops, the incident radiation does not vary greatly from year to year, and for an autumn-sown crop, full ground cover is attained early. From this, calculations of varying complexity have been used to estimate maximum dry matter yields, e.g. 20–25 t ha^{-1} dry matter for winter wheat. There is usually a fairly clear correlation between total dry matter yield and total N content, modified in part by the variation in per cent of N (Benzian and Lane, 1979), so this implies a maximum nitrogen content of some 200–250 kg ha^{-1} of N. In fact the real total dry weights of crops vary very widely, e.g. in the recent ICI Ten Tonne Club surveys the range of grain weights was from 3–11 t ha^{-1}. The calculation of maximum nitrogen demand at the end of the season is thus scientifically valuable, but tells us little about nitrogen demand on particular fields.

Alternatively, demand may be considered as crop growth and the need for additional nitrogen each day or week. This is relevant to whole-crop models, in which the increase of dry matter with time is modelled. Where growth is linear with time this is relatively easy, because there is a constant dry matter addition each day. The percentage of nitrogen may change with time, but the course of this is usually fairly well known for a single crop, and general relationships have been presented by Greenwood *et al.* (1978). Uptake rate will not, therefore, vary very much in this growth phase. Maximum rates found at Rothamsted, for winter wheat crops yielding finally about 10 t ha^{-1} of grain were rarely above 2 kg ha^{-1} day^{-1} of N, but much larger values, over 5 kg ha^{-1} day^{-1} have been found for other crops. If the crop cover is incomplete, or the day length is varying markedly, linear growth will not be obtained. Isolated plants should grow at an exponentially increasing rate, which changes gradually to a linear rate as the plants compete for light. This is given by the equation of Greenwood *et al.* (1977),

$$\frac{dW}{dt} = K_2 W \bigg/ (K_1 + W),$$

for crops growing in a period of fairly constant daylength. More complex methods are available in whole crop modelling, such as the work of Porter *et al.* (1982). The major distinction between such models lies in the number of constraints which are assumed to affect the crop. If there are no constraints other than radiation and temperature, ideal growth curves can be predicted by very complex whole-crop models based upon detailed information on crop geometry, radiation and temperature (Porter *et al.,* 1982), or on simple empirical equations (Greenwood *et al.,* 1977). Cereals are particularly difficult to model in this way, because of their tillering habit, and the shift from a vegetative to a reproductive stage. The result may be unrealistic, though good fits have been obtained with very good crops of winter wheat. In any event, the basic idea of a 'maximum biological yield' is a very useful concept (see Tinker and Widdowson,

1982). Models by Greenwood and collaborators (Greenwood *et al.*, 1974; Barnes *et al.*, 1976) start from the definition of a growth curve under 'optimal conditions', and then apply constraints. At a more practical level, the prediction of nitrogen requirement in several current schemes depends upon identification of a 'target yield', which assumes that the crop grows as well as can be expected in those conditions.

The modelling of constraints to growth is far more complex, and less well understood. The simplest step is to deal with the rate of supply of the major factor in the model, e.g. supply of N in a nitrogen model (Baldwin, 1976), or P in a phosphorus model (Nye *et al.*, 1975). Any models of field crops must also include the effects of water stress (Barnes *et al.*, 1976) and probably disease.

It is, therefore, now possible to model the nitrogen demand of a cereal crop suffering from no restraints to growth other than nitrogen supply. Our problem is that so few crops ever approach this ideal, because their yields are decreased by other constraints. Some progress in modelling the nitrogen uptake of field-grown cereals, in the presence of other constraints such as water stress, is now being made (Godwin, personal communication), though it is still in its early stages.

Root uptake processes

It is now generally accepted that all nitrate, and most of the ammonium ions in the immediate neighbourhood of roots are readily absorbed, so that almost all mineral nitrogen in a densely rooted soil volume can easily be taken up at very low concentrations (Burns, 1980a). If root density is less, then uptake must be progressively slower, both because of the physiological limitation on the uptake rate by the root, and because of the finite speed at which nitrate and ammonium ions can diffuse to the root. We can therefore assume that in moist topsoil the nitrate can be wholly exploited over a short time and in this case only the total quantity of nitrate is of interest. Lower down there is a maximum depletion rate, depending upon root density. Burns (1980a) used a root uptake model to calculate that a whole crop could be supplied by about 7 cm root cm^{-2} surface area, if it absorbed at maximum rate. Clearly a very great deal depends upon the nitrate concentration at these depths where rooting density is very small – if it is high, the exact definition of the effectiveness of these deepest roots could become very important in any attempt to model whole-crop uptake.

At the present time no really convincing model of root system development which takes into account soil conditions and crop growth is available, though attempts have been made (Hackett and Rose, 1972). In practice we must rely on the generalisation of Gerwitz and Page (1974), which stated that the density of root length declines exponentially with depth. This appears to be sufficiently near the truth in most cases.

Simultaneous simulation of transport, microbial and crop processes in the field

Nitrate produced by mineralisation and subsequent nitrification is at risk of leaching during winter and sometimes at other times of year, but nitrate and ammonium taken up by the crop are safe. Transport, microbial and crop processes should therefore be modelled simultaneously if the results are to be relevant to what happens in the field and therefore useful for prediction purposes. Some progress has been made in this direction.

Burns (1980c) developed a model that calculated (a) the amount of nitrate present in the soil in autumn from estimates of mineralisation (treated as a long-term first-order decomposition reaction), and then (b) the proportion of this nitrate still present in spring after winter leaching. This model does not seem to have treated mineralisation and leaching simultaneously but gave fair results when the measured optimum N dressings for nine winter wheat crops were plotted against the predicted residual nitrate contents in spring (Figure 5).

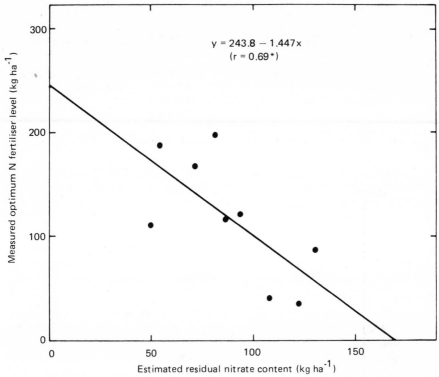

Fig. 5 Relationship between the estimated contents of residual nitrate in spring and the measured optimum N fertiliser dressings for nine winter wheat crops in the UK between 1969 and 1977. (Burns, 1980)

At Rothamsted a predictive system is under development by Addiscott in which mineralisation is treated as in Equation (4) (Tabatabai and Al-Khafaji, 1980; Addiscott, 1983), with the rate determined by the Arrhenius relationship (Figure 6). Leaching is computed from the model of Addiscott (1977) and crop dry matter and its N concentration are calculated from equations developed by Greenwood *et al.* (1977) and Greenwood (1982). In this system each process occurs daily so that mineralised N can be leached or taken up by the crop within one day. Results, expressed as comparisons of measured and predicted amounts of mineral N to 90 cm in spring, and the decline in the amounts between autumn and spring (Figure 7) have been encouraging. This system is also designed to give a warning if the growth of the crop is being held back for lack of mineral nitrogen.

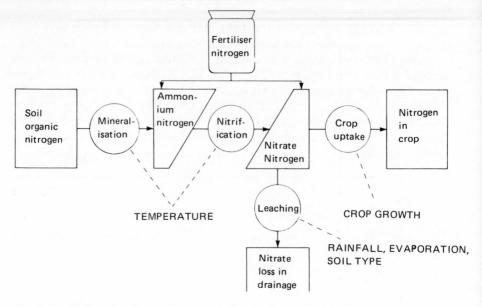

Fig. 6 Outline flow-chart for the Rothamsted N-prediction system.

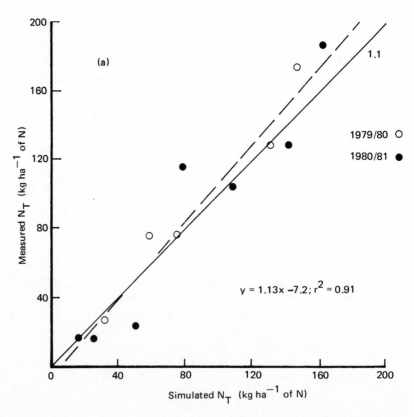

Fig. 7a Measured and simulated quantities (N_T) of mineral N found in the soil profile (0–90 cm) in spring.

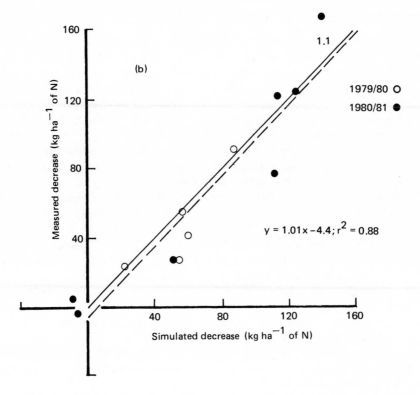

Fig. 7b Measured and simulated decreases in N_T between autumn and spring. (From Addiscott, T. M. Computer assessment of the N status during winter and early spring of soils growing winter wheat. In: *The assessment of the N status of arable soils.* Proceedings of a workshop held at the University of Leuven 12–14 January 1982. In Press.)

Practical use of modelling N requirement of cereal crops

The utility of the results of modelling the processes involved in nitrogen supply and uptake must be considered in terms of the practicalities of farming. A decision on the amount of nitrogen to be applied as seedbed N for winter crops must be made in early autumn, but the value of this is debatable. Modelling of the soil nitrogen cycle in the preceding year may be of value in this respect, but such work is still in its early stages (Frissell and van Veen, 1982). The decision on the main application of seedbed or top dressng nitrogen in spring is more important, and involves the additional questions of split or single dressings, and the timing. The twin aims must be to ensure that the crop always has access to sufficient nitrogen to grow at the maximum possible rate, in the prevailing climate, and that the final dressing shall supply a sufficient, but not excessive, amount to maintain the crop through to maturity.

Control of autumn, winter or early spring dressings

The first aim demands that the level of mineral nitrogen (especially nitrate) in the profile shall be known at all times. The level of soil mineral nitrogen is particularly important during tillering, and it may be possible to control the latter more exactly. It is totally impractical to analyse the soil to depth at frequent intervals, but it should be possible to use modelling to give early warning if the soil nitrate supply is near exhaustion, particularly if this is due to unusual weather conditions. For example, at Woburn in 1981 soil analyses (to 90 cm) indicated that the supply of mineral nitrogen in the soil was virtually exhausted by mid-March, and indeed there was increased yield of 0.5 t ha^{-1} grain where some of the nitrogen was given early (Welbank *et al.,* 1982). Such an early warning system demands that all important parts of the nitrogen cycle shall be modelled during winter as in the system described above. These processes appear to be:

1. Leaching – important on almost all soils in almost all winters.
2. Mineralisation – important in all except very cold winters; certainly important in autumn and spring.
3. Denitrification – importance under cereals is not yet clear. May be important in wet springs.
4. Crop uptake – important for early sown crops, and importance increases rapidly during early spring.

A major problem with such modelling is to decide at what point the simulations shall start, and how to determine the necessary starting conditions. The possibilities seem to be:

1) Any convenient time during winter when a deep profile (90 –100 cm) sample set can be obtained and analysed for mineral nitrogen (Jungk and Wehrmann, 1978).
2) At the time of the previous harvest, if free nitrate can be assumed to be very small, and the increase can be modelled, or if mineral nitrogen can be assessed from soil type and previous cropping.
3) Shortly after the harvest of any crop, with analysis to topsoil depth for residual nitrate, if it can be assumed that any nitrate in the subsoil at that time will be leached out during winter.

Control of main spring dressing

The decision on the size of the main dressing of nitrogen depends heavily on the assumptions about the final size of the crop, as is clear from the above discussion on crop N demand. This general approach is already used in the 'Balance Sheet' approach (Remy and Herbert, 1977) and the Hannover system (Wehrmann and Scharpf, 1976). The need to make such assumptions is a major source of uncertainty in any predictive system, and it is difficult to see how it can be overcome until better long-range weather forecasts and whole-crop models are available. The responsibility for deciding on which crop size to aim at must be left to the farmer at present, but new computerized recording systems may help to make the decision more realistic. Some success has been obtained with a system of this type at Rothamsted (Widdowson *et al.,* this volume, pages 125–128).

The predicted size of crop must be used to estimate the amount of nitrogen which will be contained in it. More information on the factors affecting the mean per cent N in crops at harvest seem to be needed. There are certainly varietal effects on per cent N in grain (Pushman and Bingham, 1976) and seasonal and climatic effects are extremely important (Benzian and Lane, 1979), though there are some indications that high yields tend to go with lower per cent N in grain, so that the variation in nitrogen content between crops is less than in grain yield. The efficiency of use of the soil nitrogen and the fertiliser to be applied is not easy to predict at present (Tinker, 1979).

The timing of the main decision on nitrogen rate may be important. The later this is made, the longer predictive modelling can continue, and the more accurate the final prediction is likely to be. The ideal would thus be to use split dressings, so that the final decision on the total amount could be left as late as possible. More exact information about the behaviour of nitrogen in the soil, together with a deeper understanding of the physiology of nitrogen in the plant, may also ensure that reliable benefits from the splitting and exact timing of the nitrogen applications can be obtained. However, there are practical objections to applying nitrogen late, and a final decision will usually need to be taken before the end of April. At this time all the biological processes are proceeding at a fast rate, and crop nitrogen content of winter wheat will already be quite large, at $50-70 \mathrm{~kg~ha^{-1}}$ of N or appreciably more for a well-supplied early-sown crop, but the possibility of leaching losses will be small.

Modelling of the changes in soil nitrogen during winter is, therefore, of clear potential value to predict or determine the amount of mineral nitrogen in the soil in spring. The value is particularly great for winter crops, where crop uptake can be large during this period. Modelling applied to a spring-sown cereal crop itself seems of less certain benefit because the period of rapid uptake is later. Burns (1980b and c) modelled the soil nitrogen changes during both winter and spring, and showed the advantages of the latter, but this was for heavily-fertilised vegetables on a sandy soil where spring leaching could be expected. Only the development and validation of such models for spring cereals can show whether the additional information they produce is worthwhile.

The technical ability to model nitrogen uptake and soil processes in detail during the summer is an important scientific aim, to ensure that we understand the whole system correctly, but at present it seems less likely to give direct practical benefits.

References

ADDISCOTT, T. M. 1977. A simple computer model for leaching in structured soils. *Journal of Soil Science* **28**, 554–563.

ADDISCOTT, T. M. 1983. Kinetics and temperature relationships of mineralisation and nitrification in Rothamsted soils with differing histories. *Journal of Soil Science* **34**, 343–353.

ADDISCOTT, T. M., DAVIDSON, J. M., HARMSEN, K., LEFELLAAR, P. L., PARTON, W. J., RAO, P.S.C., RAYNER, J. H., SMITH, K. A. and WAGENET, R. J. 1981. Migration processes in soils. In: *Simulation of Nitrogen Behaviour in Soil-Plant Systems* (eds. M. J. Frissel and J. A. van Veen), pp. 33–37. Wageningen: PUDOC.

BALDWIN, J. P. 1976. Competition for plant nutrients in soil; a theoretical approach. *Journal of Agricultural Science, Cambridge* **87**, 341–356.

BARNES, A., GREENWOOD, D. J. and CLEAVER, T. J. 1976. A dynamic model for the effects of potassium and nitrogen fertilisers on the growth and nutrient uptake of crops. *Journal of Agricultural Science, Cambridge* **86**, 225–244.

BATEY, T. 1976. Some effects of nitrogen fertiliser on winter wheat. *Journal of the Science of Food and Agriculture* **27**, 287–297.

BENZIAN, B. and LANE, P. W. 1979. Some relationships between grain yield and grain protein of wheat experiments in south-east England and comparisons with such relationships elsewhere. *Journal of the Science of Food and Agriculture* **30**, 59–70.

BOSATTA, E., ISKANDAR, I. K., JUMA, N. K., KRUH, G., REUSS, J. O., TANJI, K. K. and VAN VEEN, J. A. 1981. Soil microbiology. In: *Simulation of Nitrogen Behaviour in Soil-Plant Systems* (eds. M. J. Frissel and J. A. van Veen), pp. 38–44. Wageningen: PUDOC.

BOYD, D. A., GARNER, H. V. and HAINES, W. B. 1957. The fertiliser requirements of sugar beet. *Journal of Agricultural Science, Cambridge* **48**, 464–476.

BURNS, I. G. 1974. A model for predicting the redistribution of salts applied to fallow soils after excess rainfall or evaporation. *Journal of Soil Science* **25**, 165–178.

BURNS, I. G. 1980a. Influence of the spatial distribution of nitrate on the uptake of N by plants. A review and a model for rooting depth. *Journal of Soil Science* **31**, 155–173.

BURNS, I. G. 1980b. A simple model for predicting the effects of leaching of fertiliser nitrate during the growing season on the nitrogen need of crops. *Journal of Soil Science* **31**, 175–185.

BURNS, I. G. 1980c. A simple model for predicting the effects of winter leaching of residual nitrate on the nitrogen fertiliser need of spring crops. *Journal of Soil Science* **31**, 187–202.

COLWELL, J. D. 1978. *Computations for studies of soil fertility and fertiliser requirements.* Farnham Royal. Commonwealth Agricultural Bureau. 197 pp.

COOKE, G. W. 1979. Some priorities for British soil science. *Journal of Soil Science* **30**, 187–213.

FISHER, R. A. 1924. The influence of rainfall on the yield of wheat at Rothamsted. *Philosophical Transactions of the Royal Society of London* **B213**, 89–142.

FRISSEL, M. J. and van VEEN, J. A. 1982. A review of models for investigating the behaviour of nitrogen in the soil. *Philosophical Transactions of the Royal Society, London* **B296**, 341–349.

GERWITZ, A. and PAGE, E. R. 1974. An empirical mathematical model to describe plant root systems. *Journal of applied Ecology* **11**, 773–782.

GREENWOOD, D. J. 1982. Modelling of crop response to nitrogen fertiliser. *Philosophical Transactions of the Royal Society, London* **B296**, 351–362.

GREENWOOD, D. J., BARNES, A. and CLEAVER, T. J. 1978. Measurement and prediction of the changes in protein contents of field crops during growth. *Journal of Agricultural Science, Cambridge* **91**, 467–477.

GREENWOOD, D. J., CLEAVER, T. J., LOQUENS, S. M. H. and NIENDORF, K. B. 1977. Relationship between plant weight and growing period for vegetable crops in the United Kingdom. *Annals of Botany* **41**, 987–997.

GREENWOOD, D. J., WOOD, J. T. and CLEAVER, T. J. 1974. A dynamic model for the effects of soil and weather conditions on nitrogen response. *Journal of Agricultural Science, Cambridge* **82**, 455–467.

HACKETT, C. and ROSE, D. A. 1972. A model of the extension and branching of a seminal root of barley, and its use in studying relations between root dimensions. I. The model. *Australian Journal of biological Sciences* **25**, 669–679.

HEAPY, L. A., ROBERTSON, J. A., MCBEATH, D. K., VON MAYDELL, U. M., LOVE, H. C. and WEBSTER, G. R. 1976. Development of a barley yield equation for central Alberta. I. Effects of soil and fertiliser N and P. *Canadian Journal of Soil Science* **56**, 233–247.

JUMA, N. G. and PAUL, E. A. 1981. Use of tracers and computer simulation techniques to assess mineralisation and immobilisation of soil nitrogen. In: *Simulation of Nitrogen Behaviour in Soil-Plant Systems* (eds. M. J. Frissel and J. A. van Veen), pp. 145–154. Wageningen: PUDOC.

JUNGK, K. A. and WEHRMANN, J. 1978. Determination of nitrogen fertiliser requirements by plant and soil analyses. In: *Proceedings of the 8th International Colloquium on Plant Analysis and Fertiliser Problems*, Auckland, New Zealand, 28 August–1 September, 1978 (eds. A. R. Ferguson, R. L. Bielski and I. B. Ferguson), Vol. 1, pp. 209–234. *New Zealand D.S.I.R. Information Series* no. 134; Government Printer, Wellington, N.Z.

NYE, P. H., BREWSTER, J. L., BHAT, K. K. S. 1975. The possibility of predicting solute uptake and plant growth response from independently measured soil and plant characteristics. *Plant and Soil* **42**, 161–170.

PAUL, E. A. and van VEEN, J. A. 1978. The use of tracers to determine the dynamic nature of organic matter. *Transactions 11th International Congress of Soil Science* (Edmonton, Alberta) **3**, 61–102.

PORTER, J. R., BRAGG, P. L., RAYNER, J. H., WEIR, A. H. and LANDSBERG, J. J. 1982. The ARC winter wheat simulation model. Principles and progress. In: *Opportunities for Manipulation of Cereal Productivity.* British Plant Growth Regulator Group Monograph No. 7, pp. 97–108.

280

PUSHMAN, F. M. and BINGHAM, J. 1976. The effects of granular nitrogen fertiliser and a foliar spray of urea on the yield and bread-making quality of ten winter wheats. *Journal of Agricultural Science, Cambridge* **87**, 281–292.

RAO, P. S. C., DAVIDSON, J. M. and JESSUP, R. E. 1981. Simulation of nitrogen behaviour in the root zone of cropped land areas receiving organic wastes. In: *Simulation of Nitrogen Behaviour of Soil-Plant Systems* (eds. M. J. Frissel and J. A. van Veen), pp. 81–95. Wageningen: PUDOC.

REMY, J. C. and HEBERT, J. 1977. Le devenir des engrais azotes dans le sol. *Comptes Rendus des Seances de l'Academie d'Agriculture de France* **63**, 700–714.

SMITH, K. A. 1981. A model of denitrification in aggregated soils. In: *Simulation of Nitrogen Behaviour of Soil-Plant Systems* (eds. M. J. Frissel and J. A. van Veen), pp. 259–266. Wageningen: PUDOC.

STANFORD, G. and SMITH, S. J. 1972. Nitrogen mineralisation potentials of soils. *Soil Science Society of America Proceedings* **36**, 465–472.

TABATABAI, M. A. and AL-KHAFAJI, A. A. 1980. Comparison of nitrogen and sulphur mineralisation in soils. *Soil Science Society of America Journal* **44**, 1000–1006.

TANJI, K. K., MEHRAN, M. and GUPTA, S. K. 1981. Water and nitrogen fluxes in the root zone of irrigated maize. In: *Simulation of Nitrogen Behaviour of Soil-Plant Systems* (eds. M. J. Frissel and J. A. van Veen), pp. 51–66. Wageningen: PUDOC.

TINKER, P. B. 1979. Uptake and consumption of soil nitrogen in relation to agronomic practice. In: *Nitrogen assimilation of plants* (eds. E. J. Hewitt and C. V. Cutting), London: Academic Press, pp. 101–122.

TINKER, P. B. and WIDDOWSON, F. V. 1982. Maximising wheat yields, and some causes of yield variation. Proceedings of the Fertiliser Society **211**, 149–184.

van VEEN, J. A. and FRISSEL, M. J. 1981. Simulation model of the behaviour of N in soil. In: *Simulation of Nitrogen Behaviour of the Soil-Plant Systems* (eds. M. J. Frissel and J. A. van Veen), pp. 126–144. Wageningen: PUDOC.

WAGENET, R. J. 1981. Simulation of soil-water and nitrogen movement. In: *Simulation of Nitrogen Behaviour of the Soil-Plant Systems* (eds. M. J. Frissel and J. A. van Veen), pp. 67–80. Wageningen: PUDOC.

WEHRMANN, J. and SCHARPF, H. C. 1976. Fertiliser requirements of winter wheat as affected by the mineral nitrogen content of the soil in spring. *Proceedings of the 8th International Fertiliser Congress*, Vol. 2, pp. 182–191.

WELBANK, P. J., TAYLOR, P. J., WIDDOWSON, F. V., PENNY, A., DARBY, R. J. and HEWITT, M. V. 1982. Growth the yield of winter wheat on contrasting soils: Rothamsted and Woburn. *Report of the Rothamsted Experimental Station for 1981*, Part 1, pp. 25–28.

Discussion

Dr Dilz commented that one of the models described in the paper was currently used in the Netherlands. He suggested that the lower nitrogen requirement for high yielding crops in the Netherlands, compared to cereal crops grown in UK conditions could result from differences in plant development, particularly root growth and duration, during the season. Dr Tinker agreed with this point and felt that too much emphasis could be placed on nitrogen uptake during the winter and early spring. He thought that uptake and the nitrogen content of the soil at later stages in the growing season should be investigated in more detail up to plant senescence.

Mr Wadsworth asked about the measurements required for testing and validating the Rothamsted model. Dr Tinker replied that as many different measurements as possible should be taken during the first few years of testing. Subsequently selective tests could be made to check the accuracy of the model, for example nitrate levels in both the soil and stem sap, or crop dry matter production, to test a prediction that soil mineral nitrogen levels were declining rapidly.

Dr Greenwood commented on the considerable flexibility within different models and suggested there was great potential for obtaining appropriate data from field trials in order to test these models.

Reports of syndicate discussions

Report of Syndicate A
Relative merits of extensive and intensive experiments

Chairman: Dr D B Davies
Recorder: S J Richardson

An extensive experiment is one which involves relatively little input of labour and other facilities whereas an intensive experiment requires a much larger input.

The main value of intensive work is the opportunity it affords to look at certain parameters in great detail. Concentrated effort can be put into collecting a large amount of data on various factors at a particular site in order to identify which factors seem to have an important bearing on the results.

The advantage of extensive experiments is that a wide number of environments may be sampled. Their value usually takes the form of providing correlations such as effect of soil type or variety on yield.

The group considered that proposed experimental work should ideally begin with intensive experiments and after identifying important factors extensive work should follow in which only selected factors are varied to investigate the earlier impressions.

The cereal experiments reported in this volume have been considered as extensive experiments. This has taken a great deal of time and effort on the part of the authors and has given valuable results. However, the majority of the work has been done more intensively than described and it is hoped that the opportunity will be taken to study the experiments in greater detail in an attempt to account for the variability in the results. Thus the effect of tiller numbers at different growth stages and of previous crop as distinct from nitrogen Index might be of value.

At present ADAS nitrogen recommendations for cereals have a high degree of uncertainty. In part this is because the experiments on which they are based have been seeking 'optimum N' which is not a predictable property of a crop other than as a first approximation. The group considered that the immediate future (1983–1988 perhaps) should concentrate on improved prediction of the nitrogen supply side using a combination of intensive experiments and extensive experiments for validation and to provide an adequate data base. Both projects should, the group believed, be conducted in close collaboration with research workers and in particular those modelling soil nitrogen supply. Studies using ^{15}N would be needed in both sets of work. The result would hopefully be an improved N Index system which could be adjusted for individual site variables. This programme would be an ambitious one and would require policy decisions, and the will to see these through to fruition.

The group stressed the importance of a local co-ordinator keeping close personal surveillance on each experiment and reporting observations. It is unsatisfactory to expect a distant sponsor to account for variability from tabulated data when local observations might readily explain anomalies.

Finally ADAS must acknowledge that interpretation of experimental results takes much time and effort. Therefore, sponsors in particular should be in a position to allocate sufficient time to this important task each season to obtain the maximum value from field experiments.

Report of Syndicate B
The role of ^{15}N in future experimentation

Chairman: Dr R Dowdell
Recorder: R J Unwin

The syndicate considered that it was inappropriate to restrict consideration of this subject to future ADAS work only, and discussed it in the context of overall R and D effort. It was recognised that in order to make most efficient use of resources, effective co-ordination and collaboration between ADAS, the Agricultural Research Service (ARS) and universities should be increased. Members felt strongly that greater contact should be established between interested groups at 'worker' level.

It was agreed that ^{15}N would have a fundamental role in future studies where there was a need to identify the precise transfer of nitrogen within the nitrogen cycle. Research to improve the understanding of such processes should remain the responsibility of the ARS and universities. From this work it should be possible to better identify the 'leaks' of fertiliser nitrogen, i.e. by leaching, gaseous loss and immobilisation from the cycle under different conditions. ADAS should continue field studies with ^{15}N to improve the efficiency of fertiliser use for the benefit of the farmer and for protection of the environment. The validity of such field studies will be increased by the fundamental research work which should include confirmation of assumptions now made regarding the relative availability of ^{15}N and unlabelled nitrogen within the nitrogen cycle.

Unlabelled nitrogen fertiliser experiments will continue to be undertaken by ADAS to establish general recommendations under changing agronomic conditions. The number of such trials will be less than in recent years and simpler experimental designs may be adopted. Studies with ^{15}N should provide information on crop uptake of nitrogen throughout the season in order to detail the demand for nitrogen according to soil, climate and cultural factors. Improved advice on both rates and timing of fertiliser applications and on related cultural techniques should then be possible.

In order to achieve this aim more effort will be required to identify and record those parameters necessary for accurate interpretation of experimental results, e.g. soil moisture supply and the incidence of crop pests and diseases. The group did not consider that it would be practical or necessary for ADAS to attempt to construct an accurate nitrogen balance under field conditions.

Environmental considerations must remain a priority in interpretation of the data obtained. Whilst not unduly restricting production, ADAS should seek to identify the maximum quantity of fertiliser nitrogen consistent with maintaining environmental standards. Such an approach assumes greater importance in areas where water supplies are particularly at risk to contamination by nitrate.

The facilities to handle ^{15}N would be valuable in the investigation of other agricultural systems, notably the fertiliser requirement and fate of residues of oilseed rape, the nitrogen value of leguminous break crops, the decomposition of straw residues and work on grassland and slurry systems.

The Conference identified the limited value of the many traditional nitrogen trials, carried out in recent years. In order to make best use of future ADAS staff resources ^{15}N facilities should be provided for development work. Management should consider whether analytical facilities should be made available 'in-house', by agreed sharing of equipment, or on a contract basis.

Report of Syndicate C
Can the residual nitrogen from previous crops be better quantified?

Chairman: Dr T Batey
Recorder: M J Marks

Within ADAS the current method of estimating the residual nitrogen from previous crops is the N Index system. Although field experiments have shown the N Index to be related to nitrogen response, it has been criticised for being too simple and for having many imperfections. The group, therefore, considered that a re-evaluation of the relative significance of previous cropping to the supply of non-fertiliser nitrogen to the crop was required.

Consideration was given to methods by which this might realistically be attempted. There was general agreement that useful information could be extracted from existing records of past field experiments. In particular the offtake of nitrogen on control plots receiving no fertiliser nitrogen (N_0 plots) could be examined and the variation in nitrogen removal related to relevant site characteristics such as soil physical and chemical properties, as well as previous cropping. It was considered desirable that previous cropping records should go back for 8–10 years.

Studies using ^{15}N were considered to be invaluable as this technique allows nitrogen derived from crop residues to be distinguished from that derived from soil organic matter. More research on a range of soils was considered to be necessary.

Methods which would provide a more precise estimate of nitrogen residues from the previous crop were discussed. These residues can be broadly divided into organic nitrogen and mineral nitrogen. Knowledge of the quantity of organic residues returned to the soil from the previous crop together with its C/N ratio would allow prediction of the amount of nitrogen mineralised and also the rate of its release. The details of this calculation are given in Dr Jenkinson's paper (see pages 79–92).

A more precise estimate of the amount of mineral nitrogen remaining in the soil from the previous crop might be obtained by a nitrogen balance calculation for the previous crop. The fertiliser nitrogen input and crop yield could be readily obtained but the nitrogen offtake figure would be subject to error because the percentage of nitrogen in the crop taken off would not be known, and average figures would not be sufficiently accurate.

The possibility of soil sampling in the autumn to assess mineral nitrogen residues was discussed. This data should be collected from all future experiments but the method was considered to be impractical, at present, for routine advisory purposes.

Any estimate of mineral nitrogen residues would require correction for overwinter leaching losses using an appropriate model as outlined in the paper by Drs Tinker and Addiscott (see pages 265–281).

The emergence of computer based systems for keeping field records on farms provides an opportunity for putting a more sophisticated N Index system into operation. The group considered that any such improved system should include inputs from all factors shown to have a strong influence on the supply of non-fertiliser nitrogen to the crop. In addition to information on previous cropping, this might include soil properties, crop yields and meteorological data.

Report of Syndicate D
Prospects for improving nitrogen prediction by soil and plant analysis

Chairman: H J Lidgate
Recorder: D Hewgill

The syndicate reviewed the current methods for predicting the nitrogen supplying capacity of soils and agreed these could be separated into three broad groups, namely:

- Soil analyses (e.g. total N, nitrate-N, ammonium-N, mineralisable N)
- Plant analyses (e.g. total N, nitrate-N, nitrate reductase activity)
- Nitrogen Index (based on previous cropping history)

Although soil nitrate measurements were used for advisory purposes in certain parts of Germany, France and Holland, none of the present soil or plant analytical methods were considered to be satisfactory for predicting crop nitrogen requirements under UK conditions. The ADAS soil nitrogen Index system was thought to be reasonably reliable for large scale advisory work. However, the present method needed further refinement, particularly in arable areas where the majority of soils were classed as N Index 0.

Several papers presented to the Conference had shown that the shape of the nitrogen response curve and the optimum rate of nitrogen could differ markedly, even on soils with low nitrogen reserves. This suggested that crop response to nitrogen was governed by several interacting factors. It was therefore unlikely that any analytical value considered in isolation would give an accurate assessment of crop nitrogen requirement.

The syndicate concluded that the most likely prospect for improving nitrogen prediction would be by further refinement of the present nitrogen Index system. Possible refinements might include the use of plant nitrate analyses to modify the rate and timing of nitrogen, profile nitrate content to enable adjustments to be made according to the residues of mineral nitrogen in the soil and differential nitrogen recommendations according to the anticipated level of yield.

The syndicate also agreed that the only practical way of developing more sophisticated prediction methods would be to establish a series of permanent reference sites on major soil types. These sites would involve a range of nitrogen treatments and would require intensive monitoring. Some of the more important factors to be recorded would include:

- Soil characteristics (physical and chemical properties)
- Site management (cultivations, straw disposal, previous cropping)
- Climatic conditions (temperature, rainfall, soil moisture deficits)
- Crop growth (plant populations, tiller counts, leaf areas, tissue analysis, pest and disease assessments)

By studying the interactions between the various factors listed it should be possible to improve upon the existing prediction methods or even to generate completely new techniques of nitrogen prediction. The data collected would also be of considerable value to research workers involved in modelling nitrogen responses and would provide local information which could be used for giving day-to-day advice to farmers. Members of the syndicate were acutely aware of the large workload involved but believed this could be met by a pooling of resources from ADAS, ARC and the universities.

Report of Syndicate E
The relevance of growth and developmental stages for nitrogen applications

Chairman: R W Swain
Recorder: G A Wadsworth

The nitrogen requirement of a cereal crop is largely a function of its growth, growth meaning the increase in the size of the plants. If the requirement exceeds the supply then the plant is under nitrogen stress. This stress may or may not be disadvantageous depending on the growth stage of the plant and its environment. The timing of the nitrogen fertiliser applications should be arranged to prevent any stress which would reduce yield.

The time of maximum nitrogen demand is the period of stem extension: nitrogen stress at this time reduces growth and tiller survival. There are two other times when nitrogen may be important. Firstly in the very early life of the plant when lack of nitrogen may prevent emergence of the first tiller on a few crops with low tiller numbers. Secondly nitrogen deficiency during tillering may restrict tiller numbers and reduce yield. However, visible nitrogen stress at this time often has no deleterious effect, as most crops have ample tiller production. Nitrogen stress late in the life of the crop is unlikely to affect yield but may affect protein production.

The practical interpretation of this data is that only occasionally is autumn application of nitrogen required for winter cereals, but crops on soils usually low in mineral nitrogen or late sown crops may occasionally need a little.

It is not possible to define the time of spring applications solely by growth stage. Early sown crops will usually reach a growth stage at which the nitrogen demand is potentially high at a time when temperatures are limiting, so application needs to be delayed until temperatures increase and the risk of leaching is reduced.

Late sown crops may reach the critical growth stage in a period of high temperatures when growth is rapid and the timing of nitrogen is growth stage dependent. At this time, because growth is so rapid, it is possible to miss the critical stage. There is usually little risk of leaching under these conditions so that there is no harm in applying the nitrogen before the critical stage.

These considerations give a system which should be applicable to most crops. Average temperatures and the risk of leaching define a period in calendar time when applied nitrogen is likely to be used efficiently, and within this period growth stage can be used to define the time of application more closely.

For the early nitrogen application at tillering the use of the Zadoks growth stage scale has disadvantages in that the number of tillers is no guide to the plant's development. Plant dissection to find the development stage may be required for accurate timing, but this early application must be before Zadoks growth stage 30.

The main nitrogen application to winter cereals should be applied at early stem elongation. This is defined as '1 cm ear' (the French system) or Zadoks GS31.

In all cases timing is unlikely to be very critical due to the reservoir of mineral nitrogen in the soil and the capacity of cereal plants to compensate. Practical

293

considerations of the risk of leaching and the feasibility of machines travelling over the land are also important.

Report of Syndicate F
Prospects for improving the prediction of nitrogen fertiliser requirements of cereal crops by modelling methods

Chairman: R B Austin
Recorder: Dr A D Hughes

The syndicate considered that an appropriate computer based system for determining the nitrogen fertiliser needs of cereals could:

1. Make better use of data from experiments and available information on the nitrogen requirements of crops and the fate of nitrogen in soils.
2. Make better use of local meteorological data and information on soil type.
3. Provide more precise recommendations on a field-by-field basis (for a particular soil, variety, sowing date, winter rainfall etc), than can be produced by existing systems.
4. Be more acceptable to farmers and the agricultural industry in general than the present nitrogen Index system.

Such a system could increase the efficiency with which nitrogen fertiliser is used and decrease waste of fertiliser and adverse environmental effects.

The syndicate considered that thorough analysis should be undertaken before launching into any ambitious and expensive development, to quantify the likely costs and benefits involved. The analysis should compare the costs and returns which would be entailed if:

(a) A single 'blanket' application were to be used throughout the country, regardless of local conditions.
(b) The current nitrogen Index system were used.
(c) A 'perfect' system were used.

A sufficient number of well-defined, experimentally determined response curves exist to enable the relative costs and benefits for the three systems to be calculated for a large number of site-years.

The syndicate considered that several types of model should be developed. These would range from a combination of tabulated data used in the field with a pocket calculator, to sophisticated models requiring a computer. Only by developing the full range of systems concurrently would it be possible to ensure the necessary interactions between groups working at different levels of complexity whilst also catering for the needs of potential users with a range of expertise.

A comprehensive computer model would be made up of elements dealing with each of the major processes of the fertiliser/soil/crop system. For winter cereal crops the model would take account of:

1. The nitrogen content of the soil in autumn, after harvest of the previous crop.
2. Changes in soil mineral nitrogen content and soil nitrogen transformations in winter time, allowing for rainfall, temperature and crop uptake.

From this information the model would calculate the nitrogen content of the soil and crop at the end of winter. An estimate of the likely yield is necessary for a precise prediction of the nitrogen fertiliser requirement of the crop. Satisfactory models already exist to calculate(2) above, and work on (1) is in progress. Some data from past trials may be suitable for testing these important components more thoroughly and the syndicate recommended that this be investigated as a matter of priority.

To complete the calculation of the nitrogen requirement of a crop, an estimate of the expected yield is needed. There can be little doubt that given the present state of knowledge, yields of previous crops will provide the most reliable basis for estimating expected yield. For the future, the syndicate considered that extension of current work on modelling crop growth would eventually provide a better technique. It was pointed out that this must be considered as a long-term development. The factors responsible for the large differences between predicted yield assuming ideal conditions, and actual field yields are not understood at present and therefore are not likely to be reliably quantified for some time.

The syndicate felt that both the development of more sophisticated models and the validation of those at present in existence or currently under development is likely to be hindered by a lack of suitable experimental data. They recommended that ADAS should consider more extensive monitoring of soil nitrogen status and water use in some of its field experiments to provide such data. Any such field work would need to be planned and conducted in consultation with groups constructing and testing the models.

The syndicate was optimistic about the prospects for improving fertiliser recommendations and the efficiency of fertiliser use by the adoption of computer modelling techniques, and recommended that support be given to those working in this area.

Report of Syndicate G
Opportunities for improved co-ordination of cereal nitrogen experiments

Chairman: Dr R Q Cannell
Recorder: R J W Dight

The Conference highlighted the depth of knowledge of many of the participating individuals and organisations. It has also focussed attention on the complexity of the problem to be solved. This syndicate report may appear to be critical, but the aim is to offer positive recommendations.

Science begins with data collection but a deficiency in the standardisation of terminology and techniques was noted. The description of cereal growth stages is a good example where an agreed terminology exists. Standard methods of chemical and physical soil analysis have been published, and it is recommended that standard experimental methods of measurement be agreed and published. Training of field staff to ensure comparability of results is desirable.

A clearer definition of the objectives of experiments is required. The number of trials or sites, the measurements needed and the analysis of results necessitates more planning before the experiment commences. Planning should involve all the participating parties and a psychological barrier to co-operation was highlighted. It is important that all participants must obtain positive recognition and not provide data for someone else who gets the credit. Insufficient use is made of more modern statistical methods, and there is a case for training in more advanced experimental design and analysis.

The overall co-ordinator or trial sponsor should be given authority to ensure the agreed objectives are achieved. There is a need for improving scientific management to ensure this. The cost of experiments in labour and finance required budgeting. The GM series of grassland trials (although not without some problems) is an indication of the attainment required. Other co-operators who were not present at this Conference are the Soil Survey and the Met Office. Co-ordination of experiments where several regions or centres are involved should entail briefing of the staff involved in the field and lab work to help ensure standardisation of methods, inspire personal involvement and provide job satisfaction. The participation of junior staff is often neglected.

There is a need for some improvement in ADAS in-house co-ordination but the basic organisation exists and personal contacts are very important to ensure co-operation. The ADAS structure includes relevant ARC members who can and should be co-opted where necessary. Scotland should be included to rectify past omissions. European co-operation does not appear to exist in this field. Trace elements, tillage and cultivations are examples where co-operation already exists and these can be taken as models. The mechanism for closer co-operation is not clear but existing contacts should be encouraged and expanded.

To promote overall co-ordination the establishment of a 'User Group' is suggested, similar to that dealing with 'tillage and cultivations'. Its responsibility would be to provide a link, appraise work done, maintain a register of interested parties, and generally take an overall view of the state of research and development in nitrogen use for cereal production. The proposed user group would be jointly constituted and chaired by ARC and ADAS (as in the Cultivations User Group).

Printed in the UK for HMSO
Dd 736428   C15   5/84

298